C.H. Walther

SEMICONDUCTOR

and
Conventional

STRAIN GAGES

SEMICONDUCTOR

and

Conventional

STRAIN GAGES

EDITOR

MILLS DEAN, III

Department of the Navy
David Taylor Model Basin
Washington 7, D. C.

ASSOCIATE EDITOR

RICHARD D. DOUGLAS

Newport News Shipbuilding and Dry Dock Company
Newport News, Virginia

1962

ACADEMIC PRESS · NEW YORK-LONDON

ACADEMIC PRESS INC.
111 FIFTH AVENUE
NEW YORK 3, N. Y.

United Kingdom Edition
Published by
ACADEMIC PRESS INC. (LONDON) LTD.
BERKELEY SQUARE HOUSE, BERKELEY SQUARE, LONDON W. 1

Library of Congress Catalog Card Number 62-16906

PRINTED IN THE UNITED STATES OF AMERICA

LIST OF CONTRIBUTORS

ROSCOE L. BLOSS, *National Bureau of Standards, Washington, D. C.*

WALTER ENGL, *Siemens & Halske Aktiengesellschaft Wernerwerk für Messtechnik, Karlsruhe, West Germany*

J. J. FORST, *Bell Telephone Laboratories, Incorporated, Murray Hill, New Jersey*

EUGENE FRANK, *B & F Instruments, Incorporated, Philadelphia, Pennsylvania*

FRANK F. HINES, *Baldwin-Lima-Hamilton Corporation, Electronics Division, Waltham, Massachusetts*

ARNOLD U. HUGGENBERGER, *Physical Instruments Huggenberger, Zurich, Switzerland*

W. R. HUMPHREY, *General Electric Company, Aircraft Nuclear Propulsion Department, Cincinnati, Ohio*

YOSHIKAZU IZUMI, *Kyowa Electronic Instruments Company, Ltd., Tokyo, Japan*

ANTHONY D. KURTZ, *Kulite-Bytrex Corporation, Newton, Massachusetts, and Kulite Semiconductor Products, Incorporated, Ridgefield, New Jersey*

W. P. MASON, *Bell Telephone Laboratories, Incorporated, Murray Hill, New Jersey*

R. O'REGAN, *Bell Telephone Laboratories, Incorporated, Murray Hill, New Jersey*

E. D. PADGETT, *Picatinny Arsenal, Dover, New Jersey*

J. C. SANCHEZ, *Micro Systems, Incorporated, San Gabriel, California*

I. G. SCOTT, *Australian Defence Scientific Service, Aeronautical Research Laboratories, Department of Supply, Melbourne, Australia*

PETER K. STEIN, *Arizona State University, Tempe, Arizona*

L. M. TORNILLO, *Bell Telephone Laboratories, Incorporated, Murray Hill, New Jersey*

C. O. VOGT, *Century Electronics & Instruments, Incorporated, Tulsa, Oklahoma*

OSAMU WATANABE, *Kyowa Electronic Instruments Company, Ltd., Tokyo, Japan*

LEON J. WEYMOUTH, *Baldwin-Lima-Hamilton Corporation, Electronics Division, Waltham, Massachusetts*

E. D. WRIGHT, *Electro-Optical Systems, Incorporated, Pasadena, California*

M. A. XAVIER, *Century Electronics & Instruments, Incorporated, Tulsa, Oklahoma*

v

PREFACE

This book has been assembled to provide up-to-date information on the characteristics, limitations, applications, and peculiarities of modern strain gages with emphasis on semiconductor types. It gives background information on semiconductor materials, adhesives, temperature problems, and instrumentation developments. Also included are an Index and a comprehensive Bibliography on semiconductor strain gages and allied topics.

Today, understanding the limitations of the semiconductor gage is at least as important as knowing its distinct and enticing advantages. Papers on recent developments in this new field are much sought after, and the Instrument Society of America is proud to be the leader in disseminating such information. This volume represents the apex of the present state of the art, and as far as is known, it is the first compilation of work in the field.

This volume contains 16 papers prepared by leading authorities. Most of the material was presented at the ISA 15th Annual International Instrument–Automation Conference and Exhibit held at the New York City Coliseum September 25–30, 1960. At this Conference papers were presented under the sponsorship of the Technical Department of the ISA Physical and Mechanical Measurement Instrumentation Division, Strain Committee 6J-1, during a 2-day symposium on "Recent Developments in Semiconductor and Conventional Strain Gages."

Because of the excellent attendance and the high interest shown at the above Conference, a 1-day "Workshop on Semiconductor Strain Gages" was held on January 18, 1961 during the ISA Winter Conference in St. Louis, Missouri, at the Sheraton-Jefferson Hotel. Several contributions presented at this conference are included.

Originally, the scope of the book was to be limited to papers presented at the above-mentioned meetings. However, an exceptionally timely paper discussing a strain indicator for semiconductor gages was given at the ISA 16th Annual Meeting in Los Angeles, California, in September of 1961 and accordingly, is included to make the compilation complete. The first page of each chapter carries the specific conference identification.

Responsibility for the technical accuracy of each paper understandably rests with its author(s).

ISA Technical Conference provides one of the best mediums in our field for discussional interchanges because of the timeliness of the information presented and the give-and-take atmosphere that often prevails at such meetings. It is hoped that this volume will aid in disseminating scientific information relating to the strain gage art and will minimize the loss to those unable to attend the conferences. Although much valuable information has been written in the literature relative to the accomplishments of conventional gages, it might not be remiss to mention briefly that several universities offer special academic strain gage training sessions annually as *short courses* of from one to several weeks duration. Such courses are currently offered by Arizona State University, Tempe, Arizona; University of California, University Extension, Los Angeles, California; and the Massachusetts Institute of Technology, Cambridge, Massachusetts.

The semiconductor strain gage is with us. Transistors and diodes have been familiar items on the electronics scene for more than a decade. Now the newly arrived piezoresistive semiconductor strain gage is passing through a period of initial trial and familiarization by the users. It offers intriguingly high gage factors to 230 with factors of 30,000 on the development horizon.

The conventional wire strain gage was put to immediate use as a new tool for the stress analyst after its introduction in 1939. The theoretical and practical understanding of its potentials and limitations developed gradually over the years with widespread use in the aircraft and other industries. Circuits and instrumentation were initially developed by individual users and one or two instrument manufacturers. During the past 12 years the commercial market has provided sophisticated instrumentation meeting most of the needs of the advancing technological research and test applications of wire and foil strain gages and similar resistance devices.

About 2 years ago semiconductor strain gages emerged commercially after a period of deliberate theoretical and attendant laboratory investigation followed rapidly by marked improvements in manufacturing techniques. Thus, the semiconductor strain gage was introduced to an experienced and knowledgeable technical community with a reasonably complete theoretical pedigree.

It seems unlikely at the present time that the semiconductor gage will entirely supersede the wire and foil types. Rather it will permit measurements not previously thought possible and allow other measurements with simplified instrumentation.

Studies and evaluations of the piezoresistive hydrostatic pressure effects in metals and crystals, including a type of silicon, were first reported by the late Dr. Percy Williams Bridgman beginning in 1917. His extensive work and reporting in this field spans 35 years and provides an important contribution related to the development of the wire strain gage. After the development of controlled purity in semiconducting metals, investigations were conducted on their piezoresistive pressure and strain characteristics but the practical application of this effect as a strain gage transducer lay dormant. Dr. Warren P. Mason, of the Bell Telephone Laboratories, was the first to suggest the study and application of the piezoresistive shear phenomenon in semiconducting silicon and germanium for strain gage transducers in 1954. A recent paper on his strain gage work is included in this volume.

Future technological development of semiconductor gages for the high temperature realm above 600°F will be interesting to follow. For many reasons it appears that further work in this area offers the best present possibility of effecting a break-through in high temperature strain gage technology.

MILLS DEAN, III

Instrumentation Division
Department of the Navy
David Taylor Model Basin
Washington, D. C.
July, 1962

ACKNOWLEDGMENTS

The Introduction to this book was contributed by Dr. William M. Murray, Professor-in-Charge of the Laboratory for Experimental Stress Analysis, Department of Mechanical Engineering, Massachusetts Institute of Technology. On behalf of the Instrument Society of America I wish to thank Dr. Murray not only for the Introduction but also for his dedicated interest in participating in many of the special ISA symposia on strain gages and for his contributions to the *ISA Journal.*

This compilation was suggested originally by Mr. D. J. De Michele of the General Electric Company, Schenectady, New York, and his encouragement and support are acknowledged. Technical arrangements were handled by Mr. Herbert S. Kindler of the ISA Headquarters' staff.

Mr. Frederick B. Bryant of the David Taylor Model Basin staff* provided the first incentive which led to the subsequent development of the special ISA sessions on semiconductor strain gages. He suggested, in early 1960, that the Model Basin should extend its information and knowledge of strain gages into the semiconductor transducer field. Mr. Vernon E. Benjamin, also of the Model Basin staff, has contributed continuing encouragement for my ISA activities and has been most generous with suggestions for the preparation of this volume.

I wish to acknowledge the interest and support given by the David Taylor Model Basin management in encouraging active employee participation in professional technical societies.

I am especially grateful to my wife, Jenny, who assisted in the painstaking details of proofreading and in the preparation of the Index and the Bibliography for this book.

Gratitude and appreciation are extended to the ISA 6J-1 Conference Paper Review Committee members, Mr. Richard D. Douglas and Dr. John Verna of the Newport News Shipbuilding and Dry Dock Company, Newport News, Virginia, and Mr. Theodore M. Mathison of the Boeing Company, Renton, Washington.

Lastly, I wish to express specific appreciation to the authors for their unique contributions without which this book would have been impossible, and to the many other people who have contributed of their time and talents in its preparation.

MILLS DEAN, III

* *Present address:* National Aeronautics and Space Administration, Washington, D. C.

INTRODUCTION

(Introduction for ISA Volume on *"Semiconductor and Conventional Strain Gages."* Prepared by W. M. Murray at the request of Mills Dean, III, July 1, 1962)

The Purpose of the Strain Gage

The recent spectacular achievements with missiles and space vehicles have focused attention on engineering and technological advances which are unparalleled in the history of mankind. However, the headlines in the public press, as a rule, mention only the ultimate results and give little information concerning the breadth and depth of the advances which have been made in the individual skills that must be combined to produce an over-all result such as a successful orbital flight or probe into space. Nor do they tell us about the comparable advances which have taken place in the more prosaic but less publicized industries.

In the area of mechanical design, the old-fashioned *factor of safety* has long ago given way to resolution into its components of *a margin of safety* and *a factor of ignorance.* Today, the latter component, the ignorance part, can be almost eliminated from mechanical design as a result of improvements which have been made in the techniques for the measurement of strain. This applies not only to improvements in strain gages themselves, but also to the procedures for installing them, and to the associated instrumentation for obtaining the readout, either directly in terms of strain, or automatically calculated into terms of some other quantity whose value may depend upon the simultaneous observation of several strains at different locations. In passing, one cannot help noting that in the aero-space industry, where weight must be held to an absolute minimum, the difference between success and failure often depends upon the virtual elimination of the ignorance factor from structural or mechanical design.

Milton M. Leven* who is internationally renowned for his work on photoelasticity, particularly the stress freezing techniques as applied to three-dimensional problems, has given us an interesting graphical presentation to illustrate the manner in which the various methods of Experimental Stress Analysis, especially "Strain Gages," are related to the general problem of design. This concept is shown in Fig. 1, from which one can see

---

* Milton M. Leven, past president of the Society for Experimental Stress Analysis, is affiliated with the Westinghouse Research Laboratories at East Pittsburgh, Pennsylvania.

that strain gages of various kinds are utilized in both model and prototype testing.

Depending on the size of the structure (or machine part), the number of units to be produced, and considerations relative to safety of human beings

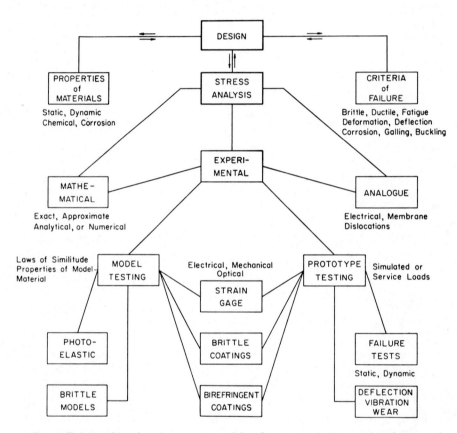

Fig. 1. Relationship of strain gages to model and prototype testing, and to the general problem of structural design.

or financial investment, either model or prototype testing, or both, may be conducted. In any case, there is little question about the importance of strain gages as devices which can be used for preliminary estimates, checking or proving prototypes, and the accumulation of service information for future requirements.

Historical Development of Stress-Strain Relations

The first uses of strain measuring devices are lost in obscurity but quite likely they involved observations of some sort of deflection, such as the bending of the branch of a tree, the sag of a primitive bridge, or perhaps the sway of the mast of a ship. We do know, however, that by the latter half of the seventeenth century some attention had been paid to strain measurement. It was in this period that Robert Hooke (1635–1703) announced his famous law—"within certain limits, stress is proportional to strain"— from which one can infer that there must have been some observation of strain (or deflection) in order to postulate the proportionality between stress and strain. Hooke's work, although of great fundamental significance and importance, must have been relatively crude, at least by modern standards, since about 100 years elapsed before Robert Young (1773–1829) and S. D. Poisson (1781–1840) set forth the quantitative relationships which form the basis of numerical calculations of stress values from strain observations.

When numerical values are mentioned one cannot help thinking of a well-known quotation from Lord Kelvin:

> I often say that when you can measure what you are speaking about, and express it in numbers, you know something about it, but when you cannot express it in numbers, your knowledge is of a meagre and unsatisfactory kind; it may be the beginning of knowledge, but you have scarcely, in your thoughts, advanced to the stage of science, whatever the matter may be.

The modern bonded resistance strain gage is capable of fulfilling Lord Kelvin's requirements under a great variety of conditions and environments.

Strain Gage Characteristics

If one were starting from scratch to design and develop a good general purpose strain gage, the following ten characteristics would probably be included in the specifications:

1. Ability to measure strains precisely under static or dynamic conditions.
2. Small size and negligible weight.
3. The possibility of remote observation and recording.
4. Independence of temperature changes.
5. Easy installation.
6. Stability of calibration.
7. Linear response to strain.
8. Low cost.
9. Dependability under a wide variety of environments.
10. The possibility of operation as an individual strain gage for measuring

strain *per se*, or in multiple arrangements for determining quantities from simultaneous observations of strain at several different locations or orientations.

Of the many instruments which have thus far been developed for strain measurement, whether mechanical, optical, electrical, or combinations thereof, the bonded electric resistance strain gage (wire, foil, or semiconductor) has, by far, come the closest to fulfilling the above ten requirements.

THE BASIC PHENOMENON

Publication of the basic operating principle applicable to wire and foil gages dates back to 1856, when Lord Kelvin reported that certain metallic conductors when subjected to mechanical strain exhibited a corresponding change in electrical resistance.

Within the last 15 years intensive research on semiconductors has brought forth the discovery that certain of these materials also exhibit a change in electrical resistance with change in strain. However, as the readers of this volume will find out, the physics of what takes place in the semiconductors appears to be somewhat different from that in metals, although the over-all effect is comparable.

As of the moment, silicon appears to be the preferred material for the sensing element of semiconductor gages. In general, semiconductors show a much larger percentage change in electrical resistance per unit of strain than do the metals. Furthermore, the effect is controllable and can be varied both in magnitude and in sign by suitable production procedures.

DEVELOPMENTS—PAST, PRESENT, AND FUTURE

It is characteristic that in many cases a considerable time lag exists between the discovery of some physical phenomenon and its commercial exploitation. The resistance strain gage is no exception, as approximately 75 years elapsed between Lord Kelvin's announcement and the commercial application of the principle to an unbonded gage with wire sensing elements mounted on a mechanical carrier. However, during the last 25 years there have been numerous developments and improvements which have contributed to making the bonded resistance strain gage into the precise, versatile and reliable instrument which it is today. Of all these developments the following four (in chronological order) are outstanding:

1. The concept of using a sensing element in the form of a very fine wire which could be cemented directly to the surface and then forced, by the cement, to follow the strains. (This is possible with a very fine wire because the surface area greatly exceeds the cross-sectional area

and the bond stress in the cement is low enough to avoid creep or rupture in the bond.)

2. The scheme of premounting the sensing element on a paper or plastic carrier to facilitate installation. This makes the gage commercially attractive.
3. The development of the foil gage.
4. The development of the semiconductor gage.

What the future holds in the way of strain gage developments cannot be predicted with too much accuracy. There are bound to be refinements of present techniques and quite likely the introduction of something entirely new, especially for high temperature applications. However, it seems reasonable to expect that future developments will certainly be as outstanding as those of the past and possibly a good deal more so. If enough competent people carry on research for a sufficient length of time they are bound to achieve results, provided, of course, that information can be distributed from one person or one group, to another.

DISSEMINATION OF INFORMATION

The dissemination of information has two interrelated aspects. One is purely a matter of communication and the other is educational. For exchanging information the symposia and workshops held by the ISA and other technical organizations, as well as *short courses* at universities, are of tremendous value in transmitting knowledge and stimulating those who are able to attend in person.

On a much broader scale, however, are the publications which have resulted from such meetings, and publications by individuals. There are hundreds of articles on strain gages distributed throughout the technical periodicals with heaviest concentrations to be found in the *Proceedings of the Society for Experimental Stress Analysis* and the magazine, *Strain Gage Readings*.

In addition to the articles which have appeared in periodicals, there is a modest number of books in which the basic information on strain gages has been gathered and correlated. This volume is therefore a most welcome addition to the books which have been written on the subject since it contains a fine collection of the latest technical data on the newest developments in the realm of strain gages.

The organizers of the symposia at which the following papers were presented are to be congratulated not only upon the success of the meetings but also for their efforts in collecting the technical information and making it available in a book which will provide a permanent record of the transactions. In this manner a large amount of very useful information has been preserved for the benefit of a considerably larger number of people than had the good fortune of being able to attend the original presentations in person. This is an exceedingly worthwhile achievement and a great credit to all concerned, authors, editors, and organizers alike.

WILLIAM M. MURRAY

Massachusetts Institute of Technology
Cambridge, Massachusetts
July 1, 1962

CONTENTS

SILICON PIEZORESISTIVE DEVICES

E. D. Padgett

Picatinny Arsenal, Dover, New Jersey

AND

W. V. Wright

Electro-Optical Systems, Inc., Pasadena, California

Abstract

The basic properties of semiconductor piezoresistive materials must be "characterized" if they are to be used properly in strain gage and transducer applications. This paper describes some basic properties of various forms of silicon piezoresistive materials. Important techniques associated with the use of these materials as transducer elements as well as some problem areas are introduced.

Introduction

The piezoresistive effect is the name given to the change in electrical resistivity that occurs with the application of stress. Here stress is understood to mean "distributed force per unit area." Most materials exhibit the effect to some degree.

The piezoresistive effect in semiconductors is unusually large. For analytical purposes the terms electrical resistance and stress are understood to be tensors. The effect in semiconductors was first noted by Smith[1] and explained later by Herring,[2-5] and others. The effect in highly doped silicon and germanium is attributed to the large values of "piezoresistance coefficients" (three terms of a fourth rank tensor) that are associated with the symmetrical structure of these materials. In p-type silicon (and n- and p-type germanium) the presence of a large *shear coefficient of piezoresistance*, π_{44}, yields very high gage factors, which makes these materials useful for strain gage and transducer applications.

The optimum piezoresistive effect depends on physical form, type of material, its resistivity or doping, and crystallographic orientation, in the region near room temperature. Of about 24 varieties of p- and n-type silicon characterized to date, the optimum form for strain gage applications appears to be a slender filament of p-type silicon with a resistivity of 0.1 ohm-cm and a 111 orientation in k-space.

1

Theoretical Considerations

The piezoresistive effect in semiconductors has been discussed by several investigators.[2-5] The theory is complex and concerns intervalley carrier scattering and, in some cases, impurity scattering in germanium and silicon. A useful analysis of this art has been contributed by Mason and Thurston,[3] who derived detailed equations to explain the effect in terms of "changing properties" of the material. It has been stated that if a shear stress is applied to a suitable form of semiconductor material, the property that changes is the ratio of an electric field component to a perpendicular current density component. In the absence of a shear stress this ratio has a value of zero.

In a semiconductor the piezoresistive effect is described by stating the relationship between a stress tensor and an electrical resistance tensor. It can be shown[3] that the piezoresistive tensor is a fourth rank tensor which, in general, contains 81 terms. Since the material (silicon) has a symmetrical cubic structure, only three terms of the tensor are retained and these are of the fourth rank tensor type π_{1111}, π_{1122}, and π_{1212}, which can be reduced to the simpler notation, π_{11}, π_{12}, and π_{44} to identify the piezoresistive coefficients.

This paper is concerned with the characteristics of long, thin, filamentary types of piezoresistive elements, sometimes called "piezors." In this case the stress is a tension, which is applied to the element along the longitudinal axis. If the electric field component, E, and current density component, i, are in the same direction, a simplified expression can be written

$$\frac{E}{\rho} = i[1 + \pi_e T] \qquad \text{or} \qquad \frac{E}{i} = \rho[1 + \pi_e T] \qquad (1)$$

where ρ is resistivity under zero stress, π_e is the longitudinal stress gage factor (coefficient), and T is longitudinal stress. The ratio E/i describes the quantity that is changing. It is the "longitudinal resistivity under tension T."

Some investigators prefer to consider the situation wherein the change in electrical resistance is measured along the longitudinal axis when the stress is applied in the same direction. For this condition a definition of a simple scaler gage factor for the element can be written. In terms of the piezoresistive coefficients and the orientation of the crystal comprising the element, this factor is

$$\pi_e = \frac{\Delta R/R_0}{T} = \frac{\Delta R/R_0}{F/A} \qquad (2)$$

where π_e and T are defined as above, ΔR is the change in electrical resistance with applied stress, R_0 is the initial electrical resistance of the element (at initial ambient temperature), F is applied longitudinal force, and A is cross-sectional area of the element.

Another useful form of the above expression in terms of piezoresistive coefficients, π_{44}, π_{12}, and π_{11}, and direction cosines, l_{11}, l_{12}, and l_{13} from the cubic crystal axis to the longitudinal axis of the element, is

$$\pi_e = \pi_{11} + 2[\pi_{44} + \pi_{12} - \pi_{11}][l_{11}^2 l_{12}^2 + l_{11}^2 l_{13}^2 + l_{12}^2 l_{13}^2]. \tag{3}$$

The gage factor of the element can be expressed in terms of the piezoresistive coefficients and the Miller indices (h, k, l) of the crystal with respect to the axis of the element. This is

$$\pi_e = \pi_{11} + 2[\pi_{44} + \pi_{12} - \pi_{11}] \left[\frac{h^2 k^2 + h^2 l^2 + k^2 l^2}{(h^2 + k^2 + l^2)^2} \right]. \tag{4}$$

For a thin semiconductor element the *stress gage factor* is related to the *strain gage factor* by the scaler expression

$$G = Y\pi_e \tag{5}$$

where G is the strain gage factor or fractional change in resistance per fractional change in longitudinal strain, and Y is Young's modulus of elasticity along the axis of the element.

An additional comment may be useful inasmuch as the concept of "fractional change" was introduced above. By using Young's modulus, $Y = T/S$ and Eqs. (1) and (2), the expression in Eq. (5) can be rewritten

$$\pi_e T = \pi_e Y S = \frac{\Delta \rho}{\rho} \tag{6}$$

where ρ denotes the resistivity of the material, and S is longitudinal strain.

The conventional expression for "resistance" of a thin wire is $R = \rho L / A$ where L is length and A is cross-sectional area. Let $\Delta L/L$ denote the *resistance change due to a change in length*, $\Delta A/A$ denote the *resistance change due to a change in cross-sectional area*, and $\Delta \rho / \rho$ represent the *change in specific resistance*. If $\Delta R/R$ denotes the unit change of resistance, then

$$\frac{\Delta R}{R} = \frac{\Delta L}{L} - \frac{\Delta A}{A} + \frac{\Delta \rho}{\rho}. \tag{7}$$

By introducing Poisson's ratio (usually about 0.3) which is an expression of the ratio of the magnitude of transverse to longitudinal strain resulting from a simple tension, Eq. (7) can be rewritten as

$$\frac{\Delta R}{R} = \frac{\Delta L}{L} - \frac{\Delta A}{A} + \frac{\Delta \rho}{\rho} = S + 2\sigma S + \pi_e Y S \tag{8}$$

$$= (1 + 2\sigma + Y\pi_e)S$$

where σ is Poisson's ratio. This expression says that $\Delta R/RS$ is a constant. It can be rewritten to express the strain gage factor of a semiconductor as follows:

$$\frac{\Delta R}{RS} = 1 + 2\sigma + Y\pi_e. \tag{9}$$

The strain gage factors of the silicon semiconductor elements used in this investigation were dependent upon electrical resistivity, crystal orientation, and ambient temperature. Values of from 40 to 200 were obtained. For the temperature range $-40°$ to $+48°C$ the authors feel that a gage factor of 125 ± 5 could be obtained on a practical, repeatable basis, if desired. For comparative purposes theory predicts that gage factors for some semiconductors can be as much as 150 times larger than those of conventional conductors.

For a more detailed mathematical discussion of the piezoresistive effect, see the Bibliography at the end of this paper.

Practical Considerations

A number of considerations must be kept in mind when considering the use of semiconductor "piezors" in strain gage and transducer applications. A brief summary of some important properties of a p-type silicon element as compared to Karma strain gage wire is presented in Table I in order to emphasize effects of temperature.

The temperature dependence of gage factor and electrical resistance will be discussed later. The effects of temperature change and expansion of materials can be reduced by using these "piezors" in bridge type electrical circuits similar to those used in wire strain gage applications. The problem of expansion (in dissimilar materials) can be reduced by using an unstressed inactive semiconductor element, or gage, bonded to a similar material and placed near the active gage. Both gages are then connected in a bridge type circuit. A four-active-arm bridge circuit, wherein the element in each arm is a "piezor," is shown in Fig. 1. The current applied to the semiconductor elements should not exceed that value which would cause appreciable heating of the element or thermal drift. For elements available at this time (September, 1960) a practical value is about 20 to 25 ma.

Among other items that must be considered are the following: (a) methods of mounting bonded and unbonded gages and absorption of deflective energy by bonded members and bonding material, (b) method of attaching electrical connections to the semiconductor, and (c) response time of the "piezor" itself.

Mechanical mounting methods, the use of bonded or unbonded designs, and problems of absorption of deflective energy are complex matters. The "best" solution must be determined by experience or practical analysis of the task to be performed. If the decision is for a bonded design, the devices can be bonded to the test surface (usually metal) by a thin film of adhesive. A number of epoxy resins and elements have been used successfully for insulation and for bonding silicon gages to metal surfaces. Mixing and curing cycles as stated by the manufacturer of such materials have been satisfactory.

TABLE I

COMPARISON OF SEVERAL PROPERTIES OF A SEMICONDUCTOR "PIEZOR" TO LIKE PROPERTIES OF A STRAIN GAGE WIRE

Property	Material		Ratio
	0.1 ohm-cm p-type Si, 111	Karma strain gage wire	
Strain gage factor	125 (nom)	2.0	62.5
Thermal coeff. res., $\dfrac{dR}{R_0} \cdot \dfrac{1}{\Delta T} \left(\dfrac{\%}{°C}\right)$	12×10^{-4}	0.2×10^{-4}	60
Thermal coeff. G.F., $\dfrac{dG}{G_0} \cdot \dfrac{1}{\Delta T} \left(\dfrac{\%}{°C}\right)$	16×10^{-4}	5×10^{-4}	3
Seebeck coeff., alpha $(uv/°C)$	600	40	15
Linear expansion coeff., K $\left(\dfrac{\text{inch/inch}}{°C}\right)$	4×10^{-6}	10×10^{-6}	0.4

In general, the "alloy method" of connecting lead wires (usually a gold alloy wire) to the semiconductor element is preferred. Alloying provides a good ohmic contact with reasonable mechanical strength.

The response time of a thin piezoresistive element itself is of the order of 10^{-10} second. Since this is much shorter than the time required to propagate an elastic wave along the element, the total response time of the system will be limited by the time constants of the mechanical system used.

The temperature dependence[4] of important parameters of piezoresistors is emphasized so that an engineer can use compensating techniques when necessary. It has been pointed out that changes due to thermal variations can be reduced by using the "piezors" in bridge type electrical circuits.

Also, it is important to note that a semiconductor element can be no more *sensitive* to thermal drift than a conventional wire strain gage element. The following example will illustrate this point. Assume that semiconductor gages and metal wire gages are operating at 0.05% strain (500 microinches/inch) in suitable bridge circuits excited at 10 volts. The output signal from the semiconductor bridge circuit would be 0.600 volt while that from the wire gage bridge would be 0.010 volt. The larger output from the semiconductor device is one of its greatest advantages. Now introduce a thermal change and let it unbalance the wire gage circuit by 0.0005 volt (5%).

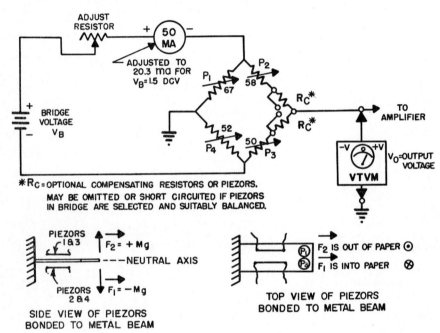

FIG. 1. Bridge type test circuit.

The same thermal change on the semiconductor circuit would result in a bridge unbalance 60 times greater or 0.030 volt. This represents a drift of 30 mv/600 mv, or approximately 5% for the semiconductor gage as compared to 5% for the wire gage. While the rate of change of resistance of the semiconductor gage with temperature is higher than in a conventional wire gage, the effect is compensated by the higher gage factor (and greater output) of the semiconductor gage. The resistance of a semiconductor gage is a function of temperature which is shown in the graphs.

It will be shown later that the gage factor of a *p*-type silicon element decreases in essentially a linear manner, with increasing temperature in the range $-50°$ to $+125°C$ at a rate of about $-0.20\%/°C$ or $-0.10\%/°F$. For the same condition the gage factor of n-type silicon decreases linearly with a slope of about $-0.10\%/°C$ or $-0.06\%/°F$.

OTHER CONSIDERATIONS

The chronological development of semiconductor piezoresistive elements is depicted in Fig. 2. In the past, basic segments were cut by saw from a master rod or bar (the proper crystal orientation being along the axis or

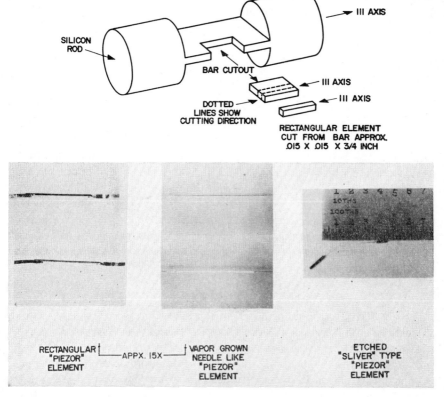

FIG. 2. *Upper:* Sketch to show method of cutting elements from bar. *Lower:* Silicon piezoresistive elements.

length of the bar). These elements were rectangular in shape. After being cut from the bar these elements were lapped and etched in an acid solution to remove saw marks and irregularities. Lead wires were then affixed and the semiconductor elements would be ready for use as strain gage or transducer.

The above method has the following disadvantage. Such elements are relatively large in size and very brittle. Hence, they can be broken easily.

An objective of the present work was to develop "tougher" units with a reasonable degree of flexibility. Two experimental methods were used to improve the durability and flexibility of silicon elements.

One method used was a vapor growth process. Ultra-thin elements were formed by letting silicon vapor condense on the relatively cool walls of a quartz tube (located in a thermal gradient). These needle-shaped or "whiskerlike" elements that grow from the walls of the tube are hexagonal in cross section. They vary from about 0.001 to 0.003 inch in diameter and are about $\frac{1}{4}$ to $\frac{5}{8}$ inch in length. These elements have great structural strength[5] and can be bent into a "springlike" loop without breaking. One of these experimental units is shown in Fig. 2.

The second method used to obtain flexible specimens was to use a carefully controlled bath process. Here, rectangular slabs roughly $0.015 \times 0.015 \times$ about $\frac{3}{4}$ inch in length were cut from a properly oriented master rod. These were lapped to a size of about $0.010 \times 0.010 \times \frac{3}{4}$ inch. Regions about 0.063 inch square on the ends were masked with a protecting film of "resist." The unit was then placed in a controlled bath to etch away unwanted material. The result was a *dumbbell-shaped* unit with a thin cylindrical center portion which was about 0.002 inch in diameter by about $\frac{5}{8}$ inch in length. The "resist" was removed from the end areas and lead wires were attached by an alloying process. One of these sliver type elements is shown in Fig. 2. A disadvantage of this method is that "voids" or "hollow" areas (due to imperfect or nonhomogeneous regions) sometimes are etched out of the semiconductor wafer with resultant loss of structural strength in this type of element.

CHARACTERISTICS OF SILICON ELEMENTS

To obtain the optimum type of semiconductor for use in strain gage (and transducer) applications, it is necessary to "characterize" the basic properties of such piezoresistive materials. The present work emphasizes the static properties of thin elements of silicon. To date approximately 24 forms of n- and p-type silicon have been studied. The word *form* as used here means that the specimens tested had crystallographic orientations in the 111, 110, and 100 directions in k-space for five different values of resistivity in the range 0.001–100 ohm-cm. Over-all temperature environment was from about $-80°$ to $+160°$C. Some of the characteristics are shown in graphical form in Figs. 3–10.

In general, two basic methods were used to establish the properties of the silicon devices discussed in this paper. One of these was to arrange the piezor in a static test setup so that current or resistance changes were measured upon application of longitudinal stress for the stated environment. Another method involved bonding of matched gages to the top and bottom surfaces of a horizontal cantilever beam or a "constant moment" beam. The latter was used to minimize "shear effects" and the bonding

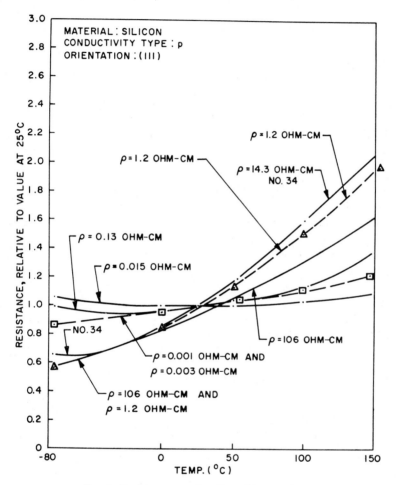

FIG. 3. Resistance as a function of temperature.

material insulated the piezors from the beam. The elements were connected in a bridge circuit. Voltage or current changes were measured when a steady load was applied to the beam. When known forces were applied, the beam deflected from its neutral or unstressed position. This action placed the piezors on the beam in tension or compression, thus causing a change or unbalance in bridge resistance. All of the variables involved can be measured and plotted graphically.

Linear relationships exist between change in resistance of thin p-type silicon elements and applied longitudinal stress at strain levels less than

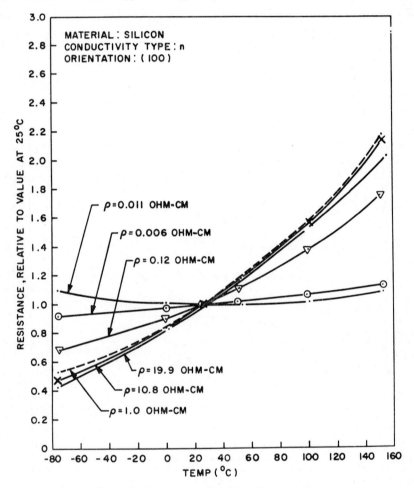

FIG. 4. Resistance as a function of temperature.

1000 microinches/inch. All types of n-type silicon do not exhibit this linear relationship.

Figure 1 shows one type of four-active-arm bridge circuit and cantilever beam that has been used successfully.

Figure 2 shows some of the varieties of silicon piezors that were developed and tested.

Figures 3–6 show variations in electrical resistance and gage factor as functions of temperature. Figures 7–9 show outputs as functions of stress for stated conditions. Figure 10 is a graph of output as a function of strain.

Figure 3 shows relative electrical resistance as a function of temperature

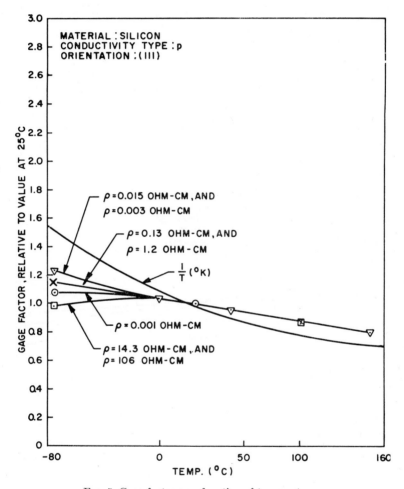

Fig. 5. Gage factor as a function of temperature.

for various values of resistivity of p-type silicon with the 111 orientation. The graph shows that the temperature characteristic varies widely for various resistivities. Materials with resistivities in the neighborhood of 0.100 to 1.0 ohm-cm have the smallest slope. A horizontal line would denote a perfect characteristic.

Figure 4 is the same characteristic for n-type silicon with the 100 crystal orientation. Here again, low resistivity materials exhibit the best temperature stability.

Figure 5 shows the gage factor-temperature characteristic of p-type silicon with the 111 orientation. Once again materials with resistivities

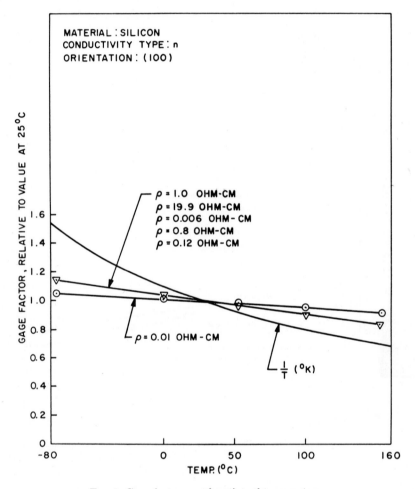

FIG. 6. Gage factor as a function of temperature.

near the 0.100-ohm-cm region exhibit relatively good stability. For convenience in comparison this graph (and Fig. 6) includes the $1/T(\mathrm{K}^0)$ characteristic.

Figure 6 is the gage factor-temperature characteristic of n-type silicon with the 100 orientation. The low resistivity material exhibits the best temperature characteristic.

Figure 7 shows the output-stress characteristic of low resistivity, p-type silicon with the 111 orientation. Temperature is the parameter.

Figure 8 is the same characteristic for low resistivity n-type silicon with the 100 orientation.

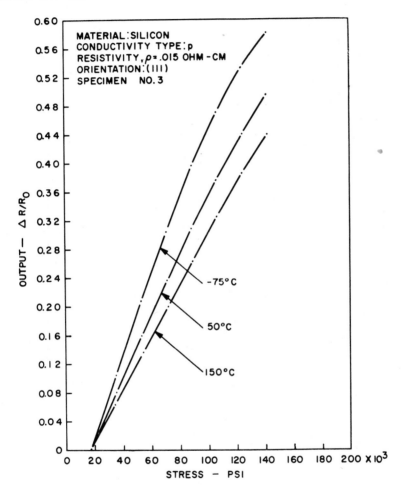

MATERIAL : SILICON
CONDUCTIVITY TYPE : p
RESISTIVITY, ρ = .015 OHM - CM
ORIENTATION : (III)
SPECIMEN NO. 3

-75° C

50° C

150° C

OUTPUT — $\Delta R/R_0$

STRESS — PSI

FIG. 7. Output characteristic of p-type silicon at selected temperatures over selected stress ranges.

Figure 9 is a graph of output level as a function of tension for n-type silicon with the 100 orientation. The parameter is resistivity. The ambient temperature was about 50°C. Note that the output characteristic of this type of material is nonlinear. This is a disadvantage. Test conditions are explained in the sketch.

Figure 10 is a graph of per cent output as a function of strain for the *p*-type, low resistivity, "vapor grown piezor." The nonlinearity of the output as a function of strain is hardly noticeable (at room temperature). In this case two elements were bonded to the surfaces of a constant moment

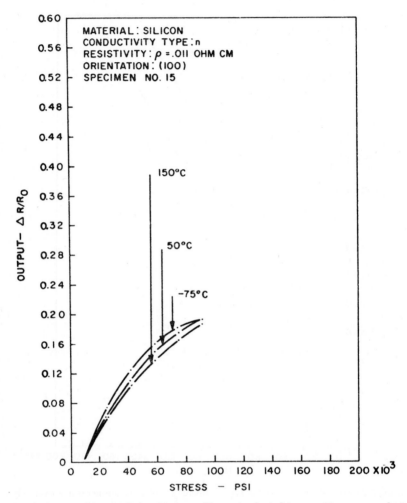

FIG. 8. Output characteristic of *n*-type silicon at selected temperatures over selected stress ranges.

bending beam as shown in the sketch. Compression loading is shown. The elements were connected in a bridge type circuit. Known values of load were applied to deflect the beam in order to place the gages in compression and tension. This unbalances the bridge by an amount proportional to applied force. Then the applied force was removed and the beam was allowed to return to its neutral position. The direction of the applied force was reversed to reverse the compression and tension stresses applied to the gages. This graph illustrates the fact that if one element is put in tension, and the other in compression the bridge unbalance is such that there will be a linear change in electrical output in the stress range indicated. If the stresses are reversed the electrical output remains essentially linear. In

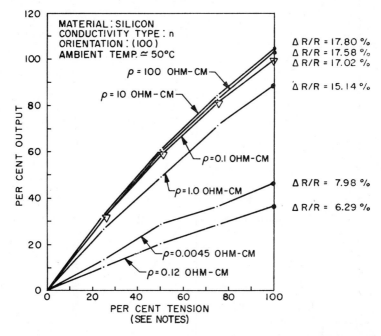

FIG. 9. Output level as a function of tension. *Notes:* Outputs normalized for specimen with $\rho = 0.1$ ohm-cm, n-type; 100% tension (uniaxial) stress level $\simeq 30,000$ psi.

other words, applied stresses in one direction cause an increase in resistance, but when applied in the opposite direction such stresses cause a decrease in resistance. It is noted that this is not a polarity reversal in the strict sense of the word.

APPLICATIONS

There are several areas for application of semiconductor piezoresistive devices. These include, (1) direct bonded structural strain measurements, (2) unbonded strain measurements, (3) and a wide range of force and pressure transducer applications. The low impedances (60–5000 ohms) of piezoresistors are well suited to a number of amplifier applications. The unusually high gage factor of these semiconductor elements undoubtedly

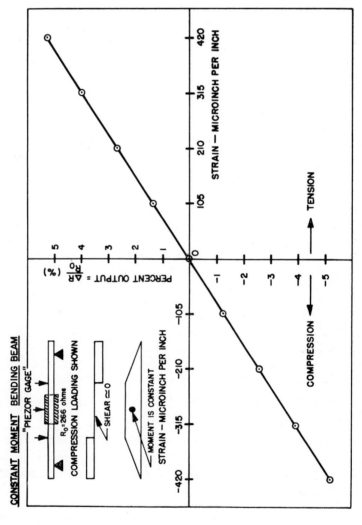

Fig. 10. Per cent output as a function of strain.

will lead to new measurement techniques in those areas where the direct output of metal wire strain gages is marginal. Applications to structures with resonances in the neighborhood of 50,000 cps are planned.

Conclusions

1. Slender elements of semiconductor piezoresistive materials have characteristics that will be useful in strain gage and transducer applications.

2. The main advantages of these devices are small size, high gage factor (amplification) and high output signal, good linearity of output, essentially instantaneous response time, excellent structural strength, and operation from low voltage batteries.

3. The main disadvantages of these devices are that gage factor and electrical resistance of the materials are temperature dependent. However, such effects can be reduced by using material of optimum type, resistivity, and geometrical form, as well as using suitable bridge type electrical circuits when making measurements.

4. Available characteristics data indicate that the optimum form of silicon for strain gage work is a thin element of p-type material with a 111 crystal orientation and a resistivity of about 0.10 to 1.0 ohm-cm.

5. Some crystallographic forms of n-type silicon have a nonlinear electrical response (output) when used in strain gage applications.

Nomenclature

ρ = resistivity (ohm-cm).

π_e = longitudinal piezoresistive coefficient when electric field component, current density component, and simple tension are all in the same direction ($cm^2/dyne \times 10^{-12}$). Other piezoresistance coefficients are denoted by the symbol π, with suitable subscripts, and their nomenclature is denoted in the text.

E = electric field component (volts/cm).

i = current density component (amp/cm^2). Sometimes represented in the three-dimensional case as the divergence of a vector, "div i."

h, k, l = Miller indices of a semiconductor crystal with respect to axis of a thin element.

T = longitudinal stress, distributed force per unit area, F/A ($dynes/cm^2$).

l_{11}, l_{12}, l_{13} = direction cosines from cubic crystal axis to longitudinal axis of a thin piezoresistive element.

G = strain gage factor, fractional change in resistance per fractional change in longitudinal strain.

Y = Young's (stretch) modulus, ratio of longitudinal stress to longitudinal strain (dynes/cm² $\times$ 10¹²). 1 dyne/cm² = 1.45 $\times$ 10⁻⁵ lb/inch². $Y\pi_e$ is dimensionless.

S = longitudinal strain, dimensionless.

$R = \rho L/A$ = resistance (ohms).

L = length (cm)

A = cross-section area (cm²).

σ = Poisson's ratio, ratio of transverse to longitudinal strain $(-\Delta w L_0/w_0 \Delta L)$.

°F = temperature, degrees Fahrenheit.

°C = temperature, degrees centigrade.

ACKNOWLEDGMENTS

The authors wish to thank the technical committees of the Instrument Society of America for their interest in this subject. Also, it is appropriate to acknowledge the interest and support of management and engineering segments of Electro-Optical Systems, Inc., Pasadena, California, and Picatinny Arsenal, Dover, New Jersey. This work was supported, in part, by the Ordnance Corps, U. S. Army, Contract No. DA-04-495-ORD-1475.

REFERENCES

1. Smith, C. S., Piezoresistance effect in germanium and silicon, *Phys. Rev.* **94**, 42–49 (1954).
2. Herring, C., Transport properties of a many valley semiconductor, *Bell System Tech. J.* **34**, 237–290 (1955).
3. Mason, W. P., and Thurston, R. N., Use of piezoresistance materials in the measurement of displacement, force, and torque, *J. Acoust. Soc. Am.* **29**, 1096–1101 (1957).
4. Morin, F., Geballe, T., and Herring, C., Temperature dependence of piezoresistance of high purity silicon, *Phys. Rev.* **105**, 525–539 (1957).
5. Eisner, R. L., Tensile test on silicon whiskers, *Acta Met.* **3**, 1–2 (1955).

BIBLIOGRAPHY

A. General Theory

    a. W. Shockley, "Electronics and Holes in Semiconductors," Van Nostrand, Princeton, New Jersey, 1950.
    b. E. Conwell, *Proc. I.R.E.* **40**, 1327 (1952); **46**, 1281 (1958).
    c. C. Herring, *Bell System Tech. J.* **34**, 237 (1955).
    d. F. Morin, T. Geballe, and C. Herring, *Phys. Rev.* **105**, 525 (1957).

B. Elastic Moduli

    e. H. McSkimen, *J. Appl. Phys.* **24**, 988 (1953).
    f. R. Eisner, *Acta Met.* **3**, 1 (1955).
    g. L. Slutsky and C. Garland, *Phys. Rev.* **113**, 167 (1959).

C. Apparatus

    h. R. Potter and J. McKeab, *J. Research Natl. Bur. Standards* **59**, 427 (1957).
    i. M. Pollack, *Rev. Sci. Instr.* **29**, 639 (1958).

D. Growth of Crystal Elements

    j. G. Pearson, W. Read, and W. Feldmann, *Acta Met* **5,** 181 (1957).

    k. R. Doremus, B. Roberts, and D. Turnbull, eds., "Growth and Perfection of Crystals," Wiley, New York, 1958.

E. Measurements of Piezoresistive Effect and Changes in Resistivity

    l. C. Smith, *Phys. Rev.* **94,** 42 (1954) (Ge and Si).

    m. W. Paul and G. Pearson, *Phys. Rev.* **98,** 1755 (1955) (Si).

    n. R. Keyes, *Phys. Rev.* **99,** 490 (1955) (InSb).

    o. See reference 3 (Ge, Si, InSb).

    p. M. Pollak, *Phys. Rev.* **111,** 789 (1958) (*n*-Ge).

F. Strain Gages

    q. C. Perry and H. Lissner, "The Strain Gage Primer," McGraw-Hill, New York, 1955.

AN EXPERIMENT ON A NEW TYPE OF RESISTANCE FOIL STRAIN GAGE FOR ANALYSIS OF CONCENTRATED STRESSES

Osamu Watanabe and Yoshikazu Izumi

Kyowa Electronic Instruments Company, Ltd., Tokyo, Japan

Abstract

In general, analysis of concentrated stress has been done by Rühl-Fischer's method. Now, more convenient resistance foil gages are manufactured, which have special configurations and electrical circuits for varying their gage length. With such gages, concentrated strain distributions around circular holes in tensile test specimens have been measured, and the results checked with theoretical computations. These gages have also been compared with commonly available resistance wire strain gages.

Introduction

Rühl-Fischer's method is commonly used for the measurement of concentrated stress in nearly all types of construction materials. In the application of the foil gages with variable gage length, it was possible to determine the elongation of each segmental length and, thus, by differentiation of the displacement distribution curve, calculate the strain distribution. Ordinarily, this measuring was done by changing the gage length of a mechanical strain gage. However, the installation of this kind of strain gage required some skill and practice. In addition, its defects, such as bias of the operator, difficulty of installation for extremely short gage lengths, and difficulty in obtaining the true gage length, added possibilities for error. Worse yet, it was incapable of remote measurement and the contact points required resetting at each change of gage length. These disadvantages resulted in attempts to produce a gage which was operationally simple, lent itself to remote operation, and could be switched electrically to change its length.

Theory of Operation

1. *Rühl-Fischer's Method*

The commonly used strain gage merely indicates the average strain value distributed over the gage length. Different strain is indicated when the gage length is changed, since all sections of the gage must indicate a constant strain. This results in difficulty in obtaining the "peak" of concen-

21

trated strain. In attempts to manufacture a strain gage by shortening the length, manufacturing technology dictates the minimum size.

According to the method of Rühl-Fischer, the distance between two measuring points is divided into several parts. The displacement of each

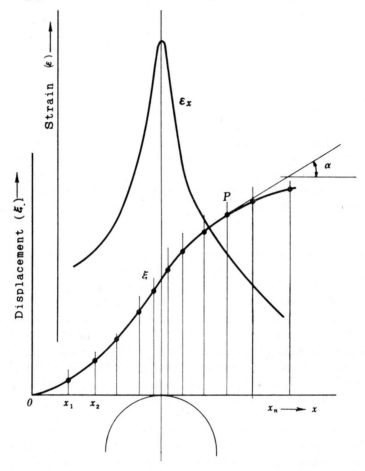

FIG. 1. Displacement curve and strain distribution by Rühl-Fischer's method.

gage length is plotted at its measuring point to describe the displacement curve. The tangent at each point on the curve, becoming the differential value of this point, is the strain shown in Fig. 1. In the measurement of concentrated stress at the minimum section of a plate, a measuring line, X, is drawn perpendicular to the lines of force at the bottom of the hole. This line is divided into intervals $X_1, X_2, \ldots, X_n$. The displacement, ξ_i, at each measuring point is given by

$$\xi_i = \int_0^{xi} \epsilon_i dx_i. \tag{1}$$

Displacements, OX_1, OX_2, . . . , between the gage lengths can be plotted at each measuring point, a displacement curve drawn, and the maximum strain concentration obtained at the inflection point. The tangent at a point, P, on the curve will be

$$\frac{d\xi}{dx} = \tan \alpha = \epsilon_x. \tag{2}$$

From formula (2), the strain in the X-direction can be obtained. Repeating this at each point on the curve will complete the information of the strain distribution curve based on the concentrated stress.

2. *Electrical Resistance Strain Gage Manufactured for Trial*

The pattern of the gage becomes complicated in obtaining a variable gage length, and a high degree of precision is required for each element. Consequently, the strain gage form is a grid pattern produced by the printed circuit technique. This is the same method used in the manufacture of etched foil strain gages. The basic pattern has an appearance as illustrated in Fig. 2, which has five elements 6 mm long and a resistance of 60 ohms

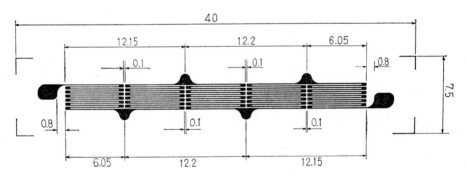

Fig. 2. The pattern of the variable length strain gage manufactured for trial.

per element. Thus, sufficient space, which makes lead wire connection much easier, is provided for the six terminals of the variable strain gage. Epoxy resin is used for the backing of the gage. Phenolic resin or epoxy resin is used to cement the strain gage to its measuring position. This procedure is the same as that used in mounting ordinary foil strain gages.

3. *Element Switching Unit*

The lead wires, connected to the six gage terminals, were wired to the element switching unit having the circuit shown in Fig. 3.

A_0 to A_n and D_0 to D_n ($n = 1 \sim 5$) form two arms of a Wheatstone bridge. These constitute active and dummy gages when two identical strain gages are connected to the terminals. Variable resistors VR_1 to VR_5 are for the adjustment of preliminary balance and are inserted into the proper circuit by the selector switch SW. Switch SW has four poles and five positions.

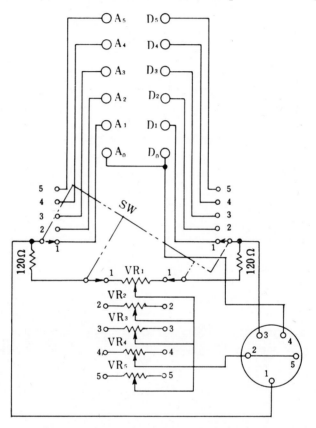

FIG. 3. Element switching unit wiring diagram.

This makes possible the simultaneous switching of the active and dummy gages for each circuit, when multiples of 60 ohms are inserted into the bridge. This is done at basic points of the A_0 and D_0 gage terminals. A 1.5-volt 400-cps carrier wave used for the input to the bridge of the switching unit was supplied from the strain indicator.

4. Testing Method

The specimen used for the measurement of concentrated stress was a steel strip with a circular hole. It was loaded in pure tension and, thus,

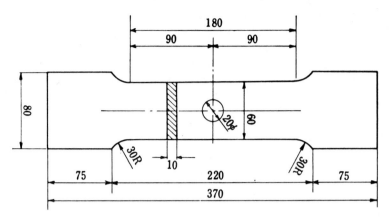

FIG. 4. Dimensions of specimen used in the test.

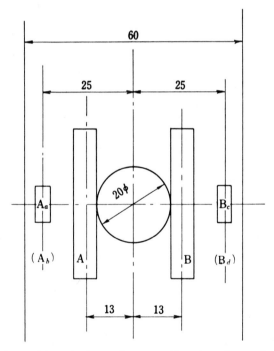

FIG. 5. Relative position of wire strain gages adhered on the specimen. Parentheses indicate the strain gage on the back surface of the specimen.

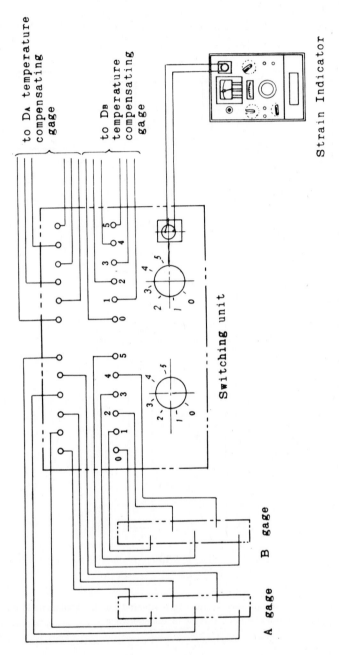

Fig. 6. Block diagram of testing equipment.

values were possible to check by theoretical analysis. Two specimens, the dimensions of which are shown in Fig. 4, were prepared and tested in separate experiments. Two gages were fixed to the specimen with their axes 13 mm from the center of the hole and parallel to the direction of force. The adhesive was Araldite type 101 which was hardened at room temperature. To measure the bending in the specimen due to chucking, two paper gages, type K-22.1, 10 mm long, were placed on each side of the specimen. These were located parallel to the variable gage length strain gages, 25 mm from the center of the hole. These gage positions and their notation are shown in Fig. 5. A 50-ton capacity Amsler-type testing machine was used to load the specimen to 1.2, 2.0, 3.2, 4.0, 5.2, and 6.0 tons. Figure 6 is a block diagram of the measuring equipment used for testing.

5. *Results of the Tests*

Tables I and II indicate displacements measured by the variable length strain gages A and B of the specified loads for gage elements G_1–G_5. The measured strains were converted to displacements when multiplied by their gage length. That is, G_1 was multiplied by 6 mm, G_2 by 12 mm, G_3 by 18 mm, G_4 by 24 mm, and G_5 by 30 mm. Figures 7 and 8 show the results in graphic form, while Fig. 9 shows the relative position of gage elements G_1 to G_5 and the hole.

It is quite easy and accurate to use formula (3)[1] to obtain the tangent at a given point on the displacement curve:

$$\epsilon_n = \left(\frac{d\xi}{dx}\right)_{x=n} = \frac{\xi_1 - 8\xi_2 + 8\xi_4 - \xi_5}{12h}. \tag{3}$$

In formula (3), h is for equally divided intervals from point n and the values for ξ_1 to ξ_5 are for relative displacements corresponding to the element number.

The concentrated strain for each load is shown in Table III. These are for the point n along the x-axis, shown in Fig. 9 and evaluated for $h = 3$ mm.

In the case of pure tension, the strains on the A and B gages are theoretically symmetrical. However, the strains in Tables III and IV are, as a result of bending, unsymmetrical.

The effects of bending stresses are shown in Figs. 10 and 11. These were measured by the K-22.1 paper gages discussed in Test Methods. Based on the experimental results, the correction for bending was done as follows:

The values measured by A_a, A_b, B_c, and B_d shown in Fig. 5 are represented by ϵ_a, ϵ_b, ϵ_c, and ϵ_d.

TABLE I
Measuring Results of Specimen No. 1

A side

Load	G_1		G_2		G_3		G_4		G_5	
	$\epsilon \times 10^{-6}$	$\xi \times 10^{-3}$ mm	$\epsilon \times 10^{-6}$	$\xi \times 10^{-3}$ mm	$\epsilon \times 10^{-6}$	$\xi \times 10^{-3}$ mm	$\epsilon \times 10^{-6}$	$\xi \times 10^{-3}$ mm	$\epsilon \times 10^{-6}$	$\xi \times 10^{-3}$ mm
0 (ton)	0	0	0	0	0	0	0	0	0	0
1.2	69	0.414	77	0.93	85	1.53	85	2.05	84	2.53
2.0	128	0.772	142	1.71	151	2.72	359	3.69	151	4.56
3.2	249	1.49	275	3.30	290	5.23	293	7.04	290	8.61
4.0	335	2.00	363	4.37	385	6.93	388	9.32	383	11.5
5.2	466	2.79	509	6.11	535	9.64	540	12.9	531	15.9
6.0	556	3.33	605	7.28	638	11.5	645	15.5	635	19.1

B side

Load	G_1		G_2		G_3		G_4		G_5	
	$\epsilon \times 10^{-6}$	$\xi \times 10^{-3}$ mm	$\epsilon \times 10^{-6}$	$\xi \times 10^{-3}$ mm	$\epsilon \times 10^{-6}$	$\xi \times 10^{-3}$ mm	$\epsilon \times 10^{-6}$	$\xi \times 10^{-3}$ mm	$\epsilon \times 10^{-6}$	$\xi \times 10^{-3}$ mm
0 (ton)	0	0	0	0	0	0	0	0	0	0
1.2	237	1.42	254	3.04	263	4.73	268	6.43	268	8.04
2.0	354	2.12	384	4.60	395	7.10	391	9.57	391	12.0
3.2	513	3.09	555	6.66	572	10.3	579	13.85	579	17.4
4.0	615	3.69	664	7.97	685	12.3	696	16.7	695	20.8
5.2	766	4.60	828	9.95	853	15.4	862	2.07	856	25.6
6.0	865	5.19	930	11.2	962	17.3	978	23.4	965	29.0

TABLE II

MEASURING RESULTS OF SPECIMEN No. 2

Load	G_1		G_2		G_3		G_4		G_5	
$\epsilon \times 10^{-6}$	$\epsilon \times 10^{-6}$	$\xi \times 10^{-3}$ mm	$\epsilon \times 10^{-6}$	$\xi \times 10^{-3}$ mm	$\epsilon \times 10^{-6}$	$\xi \times 10^{-3}$ mm	$\epsilon \times 10^{-6}$	$\xi \times 10^{-3}$ mm	$\epsilon \times 10^{-6}$	$\xi \times 10^{-3}$ mm
A side										
0 (ton)	0	0	0	0	0	0	0	0	0	0
1.2	88	0.526	98	1.17	99	1.79	100	2.42	100	3.03
2.0	165	0.991	182	2.19	190	3.44	190	4.58	186	5.60
3.2	306	1.83	336	4.03	345	6.22	345	8.30	338	10.2
4.0	394	2.37	434	5.20	444	8.00	449	10.8	438	13.1
5.2	534	3.20	581	6.98	602	10.9	664	14.5	588	17.7
6.0	630	3.77	686	8.24	709	12.8	716	17.2	700	21.0
B side										
0 (ton)	0	0	0	0	0	0	0	0	0	0
1.2	187	1.12	187	2.25	211	3.80	210	5.03	204	6.12
2.0	283	1.70	307	3.68	322	5.80	322	7.73	395	9.73
3.2	435	2.61	474	5.70	504	9.08	500	12.0	486	14.6
4.0	526	3.16	570	6.84	607	10.9	604	14.5	589	17.7
5.2	657	3.95	721	8.65	765	13.8	767	18.4	745	22.3
6.0	754	4.53	826	9.91	881	15.9	878	21.0	853	25.6

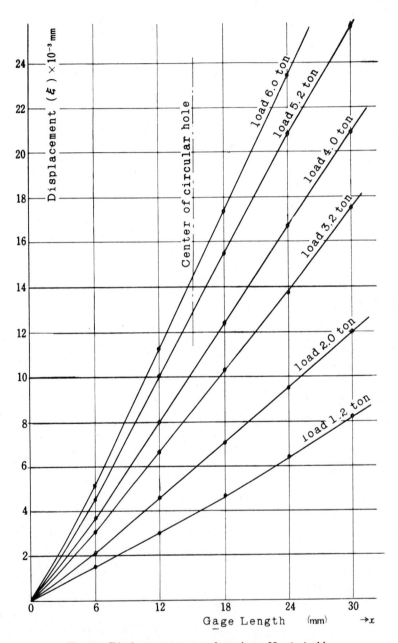

FIG. 7a. Displacement curve of specimen No. 1, A side.

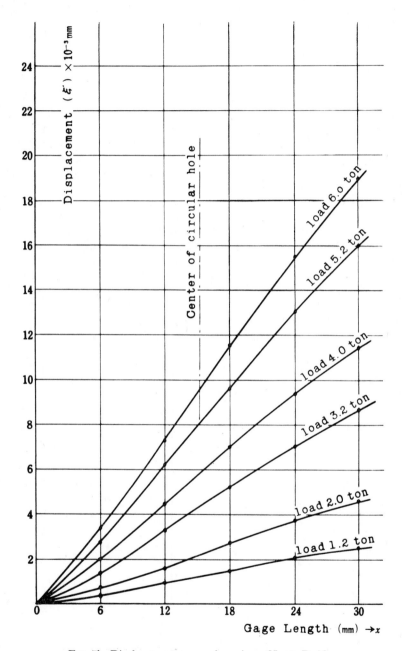

FIG. 7b. Displacement curve of specimen No. 1, B side.

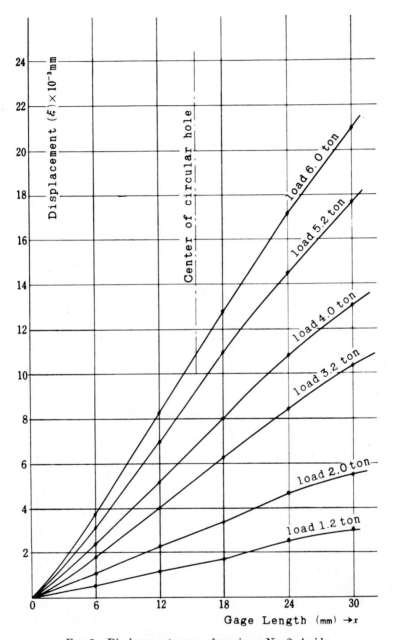

F<small>IG</small>. 8a. Displacement curve of specimen No. 2, A side.

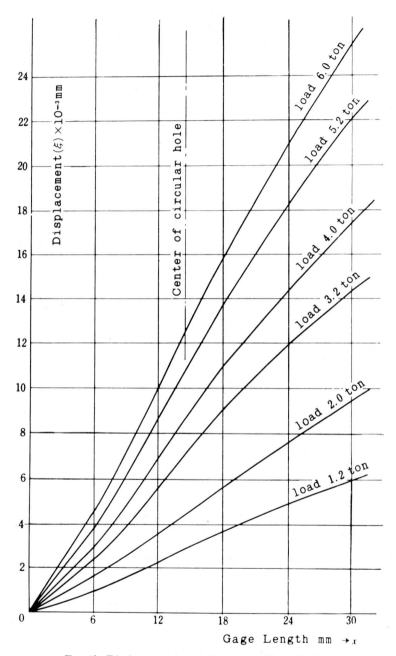

FIG. 8b. Displacement curve of specimen No. 2, B side.

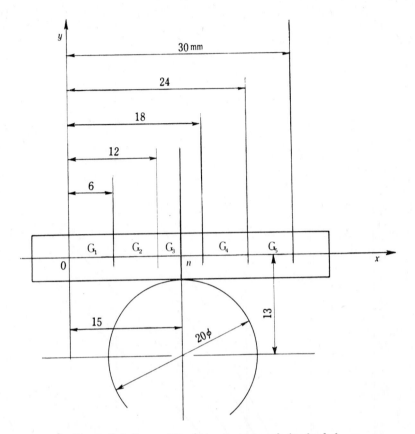

FIG. 9. Relative position between gage and circular hole.

TABLE III

MEASURED STRAIN AT n POINT AGAINST EACH LOAD OF TEST SPECIMEN No. 1

	$\epsilon_n \times 10^{-6}$	
Load	A side gage	B side gage
0 (ton)	0	0
1.2	286	96
2.0	427	170
3.2	603	324
4.0	722	430
5.2	903	595
6.0	1020	707

TABLE IV

TABLE IV

MEASURED STRAIN AT n POINT AGAINST EACH LOAD OF TEST SPECIMEN No. 2

| | $\epsilon_n \times 10^{-6}$ | |
Load	A side gage	B side gage
0 (ton)	0	0
1.2	100	246
2.0	209	378
3.2	364	570
4.0	474	693
5.2	646	852
6.0	759	1007

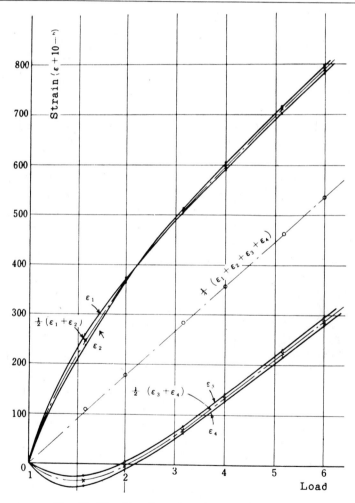

FIG. 10. Mixed bending of tension specimen No. 1.

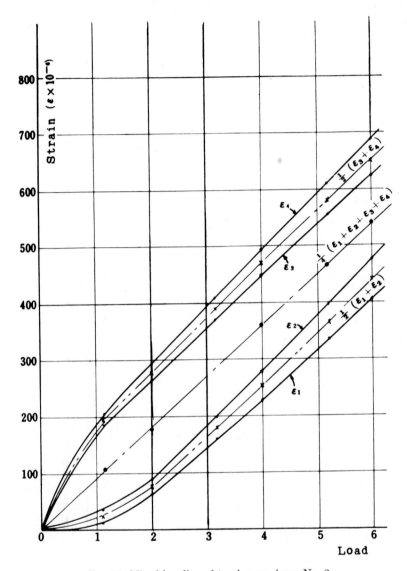

FIG. 11. Mixed bending of tension specimen No. 2.

Then

$$\frac{\epsilon_a + \epsilon_c}{2} = K$$

$$\frac{\epsilon_b + \epsilon_d}{2} = K'$$

$$\frac{(K + K')/2 - K}{K} = \frac{K' - K}{2K} = C_2 \tag{4a}$$

$$\frac{\epsilon_{nA} + \epsilon_{nB}}{2} = C_1. \tag{4b}$$

Consequently, the amount of correction could be obtained by the formulae

$$\delta_A = (C_1 - \epsilon_{nA})(1 + C_2)$$
$$\delta_B = (C_1 - \epsilon_{nB})(1 - C_2) \tag{5}$$

and added to the value of ϵ_{nA} and ϵ_{nB}. Tables V and VI show the results of this correction.

TABLE V

CORRECTION FACTOR AND CORRECTED STRAIN OF SPECIMEN No. 1

Load	$K(\times 10^{-6})$	$K'(\times 10^{-6})$	C_2 (%)	$C_1(\times 10^{-6})$	Corrected strain	
					A gage	B gage
0 (ton)	0	0	0	0	0	0
1.2	122	100	−9.02	191	182	182
2.0	185	176	−2.45	299	296	296
3.2	292	286	−1.03	464	462	462
4.0	356	359	0.42	576	577	577
5.2	464	465	0.11	749	749	749
6.0	535	536	0.09	864	864	864

TABLE VI

CORRECTION FACTOR AND CORRECTED STRAIN OF SPECIMEN No. 2

Load	$K(\times 10^{-6})$	$K'(\times 10^{-6})$	C_2 (%)	$C_1 \times 10^{-6})$	Corrected strain	
					A gage	B gage
0 (ton)	0	0	0	0	0	0
1.2	100	121	10.5	173	181	181
2.0	164	191	8.23	294	301	301
3.2	273	308	6.40	467	474	474
4.0	338	385	6.95	584	592	592
5.2	442	500	6.57	749	751	757
6.0	511	579	6.65	883	891	891

6. Theoretical Calculation

The Howland formula[2] was used for the calculation of stress at the neighborhood of a circular hole of a specimen having pure tension as in Fig. 4. In this case, the coordinates of the strip are considered as shown in

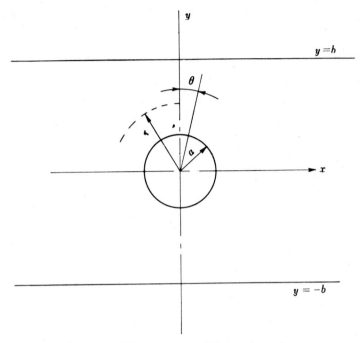

FIG. 12. The coordinates of the tension strip.

Fig. 12. Tension is also assumed to be applied evenly in the direction of the x-axis, and Young's modulus of the mild steel (SS-41) under tension was considered $E = 2.1 \times 10^4$ kg/mm², and Poisson's ratio $\nu = 0.303$.

TABLE VII
THE COEFFICIENT IN THE FINAL VALUE OF STRESS FUNCTION

d_0	5.69×10^{-2}	e_2	-6.52×10^{-2}
d_2	3.59×10^{-3}	e_4	-6.46×10^{-5}
d_4	5.25×10^{-6}	e_6	-3.50×10^{-7}
d_6	2.76×10^{-8}	e_8	-1.10×10^{-9}
d_8	1.12×10^{-10}		—
l_2	5.30×10^{-2}	m_0	6.29×10^{-3}
l_4	1.26×10^{-2}	m_2	-1.39×10^{-2}
l_6	3.22×10^{-3}	m_4	-7.04×10^{-3}
l_8	7.90×10^{-4}	m_6	-2.61×10^{-3}
l_{10}	1.91×10^{-4}	m_8	-8.43×10^{-4}

Each coefficient in the final value of stress function is obtained when

$$\lambda = \frac{a}{b} = \frac{10}{30} = 0.333$$

and the result is shown in Table VII. The X-direction stress σ_x at the minimum section of the specimen is obtained by substituting $\theta = 0$ for σ_θ. Now,

$$\sigma_\theta = T\left[\tfrac{1}{2}(1 + \cos 2\theta) + 2m_0 + \frac{d_0}{\rho^2} \right.$$
$$+ 2\sum_{n=1}^{\infty}\left\{ \frac{n(2n+1)d_{2n}}{\rho^{2n+2}} \right.$$
$$+ \frac{(n-1)(2n-1)e_{2n}}{\rho\epsilon_n} + n(2n-1)l_{2n}\rho^{2n-2}$$
$$\left. \left. + (n+1)(2n+1)m_{2n}\rho^{2n} \right\} \cos 2n\theta \right].$$

Then, if $\theta = 0$ is substituted for σ_θ,

$$\sigma_x = T\left[(1 + 2m_0 + 2l_2) + 12(l_4 + m_2)\rho^2 \right.$$
$$+ 30(l_6 + m_4)\rho^4 + 56(l_8 + m_6)\rho^6$$
$$+ 90(l_{10} + m_6)\rho^8 + \cdots$$
$$+ \frac{d_0}{\rho^2} + 6(d_2 + e_4)\frac{1}{\rho^4} + 20(d_4 + e_6)\frac{1}{\rho^6}$$
$$\left. + 42(d_6 + e_8)\frac{1}{\rho^8} + \cdots \right].$$

Additional terms in the above formula are negligibly small. When the value of each coefficient in Table VII is put into the above equation it becomes:

$$\frac{\sigma_x}{T} = 1.1186 - 1.56 \times 10^{-2}\rho^2 - 1.15 \times 10^{-2}\rho^4$$
$$- 1.02 \times 10^{-1}\rho^6 - 5.87 \times 10^{-2}\rho^8 + \cdots$$
$$+ 5.69 \times 10^{-2}\frac{1}{\rho^2} + 2.11 \times 10^{-2}\frac{1}{\rho^4} \tag{6}$$
$$+ 9.8 \times 10^{-5}\frac{1}{\rho^6} + 1.11 \times 10^{-6}\frac{1}{\rho^8} + \cdots .$$

In the same way, the Y-direction stress σ_y in the minimum section also has the condition $\theta = 0$ for σ_r. It is

$$\sigma_r = T\left[\tfrac{1}{2}(1 - \cos 2\theta) + 2m_0 - \frac{d_0}{\rho^2} \right.$$
$$- \sum_{n-1}^{\infty}\left\{ \frac{n(2n+1)d_{2n}}{\rho^{2n+2}} + \frac{(n+1)(2n-1)e_{2n}}{\rho^{2n}} \right.$$
$$+ n(2n-1)l_{2n}\rho^{2n-2}$$
$$\left. \left. + (n-1)(2n+1)m_{2n}\rho^{2n} \right\} \cos 2n\theta \right].$$

Then, if $\theta = 0$ is substituted for σ_r,

$$
\begin{aligned}
\sigma_y = T \Bigg[& 2(m_0 - l_2) - 12l_4\rho^2 - 10(3l_6 + m_4)\rho_4 \\
& - 28(2l_8 + m_6)\rho^6 \cdots \\
& - (d_0 + 4e_2)\frac{1}{\rho^2} - 6(d_2 + 3e_4)\frac{1}{\rho^4} \\
& - 20(d_4 + 2e_6)\frac{1}{\rho^6} - (7d_6 + 15e_8)\frac{1}{\rho^8} - \cdots \Bigg]
\end{aligned}
$$

Upon substituting the value of each coefficient in Table VII into the above formula, it becomes

$$
\begin{aligned}
\sigma_y/T = & - 9.34 \times 10^{-2} - 1.51 \times 10\rho^2 \\
& - 2.62 \times 10^{-2}\rho^4 + 2.88 \times 10^{-2}\rho^6 \\
& + \cdots + 2.04 \times 10^{-1}\frac{1}{\rho^2} \\
& - 2.03 \times 10^{-2}\frac{1}{\rho^4} - 9.10 \times 10^{-5}\frac{1}{\rho^6} \qquad (7) \\
& - 1.08 \times 10^{-6}\frac{1}{\rho^8} + \cdots
\end{aligned}
$$

σ_x/T and σ_y/T are evaluated by putting $\rho = r/b = r/30$ (provided $10 \leqq r \leqq 30$) into formulae (6) and (7). The results are given in Table VIII: the theoretical stress on the minimum section of the strip. With

TABLE VIII

THE TENSION T OF THE SPECIMEN IS SHOWN BY THEORETICAL CALCULATIONS AS A PARAMETER WITH THE X- AND Y-DIRECTION STRESSES ON THE MINIMUM SECTION

	Stress	
ρ	σ_x/T	σ_y/T
0.333	3.427	0.000
0.400	2.315	0.335
0.467	1.826	0.363
0.533	1.563	0.336
0.600	1.416	0.260
0.667	1.314	0.193
0.733	1.238	0.132
0.800	1.161	0.080
0.867	1.096	0.035
0.933	1.009	0.001
1.000	0.905	0.000

TABLE IX
STRAINS OF X- AND Y-DIRECTIONS (T PARAMETER)

ρ	Strain	
	ϵ_x/T ($\times 10^{-5}$)	ϵ_y/T ($\times 10^{-5}$)
0.333	16.30	−4.99
0.400	10.54	−1.78
0.467	8.17	−0.93
0.533	6.96	−0.68
0.600	6.37	−0.83
0.667	5.98	−1.00
0.733	5.70	−1.18
0.800	5.42	−1.32
0.867	5.17	−1.43
0.933	4.80	−1.47
1.000	4.31	−1.32

the values in Table VIII, Hooke's law can be applied to obtain the strain:

$$\frac{\epsilon_x}{T} = \frac{1}{E}\left(\frac{\sigma_x}{T} - \nu\frac{\sigma_y}{T}\right). \tag{8}$$

Table IX shows the results of this calculation. Figure 13, being the values of Tables VIII and IX, shows graphically the stress and strain distribution

TABLE X
CALCULATED STRAIN OF X-DIRECTION 13 MM
APART FROM THE CENTER OF CIRCULAR HOLE

Load	T	ϵ_x ($\times 10^{-6}$)
0 (ton)	0	0
1.2	2.00	184
2.0	3.33	307
3.2	5.33	491
4.0	6.67	613
5.2	8.67	797
6.0	1.00	920

around a circular hole in a strip under tension. The results in Table X are obtained by the calculation of the strain at a distance of 13 mm from the center of circular hole, conforming the calculated strain to the above stated testing conditions.

7. Comparison of Theoretical Value with Measured Value

Figure 14 is a chart of the theoretical calculated values (Table VIII) and those measurements (Tables V and VI) by a variable length strain gage. The

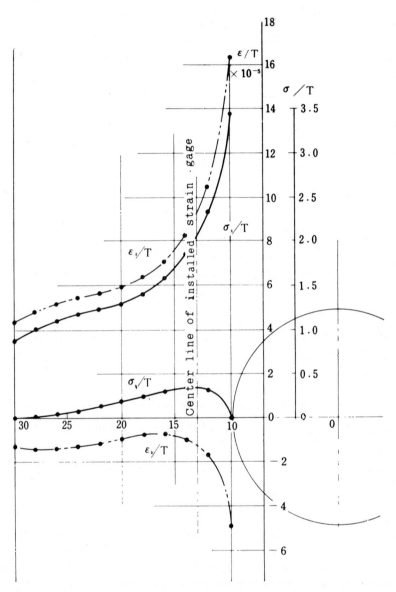

FIG. 13. Stress distribution in the neighborhood of a circular hole.

measured value indicated at the minimum section was slightly below theoretical, about 4 to 6%; a greater difference was observed in comparison of results obtained from common strain gages installed at the same position. Both of these, K-22.1 and K-18.1, strain gages are paper gages;

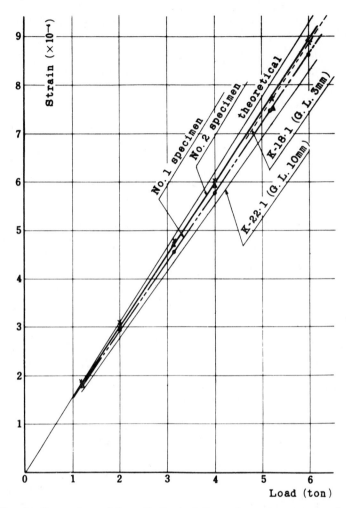

FIG. 14. Comparison of theoretical calculation value and measured value.

the standard grid type manufactured by our company. The gage length
of the former is 10 mm, and the latter 3 mm. Table XI indicates the values
of the strain in the minimum section 13 mm from the center of circular hole
of No. 2 specimen as measured by K-22.1 and K-18.1 gages. The correction
of bending was done in the same way as the case of previously mentioned
variable length strain gage.

8. Conclusion

Explanation of the fundamental experiment of concentrated strain
measuring by Rühl-Fischer's method, with the use of a variable length

strain gage manufactured for trial with a foil strain gage was done. The analysis of the data shows a remarkable effect. As seen in Fig. 14, each element of the strain gage manufactured for trial possesses a G.L. of 6 mm, which is very close to the value measured by a conventional strain gage having a G.L. of 3 mm. However, its difference from the theoretically cal-

TABLE XI

	Concentrated strain in the minimum section in the distance of 13 mm from the center of circular hole	
Load (ton)	K-22.1	K-18.1
0	0	0
1.2	161	188
2.0	274	307
3.2	435	479
4.0	547	600
5.2	718	765
6.0	826	889

culated value is still within 4 to 6%. With the skill of manufacture capable of creating a strain gage possessing characteristics obtained under trial production and the G.L. cut to 3 mm, it is quite probable that such a strain gage will be sufficiently effective for measuring concentrated stress.

By the actual use of such a strain gage, analysis of unknown stress by remote measuring will be possible. It is expected that the manufacturer's painstaking care in production of a strain gage having a short gage length, and the measurer's troubles in accurately knowing the direction to install the gage will not remain troublesome in the future. As to the resistance strain gage of G.L. about 1 mm, often seen on the market, it can be said that Rosette analysis will be considerably erratic at the spot of stress concentration because the increase of its transverse sensitivity is inevitable.

ACKNOWLEDGMENTS

We want to express deep thanks and appreciation for the kindness of Professor Masaki Watanabe of Osaka University, who directed this experiment all the way, analyzed the data, and made the theoretical calculations. We are also grateful to Yoshiharu Ideguchi, then on the staff of the same university, for his cooperative research work.

REFERENCES

1. *Prod. Eng.* **29,** 77–79 (1958).
2. Howland, R. C. J., On the stresses in the neighborhood of a circular hole in a strip under tension, *Phil. Trans. Roy. Soc. London Ser. A* **229,** 73 (1930).

ADHESIVES: HOW THEY DETERMINE AND LIMIT STRAIN GAGE PERFORMANCE

Peter K. Stein

Arizona State University, Tempe, Arizona

Abstract

A survey is presented on the manner in which adhesives determine and limit strain gage behavior. It is shown that it is not possible today to predict gage behavior on the basis of knowledge of the gage construction and adhesive properties, although competent research in this area is being carried on. Adhesive properties as they affect strain gage behavior are discussed and a number of very practical and direct operating consequences for the strain gage user are derived from these considerations. These "laws" are summarized in the section on Conclusions.

Instrumentation Requirements

The specifications written for modern instrumentation are extremely broad. It is commonly desired to measure physical quantities such as pressure, force, torque, acceleration, etc., in extremely hostile environments. Some examples of ambient operating conditions might be the following (note that no *one* instrument is expected to fit these, although it would certainly help if *one type of transducer* could be made to fulfill these requirements):

(a) temperature ambients from near absolute zero to 2000°F

(b) humidity ambients from dry desert conditions to prolonged submersion under high pressures and temperatures

(c) distance between measurement and read-out of from inches to thousands of miles

(d) pressure ambients of from thousands of atmospheres to the fractions of an atmosphere encountered in space

(e) ranges in quantities to be measured which may be apart by factors of several million to one

(f) centrifugal and vibratory environments which exert on the measuring transducer one million times its own weight, i.e., fields of one million "g's"

(g) possibilities of transmitting information from members rotating at 100,000 rpm and above

(h) frequency response from static (DC) to hundreds of kilocycles

(i) ease of application so that a Ph.D. degree is not required

(j) low enough cost so that laboratories however small can use the device

(k) stability and repeatability of calibration

(l) auxiliary instrumentation should be simple and low in cost

(m) possibility of eliminating the effects of quantities other than the desired variable which may act on the transducer; i.e., temperature fluctuations should not interfere with load measurement; bending in one plane should not interfere with bending measurement in another, etc.

One of the basic transduction processes which can be adapted to all these requirements is the resistance-strain principle which is the foundation of the bonded resistance strain gage. Commercial and research instrumentation based on the bonded strain gage have been built to satisfy all the conditions stated above. The strain gage principle is becoming more and more commonly used as its advantages become increasingly apparent.

Basic Operating Principle of Strain Gages

The basic principle of operation of the bonded resistance strain gage, as with brittle and photoelastic coating methods of stress measurement, is that strain is transmitted from the surface of the test specimen through an adhesive layer to a strain sensitive element. The mechanically induced strain in the filament is transduced into a change of electrical resistance of the filament.

The Basic Assumption

The basic assumption for all bonded strain gage work is that the resistance change in the gage is some measure of the strain beneath it. *If the strain is not faithfully transmitted from the test specimen surface to the strain sensitive filament, then no amount of expensive instrumentation attached to the gage terminals will give correct results!*

Gage Properties Affected by the Adhesive

If all other components in the gage have been properly selected (i.e., all other gage properties being equal and not the limit of gage performance) the adhesive will affect and determine the following strain gage properties among others:

Gage factor or sensitivity

Gage factor vs. temperature relationship

Gage factor vs. strain level property, i.e., linearity and hysteresis

Zero shift vs. temperature relationship especially for transient temperatures

Zero shift vs. time under zero strain

Zero shift vs. time under strain (creep).

The Problem

Since the important strain gage characteristics are, to a great extent, determined by the adhesive used to mount the gage, it becomes important to understand the nature of the effect of adhesive properties on strain gage performance, and subsequently to control and design adhesives for optimum results.*

The Purpose of this Paper

The purpose of this paper is to present a penetrating but not necessarily comprehensive analysis of the problem and to survey some of the pertinent literature. It is hoped that the simple rules formulated on the basis of this study will assist researchers in obtaining the best possible information from bonded resistance strain gages. Reference 1a gives a detailed study.

The Ideal Solution

The ideal solution to the problem, but one which unfortunately is not presently available, would be the following:

1. Obtain the characteristics of the adhesive from the adhesive manufacturer; among them would be shear strength, elastic constants, etc., and their variation with time, temperature, curing conditions, substrate material, surface preparation, etc.

2. Obtain the characteristics of the components of the strain gage type used, from the strain gage manufacturer; among them would be elastic constants of the strain sensitive element and the carrier and how these properties vary with time and temperature; strength information of similar nature; dimensions and structural specifications.

3. A theoretical analysis would be available which relates the gage component properties with the adhesive characteristics in terms of the desired performance level of the gage.

Thus could the correct adhesive be selected for a particular gage in its particular ambient condition for the specific performance characteristics required during the test.

Present State of the Art

In none of the three areas defined above is there currently available sufficient information for the solution of the strain gage problem. The following factors enter into the picture.

* It should be noted that the words "adhesive used for a strain gage installation" refer to the combination of adhesive type, filler, and curing agents if any, time-temperature-pressure cure cycle, substrate material, surface preparation procedure, humidity conditions, etc., to which the gage installation has been subjected. These effects are discussed in more detail in later sections.

Stress Distribution in Adhesive Layers

The major unknowns in the area of adhesives and of bonded strain gages are the real stresses in the adhesive layer to which the test specimen is subjected.

Relative Mechanical Adhesive Properties

The mechanical properties of adhesives are most frequently determined on the basis of some standardized test which gives *relative* information about the particular adhesive being investigated. For example, where shear strength tests are often carried out on a standardized lap-joint specimen of specified material, plate thickness, width, overlap, adhesive layer thickness, etc. Specimens may be single-lap, double-lap, butt-joined, or any of a number of configurations. The works of Davidson,[1b] Merriman,[2] and Eickner[3] are typical examples of the copious quantities of information available in this area.

Absolute Mechanical Adhesive Properties

The *average* values of shear stress obtained in a standardized lap-joint test may well serve to compare adhesives on a particular substrate with each other, but these tests do not directly give information about *the* shear strength—the maximum shear strength—of which the adhesive is capable under the conditions of an adhesive joint. It is recognized that an adhesive tested in bulk form exhibits totally different properties from one tested as an adhesive, against a given adherend, and in thin-film form. This problem of determining absolute values of adhesive properties in this frame of reference has been handled in two ways.

Determination of Stress Distribution in Standard Specimens

Theoretical analysis of standard test specimens may reveal the stress distribution to which the adhesive was subjected during the test, permitting a determination of the maximum shear stress, for example, in the adhesive layer at time of rupture. Several samples[4-9] are available of attempts at such solutions with varying degrees of rigor and complexity.

Development of Special Test Methods

Special test specimens and methods may be developed which are expected to yield information of a more absolute nature in terms of adhesive properties. Such tests may be on free films, surface films, or actual adhesive layers. Several authors[10-13] give examples of these approaches.

Stresses in the Adhesive Layer of a Gage

From the earliest days of the bonded resistance strain gage the problem of strain transmittal from the test specimen through the adhesive layer to the strain sensitive element has been studied, although notably *not* in the United States.* Several authors[14-20] treat various phases of the problem with Rohrbach and Czaika[18-20] presenting a complete mathematical equivalent for a strain gage which permits prediction of such things as creep, gage factor, etc. In these references the authors have actually determined separately the properties of each component of the gage installa-

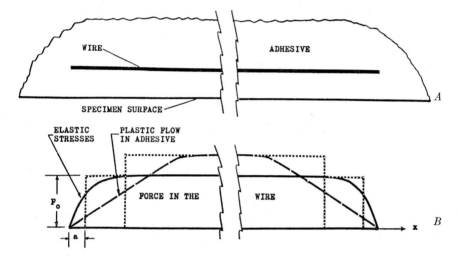

Fig. 1. Stress condition for a single wire bonded to a strained surface.

tion and then combined the individual component properties to give predictably the performance of the over-all installation. Post and Zandman[21] treat the general problem of strain transmittal to an adhesively attached layer and their investigation is directly applicable to strain gage work.

All investigators apparently agree on the following phenomena; since an understanding of these is vital to the proper application and selection of strain gages and adhesives, a brief summary will be presented. Figure 1 presents the simplest approach to the problem: a single length L of circular strain sensitive filament embedded in an infinite layer of adhesive. It can be shown that the force distribution along the length of the conductor

* This preoccupation on our part with data rather than with their validity has bothered the author considerably. A sincere attempt is being made at Arizona State University to combat this trend.[1a] Any constructive comments on these lines will be gratefully accepted.

is zero at both ends, and rises approximately exponentially towards the center, as shown in Fig. 1B.

Since the force and the strain distributions in the filament must be alike, it follows that the strain in the filament is not uniform along its length *even though the strain in the specimen beneath the gage may be uniform.* An equivalent strain distribution of the same integrated strain-distance area, but assuming uniform strain in the filament length, can be defined. The length of strained filament in this equivalent system will be less than the geometric length L by a quantity $2a$, as indicated in Fig. 1B. This means that there is an equivalent unstrained portion of the filament which does not exhibit strain-induced resistance changes but acts simply as dead resistance in series with the strain-active portion of the filament. This dead resistance desensitizes the gage such that the *gage factor* of the filament will be a factor $(1-2a/L)$ of the *strain sensitivity* of the filament. The strain sensitivity is obtained from a straight *unbonded* filament under strain whereas the gage factor applies to the bonded gage. The quantity a is a function of:

wire diameter (positive)
adhesive layer thickness (positive)
elastic adhesive modulus (negative)
elastic wire modulus (positive)
elastic adhesive shear modulus (negative),

(positive) means that an increase in the quantity results in an increase in a, i.e., an unfavorable condition; (negative) implies the opposite: a favorable condition.

Hence, most favorable results are obtained with a thin adhesive layer, fine weak wire, and strong adhesive. It should be noted that for a 0.001-inch-diameter wire the surface area per unit length is about 4000 times the sectional area; hence, even a relatively weak adhesive can exert tremendous normal forces on an embedded conductor. So large are these forces that a conductor can be forced to follow strains beyond the elastic region in either tension or compression, without buckling in compression, and with return to its original shape upon return to zero strain condition.[1a]

In addition to the above phenomenon, the axial sensitivity of the gage will be decreased if the end loops connecting parallel filament strands are of any appreciable resistance. A byproduct of this effect is that the gage also tends to respond to strains normal to its own major axis. This phenomenon of "transverse sensitivity" has been extensively treated in the literature. Figure 2 is a summary of some gage constructions as they affect this quantity.

Certain corollaries are evident from the above considerations.

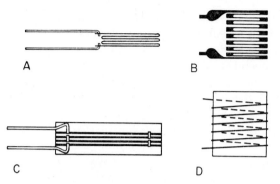

FIG. 2. *A*, Flat grid wire gage. The loops are sensitive to strains normal to the major gage axis which lies along the straight wire direction. Depending on gage type, k will be from $\frac{1}{2}$ to 6%. k can be estimated theoretically. *B*, Flat grid foil gage. The end loops are made larger than the straight portions which lie along the major gage axis. Thus the strains in the end loops do not contribute greatly to the total gage resistance change even when transverse strains are applied. k is between -1 and $+1\%$. *C*, Flat grid wire gage. End sections of heavier wire than the straight strain-sensitive elements along the major gage axis are welded to the strain-sensitive wire. Hence transverse response is very low. Shown here is G-H Tepic type of gage. *D*, Wrap-around or helical gage. The gage is three-dimensional in nature and, for some reason believed to be associated with this construction, gives negative values for k. k varies from 0 to about -6% for common gages. This gage type is outdated today since flat grid wire gages are available down to the smallest gage lengths.

PRACTICAL APPLICATION CONSEQUENCES

1. The shorter the gage length, the lower the gage factor since $2a/L$ will be a larger percentage of L.

2. Any condition which lowers the shear strength of the adhesive, while not affecting the other variables, will lower gage factor. This effect will be the more severe, the shorter the gage length of the gage.

A particular point is a rise in temperature which will result in a weakening of an organic adhesive and a subsequent drop in gage factor. Since the shear strength of the adhesive, however, depends on the type and amount of cure, any published gage factor vs. temperature curves are dangerous to interpret (see also later section on adhesives).

It should be noted that compounding short gage length with elevated temperature results in an even more accelerated lowering of gage factor with temperature.

So severe and little recognized are these effects that the results which some 19 different investigators have claimed as gage factor vs. temperature curves for Constantan (copper-nickel alloy) gages fall all over the gage factor-temperature plane depending entirely on the adhesive type, adhesive cure, gage type, gage length, etc.[1a, 22]

3. When residual stresses in the adhesive after curing are so large that superimposed strain-transfer stresses drive the adhesive into the markedly nonlinear portion of its stress-strain curve, then the lowering of the incremental shear modulus will also result in a lowering of the incremental gage factor, i.e., in nonlinearities between applied strain to the specimen and resulting strain (hence resistance change) in the filament. Similar conditions apply for large strain-transfer-induced shear stresses in the adhesive, which may result in nonlinear behavior of the filament even though the filament itself is still in the linear strain-resistance portion of its own characteristics.

4. The shear-modulus of an adhesive is a time-as-well-as-stress dependent quantity, hence a certain amount of creep may be expected in a gage installation. This creep will be worse for short gages than for long gages, at high temperature as opposed to low temperature, and for wrap-around type gage construction as opposed to flat-grid gages. This strain-induced creep must, however, not be confused with the shrinkage of the adhesive during cure which induces residual tensile strains in the adhesive layer (see later section).

The distribution of shear stress in the adhesive can be shown to be the inverse of the force distribution in the filament, i.e., zero in the center of the filament, rising exponentially to a peak at the ends. This condition implies that:

1. It is most important to get the ends of the gage well bonded to the structure. Attention to the center portion is warranted only when buckling of the gage is to be prevented in compressive strain service.

2. Anything which can be done to the ends of the filament to provide it with a larger area, thus decreasing the shear stress in the adhesive, will benefit the gage in terms of creep resistance, linearity, elevated temperature service, etc. The loops in a flat-grid gage serve as anchors of sorts to perform this function; in foil gages the larger-area end tabs perform this function even better while simultaneously lowering transverse effects. Figure 2 shows some other forms which such anchors might take.

3. It must also be noted that the wrap-around type of gage construction is the worst possible for any of the criteria mentioned above, since one of its windings is removed by an extra layer of carrier and adhesive from the specimen surface. At one time the smaller gage length gages were available only in wrap-around form. Today even the smallest gages are commercially sold in flat-grid configuration and the wrap-around construction should be discarded as outdated.

Basic Behavior of Adhesives

Why adhesives adhere has been studied by numerous investigators over many decades.[23-39] References 23-26 are samples of studies in the field of basic adhesion problems; references 27–31 are some of the many books which treat the subject, and references 23 and 32–39 are some bibliographies for the adhesive field. Apparently the first interpretation of adhesive properties specifically for the strain gage field was the article series by Stein.[1a,40–43]

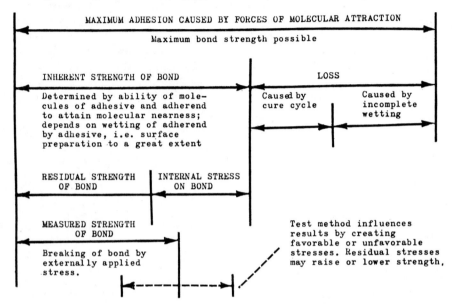

Fig. 3. Qualitative relations between the factors involved in adhesion.

On the basis of molecular considerations it is possible to arrive at some understanding of the adhesive process and to compute theoretical orders of magnitude of the forces involved. These, however, are like the theoretical maximum strength of metal computations, i.e. not realizable at present. The graphical presentation of Fig. 3 shows some of the factors involved in adhesive behavior, and will serve as a preview of following sections.

Base Material

A single adhesive will exhibit widely different properties depending on the base material or adherend to which it is attached. Rinker[23] presents some evidence that the strength of an adhesive joint is an almost linear function of the atomic volume of the adherend. Black and Blomquist[44–47] and DeLollis et al.[48] show that types of adhesive cannot be classified as stronger or weaker unless a common base material is used; the order of classification will depend on the adherend. Thus, a certain adhesive which gives good results on aluminum may not be at all satisfactory on steel. At elevated temperatures these differences are more accentuated and pronounced as shown by Black and Blomquist.[44–47]

SURFACE PREPARATION

The adhesive must be able to "wet" the surface to which it is to adhere. Surface preparation plays an important role in the strength of an adhesive installation. The mechanical and chemical surface treatments which give optimum results vary widely with the nature of the adherend or base material. References 49–56 are samples of the available literature in this area. Since this phase of a bonded installation is neither under the control of the adhesive manufacturer nor of the strain gage manufacturer, it is one of the two most critical phases in the gage installation process. (The other is the adhesive cure cycle.)

ADHESIVE TYPES

The following section is a brief attempt to cover those organic adhesive types extensively used for strain gage work. For each group, sample commercial types are given and the discussion centers mainly around the special precautions required when these adhesives are used for strain gage work. The works of Stein,[40–43,57] Follis,[58] Coover et al.,[59] and Scott[60] are applicable to this section. References 40–43 are themselves survey articles in the field of strain gage adhesives and each contains a large number of references.*

I. Solvent Setting Adhesives[40]

Typical Group: Cellulose nitrates
Typical Adhesives: Duco by DuPont; SR-4 Cement by Baldwin-Lima-Hamilton

The hardening or curing action in a solvent based adhesive is simply the evaporation of the solvent. It has been shown that about 80% of the amount of the adhesive deposited evaporates during the hardening process. Thus a residual tensile stress distribution of sizeable proportions remains in the resulting bond. These residual stresses may be relieved either by a *post-cure*† or by successive working of the bond (by applying strain to the gage in cyclic form). These processes are akin to the annealing and strengthening-through-local-plastic-flow processes in metals although the basic mechanisms bear no relation to each other. Also, as soon as the elastic limit of the strain sensing element has been passed, other phenomena occur.

It should also be borne in mind that 80% of the deposited material which evaporates must be permitted to leave the gage installation, i.e., pressure

---

* Which will explain why references to so many "standard" works in the field do not appear in this paper. The attempt here is to cover previously untreated areas.

† A post-cure is conveniently defined as holding the complete bond at a temperature 20°–100°F above the final curing temperature for some time; the time and temperature depending on the adhesive type.

pads on the gage must not be larger than the gage, or the solvents cannot get out. Furthermore, heat applied to the installation during hardening should be in the form of hot flowing air rather than radiant heat which does not assist in solvent elimination but may even promote bubble formation in the adhesive. Above all, no waterproofing must be applied to the gage until all solvents have been eliminated, or else the gage installation will never cure and creep and drift continuously.

Cellulose nitrate adhesives are hygroscopic in nature and must be water-proofed *after* cure if high humidity environments are expected.

The length of time taken to cure a gage installation with cellulose nitrate adhesive varies both with gage type and the purpose to which the gage in-stallation is to be put. For short-time tests using thin paperbacked gages, several hours may suffice. For wrap-around gages five to ten times the time is required for cure.

For long term tests where stability is required, a 10-day room-tempera-ture cure is necessary. About 24 hours at 140°F with a subsequent post-cure for 1 hour at 160°F followed by immediate waterproofing can be substituted for the lengthy cure for long term tests as will be shown later on.

Since there are numerous different varieties of cellulose nitrate which may even have the same chemical composition but vastly different molecu-lar structure and properties, only those adhesives known to have worked for strain gage applications should be used. Temperature limits for the cellulose nitrates are about 180°F and all gage installations should be held at least 20°F above the highest test temperature for about an hour to assure low creep and temperature-induced zero shifts.

The above recommendation is based on the tendency of the adhesive to shrink during cure. This means that the gage will indicate compressive strains varying with time until the cure has been completed. Cure may be near completion at one temperature and continue rapidly at a higher temperature, accompanied by further time-varying compressive strain indications by the gage even in the presence of no applied mechanical strain. This cure-induced zero shift has frequently been confused with load-induced creep and many contradictions exist in the literature because of the failure to separate these effects as will again be pointed out in a later section.

The above discussions on residual stresses, shrinkage during cure, post-cure, and waterproofing hold for all organic adhesives and will be referred to again in subsequent discussions.

II. *Chemical Action Setting Adhesives*

In general, an irreversible chemical reaction sets in under the action of a time-temperature-pressure combination, resulting in a hard, infusible

adhesive bond. Of the members of the thermosetting plastics used for strain
gage adhesives, two deserve special mention:

A. Typical Group: Phenol formaldehyde
*Typical Adhesive: Palmer Products BC-6035 (Phenolic or Bakelite Cement
     Supplied with Baldwin-Lima-Hamilton Bakelite Gages)*

The phenolic adhesive in general consists of pure resin mixed with a
filler. Fillers may vary in type and amount and completely determine the
properties of the resulting bond; elastic modulus, creep resistance, thermal
expansion coefficient, insulation resistance, shear strength, etc., and all
their variations with time and temperature.

All of these properties including nuclear radiation resistance and a host
of others are governed by type and amount of filler. Hence it is vital to
thoroughly mix the contents of the bottle of adhesive and never to remove
what appears to be "dirt" in the mixture. Fillers may be paper, flour, metal
powder, etc., for the BC 6035 it is ground marble ($CaCO_3$).

Cure is accelerated by temperature rise and the adhesive should be stored
in a refrigerator. Volatiles and water vapor are formed during the cure. In
order to maintain the water vapor in vapor form, pressure must be applied
to the bond during cure. This pressure also facilitates egress of the volatiles
—again a path for their escape must be provided. Without pressure, water
droplets and gas bubbles may form in the joint.

Shrinkage during cure is not nearly as severe for phenolics as for cellulose
nitrates, but the release of the pressure applied during cure and the volatile
evaporation process do leave residual stresses in the bond which must be
removed as described in the section on Cellulose Nitrate Adhesives. To
completely cure a phenolic resin may take several dozen hours at temperature; the bond strength will not continually increase during this time, but
continued shrinkage resulting in a cure-induced zero shift will occur in the
gage. Also, cure must be completed at the highest temperature to be met
during the test, otherwise continued cure at the higher temperature will
produce zero shifts during the test.

The adhesive strength does increase as the bond is maintained at higher
temperatures for longer times so that cure progresses. This phenomenon
explains the following curious effect frequently found in strain gage installations: the gage factor vs. temperature curve of a gage during the *first*
temperature cycle will show a drop in gage factor at somewhere near the
cure temperature of the bond. During the *second* temperature cycle the
effect of post-cure and bond-strengthening through post-cure become
evident, and the gage factor does not drop off until near the highest temperature reached during the first cycle. Much confusion in the literature is

attributed to this little recognized phenomenon which is valid for all organic thermosetting adhesives.[1a]

Phenolic adhesives are also hygroscopic and gage installations should be waterproofed. The adhesive has been used up to 700°F for short-term dynamic tests and evidence shows that the length of time at elevated temperature for which a phenolic adhesive will perform satisfactorily depends on the degree of care taken during its manufacture,[41] as well as the substrate material.

B. Typical Group: Epoxies[41]
Typical Adhesives: EPY 400 by Emerson Cuming Company, Sold by Baldwin-Lima-Hamilton; "200" by Mithra Engineering Company

The epoxy adhesive in general, consists of two components: (1) the pure resin with filler, the type and amount of which again determines all major bond properties, and (2) a hardening or curing agent also called "catalyst." The chemical reaction commences when the two components are mixed together. Some epoxies are available in "single-component" premixed form; the chemical reaction for these single-mix epoxies does continue constantly but is so slow at room temperature that practical shelf lives are obtainable. The chemical reaction is accelerated by temperature and various combinations of time and temperature of cure result in different combinations of physical bond properties.

It is not always true that a property, strength, for example, increases with increasing time and temperature of cure. In many cases certain time-temperature combinations may result in *minimum* strength properties. Cure cycles given by the manufacturer must be followed religiously unless separate and thorough tests have shown that other cures are advantageous for strain gage use.

The physical properties of the bond are also determined almost completely by the amount and type of curing agent used with the resin-filler mix. Hence the components must be weighed out carefully on a scale of at least 50-mg sensitivity unless preweighed and prepackaged units are used. It is not permissible to add an extra drop of hardener when 6 are called for: this 16% change in hardener concentration may result in drastic property variations in the resulting bond in some cases.

Epoxies do not liberate volatiles during cure, hence shrinkage is small and no path for vapor egress need be left around the gage. Post-cure is still beneficial, however, giving better gage performance from all respects.

Epoxies are known to create allergic skin reactions in some individuals and appropriate care should be taken. Temperature limits appear to be in the 700°F region for the better epoxies, but all are still hygroscopic and should be moisture-proofed. Since no volatiles are liberated only contact pressure, maintaining the gage in place, is necessary during cure.

C. Typical Group: Cyano-Acrylate
Typical Adhesive: Eastman 910 by Eastman Kodak (Contact Cement)

This adhesive sets under the action of moisture or basic chemical action especially when spread as a thin film. It hardens into an extremely thin layer so rapidly that strain gage operation within 30 seconds of mounting is possible when a suitable catalyst is used. The moisture sensitivity of the adhesive is such that even small amounts of vapor entering the adhesive container can spoil the contents—hence containers must be kept tightly closed when not in use.

The Contact cement also benefits by post-cure, a 24-hour cure at 105°F doubling its strength. After cure the bond is quite water resistant and much of its original strength returns when the gage installation is dried thoroughly after wetting.

Some of the basic properties of the adhesive are given by Stein,[57] and the application to strain gages and comparisons with other adhesives by Follis[58] and Scott.[60] The chemistry of the adhesive is treated by Coover et al.[59]

III. *Temperature Setting*

Typical Group: Thermoplastics
Typical Adhesive: DeKhotinsky (Hard) by Central Scientific

The curing process for the thermoplastic is reversible and occurs with changes in temperature: rising temperature softens the adhesive which hardens as temperature is lowered. The DeKhotinsky adhesive is one of the earliest ones used for strain gages and is still popular for rapid strain survey work: the test specimen is locally heated with a portable propane torch, for example, until the surface temperature is about 350°F. The adhesive, which is supplied in stick form, is rubbed against the hot surface leaving a thin film of molten adhesive into which the strain gage is quickly pressed. As soon as the temperature of the installation reaches ambient, tests can be made. Subsequent heating of the gage (which can be flame-proofed if necessary) permits gage removal and reuse elsewhere.

The adhesive is hygroscopic and of course not good at elevated temperatures; but it has proven an excellent means for quickly surveying a structure for strains at a number of locations and in a number of directions.

RESIDUAL STRESSES IN ADHESIVE LAYERS

Depending on the adhesive type and composition, the residual stresses in the adhesive layer may be large or small—but always are they unfavorable because they tend to vary with time and strain level making a strain gage installation appear unreliable and unrepeatable. It has been seen that the magnitudes of residual stresses are expected to be higher in cellulose nitrates than in phenolics, than in epoxies on the basis of the amount of volat.les evolved during the cure. That this consideration does not present the complete phenomenon has been studied by several investigators.[61–63] Post-cure is usually beneficial in altering the residual stress distribution in a more favorable manner as shown by McClintock and Hiza.[64] Another factor which is often ignored is that during the cure cycle the viscosity of the adhesive varies considerably before final hardening occurs. Unless the gage to be bonded is subject to some pressure (even for epoxies), viscosity, induced changes in the glue line may occur, giving rise to undesired strain transmission phenomena.[65]

Post-Cure Shrinkage

The transition of an organic adhesive from liquid to solid state, i.e., the polymerization process, is never complete at any given time or temperature. Tomkins[66] presents some criteria by which cure completion can be measured. However, polymerization-induced volume changes and residual stresses in the adhesive layer are continually changing with time and ambient temperature. The phenomenon appears such that it is possible to achieve stability at any given temperature; but should the ambient temperature rise, the cure will continue to a higher degree of completion with resulting dimensional changes in the glue line. That this is the major cause of so-called "creep" or zero drift in strain gages, has been the author's thesis for some time. Support for this point of view may be seen in the works of Chottiner,[67] Späth,[68] and Woebcken.[69] That some commercial phenolic-backed strain gages are frequently only partially cured when sold, resulting in time-dependent resistance changes in the unmounted gage, is discussed by Tiffany[70] and Scott,[71] who recommend a *pre*-cure of unmounted gages prior to installation. On the other hand some strain-gage-based transducer manufacturers frequently use very partially cured gages in their installations so that the gages and the additional adhesive form a better single entity than would otherwise be possible.

Post-Cure Strengthening

The strength and elastic constants of an adhesive usually increase as cure progresses. Thus a gage installation may well exhibit good properties insofar as gage factor and creep are concerned at room temperature, but the gage factor at elevated temperature may be found to vary with time, increasing with time. Numerous reports in the literature, for example, present data showing that the gage factor vs. temperature curve of a gage installation on the *first* temperature cycle shows a lower temperature limit for the gage than that obtained from a second temperature cycle. The strengthening of the bond during the first temperature cycle which acts as a post-cure, is responsible for this phenomenon as has already been pointed out in an earlier section. Hence, again, a post-cure to at least 20° if not 50°F above the highest expected test temperature is required if the first load and temperature cycle behavior is to be acceptable in terms of gage factor, zero shift, hysteresis, and creep.

Creep

All adhesives creep under load (as distinguished from cure-induced shrinkage). In a strain gage installation this phenomenon evidences itself as a change in gage output with time under constant strain and constant ambient conditions such as temperature, humidity, etc., the amount of creep of the installation is a function of the strain gage design, adhesive type, and the per cent completion of the cure. This problem will be discussed again in a later section.

Electrical Resistivity

Since the adhesive layer of a strain gage installation is usually expected to act as electrical insulator between the test specimen and the strain sensitive filament, the insulation resistance of the adhesive layer is an important consideration. Several investigators[66,72-75] conclude that resistivity, although it varies from adhesive to adhesive, is a function of amount and type of filler and catalyst (if any) and is also a definite function of the degree of completion of the cure. Hence it can be taken as a good indicator of this quantity which also correlates with the mechanical adhesive properties as shown above.

Adhesive Layer Thickness

Evidence exists (Rinker and Kline,[23] for example) that the shear strength of adhesive layers is inversely proportional to layer thickness; the thinner the glue-line, the stronger the joint. Various theories have been offered as explanations for this phenomenon.

Methods of Checking the Quality of the Bond between Strain Gage and Specimen[1a]

Since strain gage performance is not a predictable phenomenon, it becomes necessary to investigate methods by which the quality of the adhesive bond between the strain gage and the test specimen might be checked.

Over the years, researchers of all periods in all countries have suggested a variety of criteria to determine whether or not the conditions within the adhesive bond between the strain gage and the specimen are such that the gage can be relied upon to produce good results.

The purpose of such a checking method is twofold, and this distinction must be borne in mind in selecting one of the six methods listed:

(a) to provide a means of testing a gage installation *method*

(b) to provide a means of testing a particular gage *installation.*

When a *method* is being checked, the test can be quite elaborate, extensive, lengthy, and confined to the laboratory. Sample gage installations are investigated and the finalized method is carefully written out so that future gage installations can be duplicated exactly.

When a particular *installation* is checked the test must be quick, immediate, and applicable in the field under any ambient test conditions.

I. *Development of Gage Factor (Sensitivity)*

At various times during the curing (or drying) stage of the adhesive, the gage installation is checked for sensitivity (or gage factor). When the adhesive is liquid, this sensitivity will be low. When the adhesive is completely cured, the sensitivity will have reached a maximum value. This method suffers from the fact that adhesive cure can be far from complete when 99% of maximum sensitivity (strength) has been reached. The continuation of the cure not only strengthens the joint but adds creep resistance to the installation; it also produces shrinkage strains which give rise to zero shifts in the gage which are often falsely called "creep." Jones and Maslen[76] and Miller *et al.*[77] investigate this method.

II. *Decrease of Hysteresis*

At various times during the curing stage of the adhesive, a strain is applied to the gage and then removed. The amount of zero shift or the area enclosed in the strain-resistance change curves for increasing and decreasing strain (hysteresis) is measured. As cure progresses, the zero shift (or area) reduces essentially to zero, and the gage installation is considered fit for use. Jones and Maslen[76] and Miller *et al.*[77] also investigate this approach. The dangers in using this criterion for gage cure is that the test is essentially a short-time creep test. Gage performance can be good under short-time creep conditions, and extremely poor under longer-term creep use. The arguments used by Mika[10] also apply here.

As a general comment it may be said that a cure which is sufficient to bring about strength characteristics for structural bonding applications such as in aircraft, is usually *not* sufficient for precision strain gage work. Strain gages are more demanding than structural bonded joints.

III. *Creep Resistance*

A properly cured adhesive bond assures optimum creep resistance of the gage installation. This is the best test for a gage installation method. Since creep tests, however, do take time, this criterion may not be an acceptable one.

IV. *Stabilization of Gage Resistance*

The gage resistance is monitored continuously during cure. As the adhesive first softens the gage carrier and then proceeds to harden and cure, the induced strains in the strain gage will vary. Only when the gage resistance is stable for long periods of time can the adhesive cure be said to have been completed. This method is excellent, corresponding to the determination of the cessation of cure-induced shrinkage. Jones and Maslen[76] use this method to show, for example, that common paper-backed wire strain gages attached with Duco Household Cement (E. I. DuPont) will not be cured at room temperature conditions for about 10 days instead of the several hours which are commonly believed to suffice. This method does, however, require constant monitoring of the gage resistance and is tedious and may be inconvenient to apply, although assuring excellent results.

V. *Temperature-Cycle-Induced Zero Shift*

When the adhesive in a gage installation has been thoroughly cured, there will be no change in gage zero when the installation is returned from some temperature excursion to its original ambient temperature; that is, if the temperature limits of the gage components and the adhesive have not been surpassed. If the adhesive is *not* sufficiently cured, elevated temperature exposure will hasten completion of the incomplete cure; the resulting shrinkage stresses in the adhesive will change the gage zero reading. Hence a zero shift after a temperature excursion indicates that the adhesive cure has been incomplete. This method is a standard one used in the plastics industry as shown by Tomkins.[66]

VI. *Insulation Resistance of the Adhesive Layer*

For any adhesive, the resistivity is a function of the type of adhesive, the amount and type of filler, the ambient temperature, the amount and type of hardener (or curing agent), and the degree of completion of the cure. All mechanical and electrical properties of the adhesive are also functions of these same variables. For any one adhesive, all other things being constant *except the degree of cure* of the adhesive, the resistivity of the adhesive layer will give information as to the state of cure. For any given strain gage size and adhesive layer thickness, the insulation resistance will give this information.

Since the degree of cure for any given adhesive governs entirely the properties of the resulting joint, such as its strength, elastic modulus, creep properties, resistivity, and other electrical and mechanical properties, it also governs all the important gage performance properties. Insulation resistance, being a measure of the degree of cure is also a measure of the mechanical properties of the adhesive layer, hence of expected gage performance.

Relationship between Electrical Resistance and Degree of Cure

It is fortunate that the value of electrical resistance of an adhesive layer for any single adhesive and gage type, will correlate well with its mechanical properties and with the degree of cure of the adhesive. This correlation has been well established[70-74] with Warfield[74] offering a recent confirmation. In that work the resistivity of plastics is monitored from the instant of mixing to final cure. Excellent correlation is found between resistivity and degree of cure. It is also noted that a fast cure at elevated temperature does *not* result in as high a resistivity (and hence not in as good properties) as a longer-time, lower-temperature cure, which when followed by a higher temperature post-cure, gives far better results.

Tomkins[10] reports that over a wide variation of structure of plastics, the stress-strain characteristics were observed to be closely related to degree of cure. These observations all support the measurement of insulation resistance of a gage installation as giving a good picture of the electrical and mechanical properties of the adhesive joint, hence of expected gage performance.

It must be emphasized again that quantitative specifications of insulation resistance must first be established for the particular gage type involved by one of the other checking methods, preferably 3, 4, or 5.

The Gage-to-Specimen Insulation Resistance as a Check on Gage Performance

The simplest possible check, before using any strain gage then, is to measure gage-to-specimen insulation resistance of the adhesive layer. This measurement should be made *every time* a gage is used, since the adhesive layer may have absorbed moisture from the ambient atmosphere. Increased moisture content lowers both electrical and mechanical properties and is reflected in the insulation resistance measurement. The insulation resistance check, therefore, serves the purpose of a final check on the condition of the strain gage just prior to use.

THE MEANING OF THE INSULATION RESISTANCE VALUE

The insulation resistance value has two distinct effects on the behavior of a strain gage; in practice the second listed below will predominate in almost all cases except for high-temperature ceramic-adhesive strain gage installations.

1. *Leakage resistance:* Some of the current supplied to the strain gage will leak through the adhesive layer to the test specimen which is frequently at "ground" potential. This purely electrical phenomenon results in two effects:

A. *An apparent zero shift* of the gage installation of approximately

$$\tfrac{1}{2}(R_\text{g}/R_\text{L}) \times 10^6 \text{ microstrain}$$

for gages of about 2.0 gage factor. R_g is the gage resistance, R_L is the leakage resistance of the adhesive, both in ohms. It may be seen that if the leakage resistance varies from 100 megohms to 10 megohms, the resulting zero shift would be:

$$\tfrac{1}{2}(120/10^8 - 120/10^7) \times 10^6 = 0.6/\text{microstrain}$$

an entirely negligible quantity for most applications.

B. *A sensitivity decrease* of the gage approximately equal to

$$100R_\text{g}/R_\text{L} \%.$$

For a 1-megohm leakage resistance on a 120-ohm gage, a calibration drop of about 0.01% would result. At 10,000 ohms leakage (0.01 megohm), about 1% of error would be induced. Thus the leakage resistance itself, as an electrical circuit quantity, seldom contributes to bad gage performance. Only for ceramic-adhesive gage installations especially at elevated temperature, are the above considerations critical, because the following section does not apply to ceramic adhesives.

The following criterion, however, limits organic-adhesive strain gage installations.

2. *Adhesive mechanical condition:* For most organic adhesives the mechanical properties of the joint are adversely affected by moisture content and incomplete cure. When ceramic adhesives are used the correlation of insulation resistance and adhesive mechanical condition cannot be made. For organic adhesives, however, insulation resistance correlates with gage factor, creep resistance, hysteresis, and the ability of the gage installation to perform at higher-than-ambient temperatures.

Typical values for insulation resistance: A striking comparison in the literature is between two investigator pairs who investigated the same type of bonded resistance strain gage mounted with the same adhesive, for creep properties. Matlock and Thompson[78] use Duco cement with the very short cure cycle recommended by the strain gage manufacturer. McWhirter and Duggin[79] cured their Duco gage installations at 140°F *until the gage to specimen resistance exceeded 10,000 megohms,* and then gave them a 160°F 1-hour post-cure with immediate waterproofing thereafter. The length of cure varied with ambient oven conditions and was 12 hours for thin paper gages and 24 hours for heavier, wrap-around gages such as the SR-4 A-8 (RTM BLH Corporation). The gage-cure criterion based on *insulation resistance* of the adhesive resulted in remarkably creep-free gage installations.

It is important to note the large discrepancy in values in Table I. The low and equal creep values for tension and compression strains of high magni-

TABLE I

CREEP IN MICROINCHES PER INCH AFTER 60 DAYS FOR BALDWIN-LIMA-HAMILTON PAPERBACKED SR-4[a] STRAIN GAGES ATTACHED WITH DUCO ADHESIVE

Reference	Gage type[b]	Strain level (microinches/inch)	Creep (microinches/inch)
78	A-8 ($\frac{1}{4}$ inch)	−2000	275
		+2000	140
79	A-8 ($\frac{1}{4}$ inch)	−3000	110
		+3000	120
79	A-5 ($\frac{1}{2}$ inch)	−3000	20
		+3000	10

[a] RTM BLH Corporation.

[b] The A-8 is a paperbacked wrap-around constructio wire gage of $\frac{1}{4}$ inch gage length. The A-5 is a paperbacked flat-grid construction wire gage of $\frac{1}{2}$ inch gage length.

tudes are typical of well-cured gage installations. The large creep values at low strain levels and which are apart by factors of two depending on whether the applied strain was tensile or compressive, are typical of insufficiently cured installations. The 50 to 100 megohm value commonly accepted as a good target, is not sufficient for long term tests, although short-time tests may be conducted satisfactorily. Note that the paper gages in McWhirter and Duggin[79] behaved better than many Bakelite gage installations reported on in the literature.

In general, adhesive manufacturers' cures tend to be too incomplete for strain gage work. All cures should be tried and tested before too much stock is put in them for strain gage work.

Also note that the 50–10,000 megohm resistance range is certainly far above any insulation resistance which would affect gage behavior through leakage of current through the adhesive, and that only mechanical adhesive properties are measured when insulation resistance is checked for organic adhesive installations.

INSTRUMENT FOR MEASURING GAGE-TO-SPECIMEN RESISTANCE

The instrument used to measure the insulation resistance of a strain gage adhesive layer should be:

1. portable and battery operated for field use
2. exhibit a range of from 0.01 to 10,000 megohms
3. use a low testing voltage so as not to damage the strain gage
4. need not be very accurate since insulation resistance varies with so many things
5. should be self-calibrating
6. should be low in cost since it is only an auxiliary instrument.

Two instruments of which the author is aware which fulfill these requirements are the following:

Keithley 501 megohmmeter with a $1\frac{1}{2}$-volt DC test potential, handsize, 0.01–10,000 megohms range, self-calibrating at 0.01 and 100 megohms.

Peekel (Holland) WE 567 battery operated megohmmeter with a 5 ohm to 10,000 megohm range, 3% accuracy and a 20-volt DC test potential, self-contained, and portable.

CONCLUSION

Although a great deal of information is available in the areas of adhesive performance and strain gage properties, this information is not presently in the form in which it is possible to predict strain gage performance on the basis of basic gage construction, basic adhesive properties, and a theoretical stress analysis solution which relates these two items. Work is presently being carried out along these lines[18–20] and the "ideal solution" postulated in the paper may be available in the near future.

It is shown, however, that the performance of a strain gage installation is governed by the adhesive used and the exact method of its mixture and cure. It is important to remember that the creep, hysteresis, linearity, sensitivity, and the variation of these quantities with time and temperature depend heavily (although not exclusively) on the adhesive. No test purporting to present results of this type is complete without specifying the exact nature of the adhesive, filler amount and type (if any), curing agent amount and type (if any), time-temperature-pressure values during cure, post-cure cycle (if any), and past thermal and strain history of the installation (i.e., whether a "green" installation has been tested or whether the installation has been strain and/or temperature cycled prior to taking data).

There are these precautions among others which can be taken during gage installation to assure good results; they are based on fundamental adhesive properties or basic strain gage behavior patterns as developed in the paper:

1. Proper surface preparation and cleanliness for the test specimen and the gage are imperative.

2. Thin glue lines are preferable even though the stresses in the adhesive layer will be higher.

3. The ends of the gage, i.e., the end loops, are the critical areas in terms of attachment.

4. Any vapors formed during cure of the adhesive must be permitted to escape from the gage. Pressure pads on the gages must be small, and hot, flowing air is preferable to radiant heat. Waterproofing compounds must not be applied prior to complete cure.

5. Adhesives come specially mixed for a purpose; shake the bottle before using and do not discard parts of the mix.

6. Where different components of the adhesive are to be mixed, weigh these components carefully and accurately and do not place them in containers which may absorb one ingredient in preference to another (such as some types of paper cup).

7. Adhesive cure must be complete especially for long-term static tests. "Complete" may mean a 10-day cure in some cases.

8. Post-cure gage installations wherever possible. Post-curing implies holding the installation at 20° to 100°F above the last cure temperature or above the highest test temperature expected, for some time. Time and temperature values depend on the adhesive.

9. Gage-to-specimen insulation resistance of the adhesive layer is a good measure of expected gage performance at the instant of test. This quantity should be checked on every gage every time it is used.

10. The strain gage is a precision instrument. The "lick-'em-stick-'em" approach will get loads of data—but no results.

It is important to note that although the adhesive layer limits and determines gage performance to a large extent, there are other gage characteristics such as grid configuration, gage length, filament shape and size, etc., which also determine and limit gage performance. Strain gages must be selected carefully on the basis of at least 10 major considerations[1a, 80] of which the adhesive is only one.

REFERENCES

The references listed below are all available in the Strain Gage Readings and Engineering Measurements Laboratory (Arizona State University) Libraries, as are the references cited in survey articles references 22 and 40–43. The numbers (2-xxxx) refer to accession numbers in the SGR Library and the (R-xxx) numbers refer to review numbers in the Literature Review section of *Strain Gage Readings*.

These identifications are made so as to assist readers in checking further into any phase of special interest.

1a. Stein, P. K., "Measurement Engineering" (1200 pp.). Stein Engineering Services Inc., Phoenix, Arizona, 1962.

1b. Davidson, J. R., Shear strength at 75°F to 500°F of fourteen adhesives used to bond a glass-fabric-reinforced phenolic resin laminate to steel, *Natl. Advisory Comm. Aeronaut. Tech. Note No.* 3901 (December, 1956) (2-630).

2. Merriman, H. R., Research on structural adhesive properties over a wide temperature range, *WADC Tech. Rept. No.* 56-320 (April, 1956) (2-467).

3. Eickner, H. W., The shear, fatigue, bend, impact, and long-time-load strength properties of structural metal-to-metal adhesives in bonds to 24S-Tr aluminum alloy, F.P.L. Rept. No. 1836 (June, 1953) (2-731).

4. Sherrer, R., Stresses in a lap joint with elastic adhesive, F.P.L. Rept. No. 1864 (September, 1957) (2-751).

5. Norris, C. B., and Boller, K. H., Transfer of longitudinal load from one facing of a sandwich panel to the other by means of shear in the core, F.P.L. Rept. No. 1846 (April, 1955) (2-734).

6. Eickner, H. W., Basic shear strength properties of metal-bonding adhesives as determined by lap-joint stress formulas of Volkersen and Goland and Reissner, F.P.L. Rept. No. 1850 (August, 1955) (2-733).

7. Lubkin, J. L., A theory of adhesive scarf joints, *J. Appl. Mechanics* **24** (1957) (2-1714).

8. Lubkin, J. L., and Reissner, E., Stress distribution and design data for adhesive lap joints between circular tubes, *Trans. ASME* **78** (1956) (2-1713).

9. Perry, H. A., How to calculate stresses in adhesive joints, *Prod. Eng.* **29** (1958) (2-1102).

10. Mika, T. F., Free film properties of epoxide resin coating systems, *Offic. Dig. Federation Paint & Varnish Production Clubs* **31** (1959) (R-299).

11. Van Hoora, H., and Bruin, P., Determination of the modulus of elasticity in the study of paint films, *Offic. Dig. Federation Paint & Varnish Production Clubs* **31** (1959) (R-443).

12. Norris, C. B., Plastic flow throughout volume of thin adhesive bonds, F.P.L. Rept. No. 2092 (March, 1958) (2-1430, R-277).

13. Kuenzi, E. W., Determination of mechanical properties of adhesives for use in the design of bonded joints, F.P.L. Rept. No. 1851 (January, 1956) (2-730).

14. Longbottom, E., Reliability of SR-4 type electric strain gauges for field applications, Monogr. 8-012, Permanent Records of Research & Develop. Ministry of Supply, England, 1949.

15. Greenfield, J. F., and Bridgnell, D., The relationship between strain gauge length and the ratio of strain in gauge to strain in member, Tech. Note No. 208, De Havilland Prop. Ltd., Vibrations Dept., England (1954).

16. Fouretier, G., La Dynamometrie de Precision: Exemples d' Applications Pratiques, *Anal. Contr.* **2**, 9–10 (1958).

17. Stein, P. K., Stresses with the adhesive layer of a strain gage installation, *Strain Gage Readings* **1,** No. 3 (1958).

18. Rohrbach, C., and Czaika, N., Deutung des Mechanismus des Dehnungsmesstreifens und seiner wichtigsten Eigenschaften an Hand eines Modells, *Materialprüfung* **1,** 4 (1959).

19. Rohrbach, C., and Czaika, N., Das Kriechen von Dehnungsmesstreifen als Rheologisches Problem, *Materialprüfung* **2**, 3 (1960).
20. Rohrbach, C., and Czaika, N., Uever das Kriechen von Dehnungsmesstreifen unter statischer zugbelastung, Teile I, II, III, *Arch. tech. Messen* **243** (1959); **244** (1960) (9-2087).
21. Post, D., and Zandman, F., The accuracy of birefringent coating method for coatings of arbitrary thickness, S.E.S.A., paper 557, 1959 spring meeting, Washington, D.C.
22. Stein, P. K., Constantan as a strain sensitive alloy, *Strain Gage Readings* **1**, No. 1 (1958).
23. Rinker, R. C., and Kline, G. M., Survey of adhesives and adhesion, *Natl. Advisory Comm. Aeronaut. Tech, Note No.* 989 (1945) (2-715).
24. Alter, H., and Soller, W., Molecular structure as a basis for adhesion, *Ind. Eng. Chem.* **50** (1958) (2-1119).
25. Taylor, J., and Rutzler, J. E., Adhesion using molecular models, *Ind. Eng. Chem.* **50** (1958) (2-1120).
26. Patrick, R. L., and Vaughan, W. A., Fundamental studies on the adhesion of organic materials to metal substrates., *WADC Tech. Rept. No.* 56-663, *ASTIA* AD-118054, OTS PB 121982 (1956) (2-1285).
27. Epstein, G., "Adhesive Bonding of Metals." Reinhold, New York, 1954 (2-073).
28. Structural Adhesives: An introduction for potential users, Struct. Adhesive Assoc., Allentown, Pennsylvania, 1958.
29. Lee, H., and Neville, K., "Epoxy Resins: Their Application and Technology." McGraw-Hill, New York, 1957.
30. Carswell, T. S., "Phenoplasts." Interscience, New York, 1947.
31. "Adhesion and Adhesives: Fundamentals and Practice." Soc. of Chem. Industry, London. Wiley, New York, 1954. See particularly Reinhart, F. W., Survey of adhesion and types of bonds involved, pp. 9–15.
32. Bergler, W. H., Jr., *et al.* Structural adhesives, Struct. Adhesives Assoc., Allentown, Pennsylvania, 1958.
33. Krakeler, K., Peukert, H., and Schwarz, O., Auswertung der in-und-ausl ändischen Literatur auf dem Gebiete des Metallklebens, Forschungsbericht des Wirtschafts-und-Verkehrsministeriums Nordrhein-Westfalen No. 639 (1958) (R-295).
34. Lederman, H., Mechanical properties of high polymers, *Ann. Rev. Phys. & Chem.* **9** (1958) (R-247).
35. Hurd, J., Adhesives Guide, Research Rept. M 39, Brit. Sci. Instr. Research Assoc. (1959).
36. Engineering Societies Library Biblio. 12: Biblio. on Adhesive Bonding of Metals, 1957.
37. Bibliography on Adhesives CTR-300 with Suppl., O.T.S., 1956 and 1960 (suppl.).
38. Plastics research and technology at the National Bureau of Standards, 1950, with additional 1955 bibliography, Natl. Bur. Standards Circ. No. 494.
39. Shell Oil Company, Tech. Bull. SC 57-134: Bibliography of magazine articles for epoxy resins (1957).
40. Stein, P. K., Strain gage adhesives: Part III, Cellulose nitrate cements, *Strain Gage Readings*, **1**, No. 2, 3 (1958).
41. Stein, P. K., Strain gage adhesives: Part II, Phenolic resins, *Strain Gage Readings* **1**, No. 1, 18 (1958).
42. Stein, P. K., Strain gage adhesives: Part IV, Epoxy resins, *Strain Gage Readings* **1**, No. 3, 3 (1958).

43. Stein, P. K., Strain gage adhesives: Part I, Fundamentals, *Strain Gage Readings* **1**, No. 1, 3 (1958).
44. Black, J. M., and Blomquist, R. F., Relationship of polymer structure to thermal deterioration of adhesive bonds in metal joints, *Natl. Advisory Comm. Aeronaut. Tech. Note No.* D-108 (1959) (R-389).
45. Black, J. M., and Blomquist, R. F., Adhesive deterioration in metal bonds at high temperatures, *Adh. Age* (1959) (R-390).
46. Black, J. M., and Blomquist, R. F., Relationship of metal surfaces to heat-aging properties of adhesive bonds, *Natl. Advisory Comm. Aeronaut. Tech. Note No.* 4287 (1958).
47. Black, J. M., and Blomquist, R. F., A study of the deterioration of adhesives in metal bonds at high temperatures, *WADC Tech. Rept. No.* 55-330, OTS PB 131500 (March, 1956) (2-1204).
48. DeLollis, N. J., *et al.*, Comparative strengths of some adhesive-adherend systems, *Natl. Advisory Comm. Aeronaut. Tech. Note No.* 1863 (1949) (2-663).
49. Eickner, H. W., A study of methods for preparing clad 24S-T aluminum-alloy sheet surfaces for adhesive bonding, *F.P.L. Rept. No.* 1813-A (1950) (2-665).
50. Eickner, H. W., Adhesive bonding properties of various metals as affected by chemical anodizing treatments of the surfaces, *F.P.L. Rept. No.* 1842-A (1955) (2-732).
51. Eickner, H. W., Adhesive bonding properties of various metals as affected by chemical and anodizing treatments of the surfaces, *F.P.L. Rept. No.* 1842 (1954) (2-666).
52. Eickner, H. W., Effect of surface treatment on the adhesive bonding properties of magnesium, *F.P.L. Rept.* 1865, (1958) (2-1158).
53. Thelen, E., Preparation of metal surfaces for adhesive bonding, Franklin Inst. paper at 1957 WADC Adhesives Symposium.
54. Muchnick, S. N., Adhesive bonding of metals, *Mech. Eng.* **78** (1956) (2-747).
55. Rinker, R. C., *et al.*, Effect of pH on strength of resin bonds, *Natl. Advisory Comm. Aeronaut.* ARR 3J11, W-46 (1943) (2-821).
56. Schäfer, W., Der Einfluss der Oberflächenvorbereitung auf die Bindefestigkeit von Metallverklebungen-III, *Plaste Kau.* **5**, No. 9, 1958 (R-255).
57. Stein, P. K., Contact cement, *Strain Gage Readings* **1**, No. 3, 49 (1958).
58. Follis, G. R., Strain gages for ordinary work—new tricks and techniques, *Strain Gage Readings* **2**, No. 5, 21 (1959).
59. Coover, H. W. *et al.*, Chemistry and performance of cyanoacrylate adhesives, Soc. of Plastics Engrs., New York, January 27–30, 1959 meeting (R-169).
60. Scott, I. G., Eastman 910 as a strain gage adhesive, Aero. Research Lab., Australia, Tech. Memo. S/M 83 (1960).
61. Kobatake, Y., and Inoue, Y., Mechanics of adhesive joints: I, Residual stresses; II, Stress distribution in adhesive layer under loading; III, Evaluation of residual stresses, *Appl. Sci. Research* **A7** (1958) (R-156).
62. Weatherwax, R. C. *et al.*, A fundamental investigation of adhesion, *J. Polymer Sci.* **27** (1958) (2-1161).
63. Inoue, Y., and Kobatake, Y., Effect of fillers on residual stresses in coatings, *Kolloid-Z.* **159**, No. 1 (R-386).
64. McClintock R. M., and Hiza, M. J., Epoxy resins as cryogenic structural adhesives, *Proc. Cryogenic Eng. Conf. 2nd 1956*, Paper F-3 (1957) (2-067).
65. Schlegel, H., Technologie der Metallverklebung, *Plaste Kau.* **5**, No. 9 (1958) (R-254).
66. Tomkins, A. A., The assessment of cure, *Plastics Inst. (London) Trans. and J.* **26** (1958) (R-248).

67. Chottiner, J. Dimensional stability of plastics at high temperatures, *Machine Design* **31** (1959) (R-246).
68. Von Späth, W., Schwindung und Eigenspannungen in Klebverbindungen, *Aluminum* **35,** No. 10 (1959) (2-2142).
69. Woebcken, W., Bestimmung der Schwindung, Nachschwindung und Quellung von Presstoffen, *Kunststoffe,* **49,** No. 8 (1959) (2-2059).
70. Tiffany, A., and Wood, J., Precision strain gauge techniques, *Electronic Eng.* **30** (1958) (12-1223).
71. Scott, I. G., Resistance changes in resistance strain gauges, Aero. Research Lab., Australia, Note SM 244 (1958) (R-217).
72. Warfield, R. W., and Petree, M. C., The use of electrical resistivity in the study of polymerization of thermosetting resins, NAVORD Rept. No. 6120, OTS PB 161-028 (1958) (R-445).
73. Delmonte, J., and Cressey, K., Improving electric properties of epoxies *SPE Journal* **14** (1958) (R-224).
74. Warfield, R. W., Studying the electrical properties of casting resins, *SPE Journal* **14** (1958) (R-225).
75. Aukward, J. A. *et al.*, The change in electrical resistivity of some high polymers during isothermal polymerization, NAVORD Rept. No. 4421, OTS 131582, (1956).
76. Jones, E., and Maslen, K. R., The physical characteristics of wire strain gauges, Aero. Research Council (England) R & M 2661 (9-258).
77. Miller, B. L. *et al.*, The performance of wire resistance strain gages as influenced by the drying time of three mounting cements, DTMB Rept. No. R-213 (9-237).
78. Matlock, H., and Thompson, S. A., Creep in bonded electric resistance strain gages, *Soc. Exptl. Stress Anal.* **12,** No. 2 (1954).
79. McWhirter, M., and Duggin, B. W., Minimizing creep in paper base SR-4 strain gages, *Proc. Soc. Exptl. Stress Anal.* **14,** No. 2 (1956).
80. Stein, P. K., How to select a strain gage, *Strain Gage Readings* **2,** No. 1 (1958).

SOME TEMPERATURE EFFECTS ON RESISTANCE STRAIN GAGES

I. G. Scott

Australian Defence Scientific Service, Aeronautical Research Laboratories,
Department of Supply, Melbourne, Australia

Abstract

The effect of temperatures of up to 250°C on conventional resistance strain gages is examined. There is a review of the literature, followed by some discussion of temperature-gage factor relationships, self-heating of gages, etc. Methods of measuring gage temperature coefficients are discussed and a study is made of the temperature coefficient, in particular with respect to the use of gages in precision measurements.

Introduction

Strain gage research at the Aeronautical Research Laboratories is largely concerned with the collection of information from various sources and the supplementing of this information where necessary with the results from additional experiments. By this means it is hoped that a reasonably general picture of gage behavior can be obtained. Where this has been found impossible, attempts have been made to examine test techniques. With the increasing demand for gage operations at higher and higher temperatures it is felt of great importance to first examine the characteristics of available gages and where possible to develop suitable test techniques at comparatively low temperatures.

Heat is applied to the gage-specimen adhesive layer in order to hasten or to bring about setting or curing of the adhesive. In addition, heat applied to either attached or unattached gages is found to stabilize gage resistances. In these instances, gage performance is enhanced by the use of heat—provided of course that the gage is not damaged by excessive heating. On the other hand, conventional gages are of limited use at temperatures much above 200°C, and in precise work large errors may arise from comparatively small temperature changes in either the gage or the specimen.

The attachment and operation of gages at low temperatures will not be seriously considered. Campbell,[1] Day,[2] Day and Sevand,[3] and Majors[4] have tested gages at low temperatures and found gage-factor changes to be relatively small (of order 4%) and in many cases negligible. Further discussion is therefore concerned with the effects of above-ambient temperatures on the performance of conventional wire or foil gages.

Temperature Effects on Gage Factor

The effect of heat on gage factor is of great importance because variations in this parameter largely determine the maximum operating temperature for various gage types. The equipment used in the tests which follow consisted invariably of a beam in bending or a loaded cantilever installed in a temperature controlled oven, together with suitable resistance measuring devices.

Gustafsson[5] found for the Huggenberger gage (made using essentially a cellulose-based cement and base) an immediate and continuous decrease

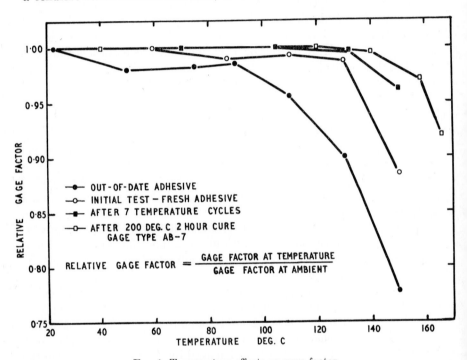

Fig. 1. Temperature effects on gage factor.

in gage factor with increasing temperatures up to 140°C, with a complete recovery of gage factor on return to room temperature. Hines[6] tested various gage types, including the type AB-3 which was found to operate satisfactorily up to temperatures of 175°C with a decrease of only 3% in gage factor. Day[7] confirmed these figures for AB-3 and AB-7 gages, while Campbell[8] tested unnamed commercial gages, one of which is believed to have been a type AB-7. In some cases the oven was taken to the highest temperature chosen for the test and gage factors were determined as the oven cooled. Hence the reduction in gage factor at the higher temperatures can be due to only *temporary* weakening of the gage bond. Maslen and Scott[9] tested an early type of foil gage, finding that the gage factor began to drop at about 45°C, a typical figure for gages attached with certain epoxy resin adhesives. Tests by Maslen[10] on a later type of foil gage produced very similar results.

Typical behavior of gages with increasing temperatures is illustrated in Fig. 1, some results of tests conducted by Saleeba and Scott[11] on type AB-7

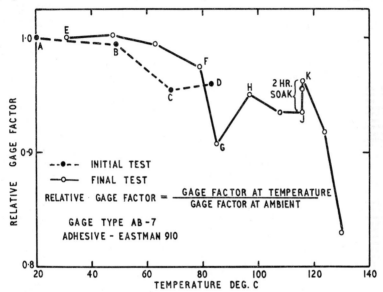

Fig. 2. Variation of gage factor with temperature.

gages being shown. A constant gage factor for temperatures up to and in excess of 120°C was found, but at 160°C the gage factor had fallen by 5% and the use of the adhesive beyond this temperature would not be recommended. The improvement in gage performance resulting from temperature cycling (accompanied inevitably by some additional adhesive cure) should be noted.

Scott[12] conducted tests on the same gage type using Eastman 910 adhesive. The decrease of the gage factor (ABC, Fig. 2) appears to be normal, while the slight increase (CD) is probably caused by the temperature cure the adhesive received during the test. On the following test on the same gage, an improvement in performance is noted until F is reached. After this the gage factor decreases rapidly to G, but recovers at H due to the additional heating. Later (JK) the gage factor is seen to recover when the gage is allowed to remain at temperature for several hours.

Thereafter the gage factor decreases rapidly with increasing temperature, the gage bond finally being completely ruptured at a temperature (130°C) below that which would damage the gage. Hence AB-7 gages can be recovered for re-use by the application of heat.

TEMPERATURE EFFECTS ON GAGE DRIFT

The increase of drift with temperature for gages attached to loaded specimens is a characteristic of most types of gages, or more correctly, the decrease in strength with temperature is characteristic of most plastics (i.e., strain gage adhesives). Jones and Maslen[13] illustrated the temperature-time-strain relationship with drift for paper-backed cellulose-based cement gages attached to Dural. Maslen[14] and Saleeba and Scott[11] were able to fit equa-

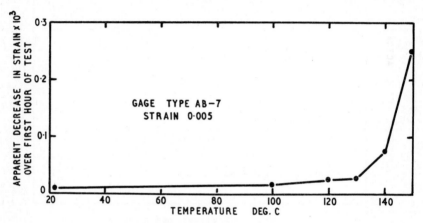

FIG. 3. Effect of temperature on drift.

tions to similar curves. This of course is comparatively easy at elevated temperatures where the gage deficiencies are generally emphasized. The effect of temperature on drift of an AB-7 gage under 0.005 strain is shown in Fig. 3.

TEMPERATURE EFFECTS ON BRIDGE OUTPUT

It is customary to assume that the output of a gage bridge is a measure of strain, but extraneous temperature effects can render this assumption invalid. As an example, consider the bridge shown in Fig. 4. Anderson[15] and Scott[16] have shown that to a good approximation the change in output voltage per unit bridge voltage V_0 is given by

$$V_0 = \tfrac{1}{4}(\beta - \alpha + \gamma - \delta)$$

which may be recognized as a very commonly used gage formula.

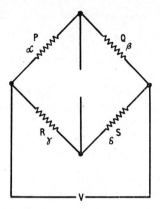

FIG. 4. Strain gage bridge.

Now the resistive changes (α's) may be due either to strain or temperature changes; hence write

$$P(1 + \alpha) = P(1 + G\epsilon)(1 + \eta\theta)$$

where G = gage factor,
ϵ = strain,
η = temperature coefficient of resistance of gage,
θ = temperature change from some fixed datum

from which $\alpha = G\epsilon + \eta\theta + G\epsilon\eta\theta$
$\doteqdot G\epsilon + \eta\theta,$

the final term being very small indeed.

Consider now the simple case where two gages are used, only one of which is affected by strain.
Then

$$V_0 = \tfrac{1}{4}(G_1\epsilon_1 + \eta_1\theta_1 - \eta_2\theta_2)$$

and provided $\eta_1\theta_1 = \eta_2\theta_2$, V_0 is solely dependent upon the strain term $G_1\epsilon_1$. If, however, this condition does not apply exactly, and assuming $G_1\epsilon_1 = 0.002$, then to obtain an accuracy of strain measurement of 1%, $(\eta_1\theta_1 - \eta_2\theta_2) < 0.00002$. This is most easily achieved by making $\theta_1 = \theta_2$ as nearly as possible, for η can be of order 0.00002 and the spread from gage to gage can be quite considerable. In this case (temperature-compensated gage pair) errors can easily occur if proper precautions are not taken.

Consider now the situation where the bridge is used to determine the difference between two comparatively large but nearly equal strains (difference bridge). We may then write

$$V_0 = \tfrac{1}{4}(G_1\epsilon_1 - G_2\epsilon_2 + \eta_1\theta_1 - \eta_2\theta_2).$$

If now $G_1\epsilon_1 = G_2\epsilon_2$ the expected condition, then the bridge output which should be zero is instead

$$V_0 = \tfrac{1}{4}(\eta_1\theta_1 - \eta_2\theta_2).$$

This output could well be large enough to cause large fractional errors, which certainly would not be tolerated in precise work and would frequently cause trouble in routine work with gages.

Gage Techniques for Precision Measurement

In transducer applications of gages, calibration of the completed device is permitted and the effects of gage factor variation and nonlinearity can therefore be largely removed. Most of the remaining errors are brought about by (small) temperature changes.

The use of dummy gages attached to small plates of the same material as the specimen and in thermal contact with the specimen, is frequently satisfactory. However, this can lead to trouble when the temperature changes. Because of the inevitable thermal resistance between the two bodies and the difference in thermal capacities, the small dummy plate heats at a much faster rate than the larger specimen.

In wind-tunnel balances, SR-4 type AB-7 gages are most commonly used. Gages forming a particular bridge are all taken from the same batch in the hope that the thermal properties of the wire will be the same or similar, are matched for resistance to better than 0.1%, and are all attached and cured together. The leakage resistance is kept high and stings are frequently stored at temperatures slightly above ambient to prevent any possibility of moisture condensing on the gages.

Although very similar techniques are used for both, it is probably harder to design suitable balances than (say) load cells. It is frequently necessary to use the difference bridge mentioned earlier, to mount gages in poor (thermal) locations, and to work in tunnels where the temperature may change by as much as 30°C, with the additional probability of temperature gradients existing along the length of the sting. Careful design is necessary to avoid, where possible, placing gages where structural strains caused by thermal expansion can be inadvertently measured, and the balance strains are kept as high as practicable in order to minimize the effects of thermally produced gage outputs. However, for various reasons strains have to be kept below 0.001.

The sources of error are varied. Bassiere[17] considered a difference bridge having an output due to temperature changes which may be written as

$$V_0 = \tfrac{1}{4}(\eta_1\theta_1 - \eta_2\theta_2 + \eta_3\theta_3 - \eta_4\theta_4).$$

If now the temperature change is the same for all gages, we may write

$$V_0 = \tfrac{1}{4}\Delta\eta \cdot \theta$$

or, if there exist temperature gradients, $V_0 = \tfrac{1}{4}\Delta\theta \cdot \eta$. Most workers prefer to make $\Delta\eta$ very small by adding short lengths of copper wire, in the appropriate arm of the bridge, attaching the wire in a low strain area near to the gage. However, Bassiere prefers to inject into the bridge circuit a signal proportional to θ. This can really be done only when using DC excitation of the gage bridge. The effects of thermal gradients are not so easily reduced. It is desirable to make $\theta_1 = \theta_2$ and $\theta_3 = \theta_4$, but frequently the gages concerned cannot be mounted close together, and hence it is almost impossible to keep them at the same temperature.

If the gage is wound using Constantan wire and the leads are made of copper, a thermocouple is formed at the lead-wire junction. Now for a 120-ohm gage bridge energized by 6 volts, a fractional resistance change of 10^{-6} results in a bridge output of only 6 μv, compared with the thermocouple output of 40 μv/°C. Hence for reasonable accuracy the temperature difference between the lead wires must be kept below 0.1°C. This in fact is one of the strongest arguments in favor of bridges energized by AC. Temperature gradients along leads can cause additional problems. It has been suggested that the copper lead wires can cool more rapidly than the gage wires and hence at junctions thermal emf's can be generated. Hansen[18] suggests that gage pairs should be kept at the same temperature, the lead wires equal in length, of adequate cross section, and side by side. Anderson[19] claims that the use of complete bridges for a sting frequently reduces lead problems. McFarland and Dimeff[20] found that the temperature coefficient of resistance of ordinary solder is rather high and that a large increase occurs at about 120°C. If the fraction of the gage resistance due to the soldered joint is 0.001, resistance errors of the order of 0.000002/°C can be readily introduced. Where solder is allowed to run along the gage wire, even higher values are found. Despite these and similar problems quite good balances have been made. Anderson[21] quotes, for a satisfactory sting, almost linear temperature effects over the range 15°–35°C of about 0.15 $\times$ 10^{-6} strain/°C.

Statham[22] analyzed the various networks used for temperature compensation of bridges. Unfortunately, calculations such as these can do no more than indicate magnitudes of compensating resistances. In practice, experimental trimming of the inserted resistance is essential, but compensation can be achieved quite rapidly.

Self-Heating of Gages

The self-heating of gages, i.e., the temperature rise occasioned by the flow of measuring current, is only of importance when either the heat capacity of the specimen is low, the gage current is high, or when high precisions are required. The allowable gage currents stated by manufacturers are generally based on heating effects for work of average quality and for specimens of average size. Where it is necessary to use different values it is best to conduct confirmatory tests.

Campbell[8] used an interesting double bridge arrangement for tests on heating. Maslen and Scott[9] passed currents through attached foil gages until steady temperatures were reached. A near-linear temperature-power output relationship was found. Two stages should be recognized. In the first, small temperature increases cause bridge output because of temperature coefficient of resistance effects. In the second, the gage bond is weakened and there is a consequent reduction in gage factor, due solely to the heating brought about by the high gage current. There is, in fact, a third stage in which the gage is destroyed by excessive current or heat.

Jones and Maslen[13] developed an expression from which the allowable gage current can be determined. However, the final expression contains a term which must be determined experimentally, but which is constant for any one method of gage construction. Using this expression Jackson[23] successfully predicted that foil gages would in general be able to dissipate more heat than conventional wire gages.

In order to reduce gage heating effects to a minimum, Tate[24] suggested the use of an auxiliary bridge by which the gage current was reduced to zero. The work of Sanders and Brodie[25] and Maslen and Coulter[26] on the use of pulse techniques with gage bridges represents largely an endeavor to increase bridge output without increasing gage or specimen temperatures, but of course the techniques can be used equally well to reduce heating effects.

The Temperature Coefficient of Resistance of a Strain Gage

The temperature coefficient of resistance for a strain gage is defined as the fractional change in gage resistance resulting from unit temperature change, the effects of temperature on gage wire, specimen, etc., being combined to give one coefficient.

The theoretical derivation of an expression for temperature coefficient in terms of various gage and specimen parameters has been discussed by various workers, including Gustafsson,[27] Gayman,[28] and Champetier[29] and the treatment given in Appendix I largely follows their work. Generally, all agree with a final expression of the form

$$\eta = \eta_0 + Gk(\lambda_0 - \lambda)$$

where η = temperature coefficient of resistance of the gage,

η_0 = temperature coefficient of resistance of the gage wire,

G = gage factor of wire,

k = factor to correct for imperfect bonding of wire or gage,

λ_0 = thermal expansion coefficient for the material of the specimen,

λ = thermal expansion coefficient for the material of the gage wire.

Unfortunately, as it is very difficult to determine values for η_0, λ_0, and λ, it is correspondingly difficult to check this equation experimentally.

Methods for the Determination of Temperature Coefficient

It is very difficult to obtain a temperature coefficient for an unattached gage. McFarland and Dimeff[20] (and others) suggested that a measure of the differential temperature coefficient for a pair of gages could be obtained from the temperature-induced resistance changes while the gages were clamped between sand-blasted plates. Tiffany and Wood[30] transferred gages rapidly from a bath of paraffin held at room temperature to a bath at about 50°C and noted the immediate change in gage resistance. It was broadly claimed that gages which behaved in the same manner under a specific set of conditions would behave in a similar manner under different conditions. Hence gage matching for temperature coefficient could be based on similarity of bridge output.

The author has so far had complete lack of success with either of these methods. Clamped gages were found to show unexplained resistance variations at sensibly constant, but slightly elevated temperatures. Saleeba and Scott[31] reduced these variations by increasing the rate of heat transfer from the heating device to the gage. In common with other workers it has been found that, associated with every temperature change, there is a rapid change in gage resistance, followed by a comparatively slow drift. Thus it is very difficult to determine the resistance change corresponding to a particular temperature change.

Constants for attached gages are more easily obtained. Maslen[10] measured the change of resistance with temperature of four gages connected in a bridge circuit to give an average temperature coefficient for the four gages. The gages were then connected so that the difference in temperature coefficient could be measured, from which the scatter of this parameter could be determined. Boyer and Scott[32] heated gages over a range of up to 40°C and very carefully measured the change in gage resistance, claiming an over-all accuracy of about 1%.

An improved arrangement which allows smaller temperature intervals to be used has been developed by Scott[33] and is shown in Fig. 5. The circuit is analyzed in Appendix II from which it can be seen that the temperature coefficient is determined directly rather than the slope of the temperature-resistance curve. To allow rapid temperature indication, a portion of the output from the measuring thermocouple is amplified, the remainder being "backed-off" using a calibrated potential source. When in use, the time between the readings at the extremities of the temperature interval is kept to a minimum (about 20 minutes) and no sensible drift can occur

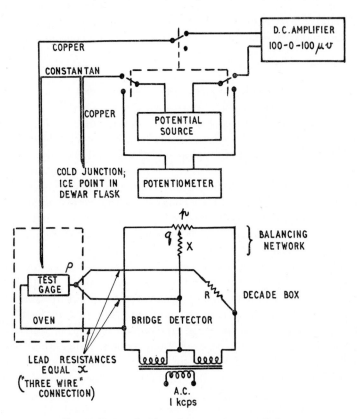

Fig. 5. Determination of temperature coefficient.

during this interval. A serious weakness of the method is the requirement to measure specimen temperature to ±0.05°C when working with temperature intervals of about 5°C. However, this technique has been found very satisfactory and a great deal of work has been done using the original arrangement.

Temperature Coefficient Variations

The results of tests conducted by various workers are shown in Table I. Temperature coefficients are seen to vary considerably even for the same wire-specimen combination—varying from −13 to +25 × 10⁻⁶/°C for copper-nickel type wire gages and aluminium alloy specimens. However, for gages from the same batch, Boyer and Scott[32] found a much smaller variation, e.g., for the type A-5 gages on Dural the values range from $15.6 - 19.3 \times 10^{-6}/°C$, while Maslen[10] found variations of only $10^{-7}/°C$ for groups of foil gages. Generally, however, the resistance-temperature relationship (from which was obtained the temperature coefficient) was linear, the equipment used was of insufficient accuracy to detect departures from linearity or only two readings were used to determine the coefficient.

TABLE I

TEMPERATURE COEFFICIENTS FOR VARIOUS GAGE TYPES[a]

Reference	Gage type	Temp. range (°C)	Temp. coeff. of resistance $\times 10^6/°C$	Remarks
Geiger and Sherlock[34]	EBDF-7D	15–250	−11 to −13	—
Ball[35]	Special	25–205	17	Gage wire wrapped around circular specimen
Jones and Maslen[13]	Unnamed	20–80	8.0, −3.3	—
Barker[36]	A-1, A-3	40–125	8.3, 23.0	—

[a] Wire or foil material—cupro-nickel alloy. Specimen material—aluminium or aluminium alloy.

However, Campbell[37] and Majors[4] found nonlinearities in the temperature coefficient-temperature relationship. Boyer and Scott[32] found significant differences in temperature coefficient between gages stretched during attachment and attached without stretching. Maslen[14] found changes in temperature coefficient of gages held at elevated temperatures (170°C) for long periods.

Saleeba and Scott[38] conducted tests on Huggenberger and AB-7 gages mounted on an aluminium alloy specimen which possessed a near-constant thermal expansion coefficient over the range of the test. The results are shown in Fig. 6. It will be seen that the temperature coefficient is quite well defined, at least sufficient to indicate a nonlinear relationship with temperature. The variation of temperature coefficient for the same gage type (AB-7) but on different materials is clearly shown in Fig. 7. The droop of the curves at temperatures in excess of 130°C is brought about by the reduction in gage factor which results from the heating of the gage.

Temperature coefficient measurements provide a very sensitive indication of poorly attached or improperly cured gages. In fact, the point at which the gage factor begins to fall is quite clearly defined from temperature coefficient-temperature curves. A sudden change in temperature coefficient (particularly when using, say, Eastman 910 adhesive) can be

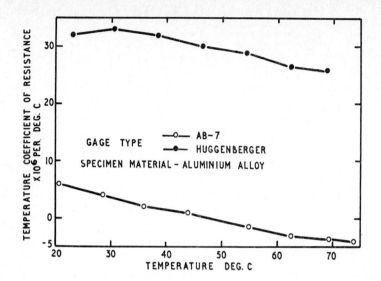

FIG. 6. Typical temperature coefficient variations. *Note:* The temperature coefficient is plotted against the mid-point of the temperature range, being assumed constant over the particular temperature interval.

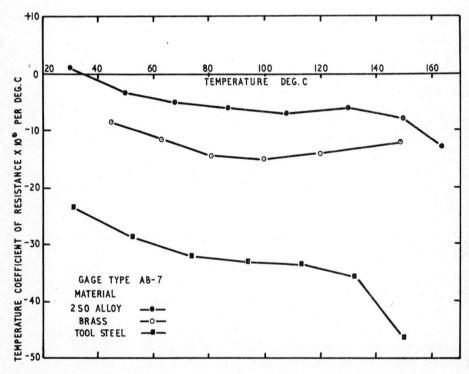

FIG. 7. Temperature coefficient of resistance of gages attached to various metals.

attributed to the gage becoming detached from the specimen. This change results from the expansion coefficient for the specimen (say, $20 \times 10^{-6}/°C$) being replaced by the coefficient for phenolic resins (about $70 \times 10^{-6}/°C$) in the temperature coefficient equation.

It is not easy to confirm many of these deductions, for both thermal expansion coefficients and temperature coefficients of resistance for the elements of the gage are greatly affected by all sorts of treatments considered common to gage attachment and handling. The temperature effect on resistance of gage wires is frequently nonlinear (see, e.g., Johnson Matthey[39]) and is greatly affected by heat treatment and mechanical working. Wiebe[40] has reported a series of attempts to produce fine wires having temperature coefficients to allow compensation, when used in gages, on various materials. Some success in this instance was achieved by using special heat treatments. Hence it is not surprising to find quite large temperature coefficient variations throughout a batch of gages. Saleeba and Scott[41] found for 20 Huggenberger gages attached to similar Dural bars a variation from 32 to $56 \times 10^{-6}/°C$, the mean being $40.1 \times 10^{-6}/°C$ with a standard deviation of $6.9 \times 10^{-6}/°C$. However, as suggested earlier, Anderson found little trouble in selecting AB-7 gage pairs so that the differential temperature coefficient was very much smaller. It is quite likely that sufficient strain can be induced in the Huggenberger gages during attachment to cause the variations listed.

Finally, one must be careful to distinguish between the temperature coefficient of an unattached gage (η') and the value which can be assigned to the gage from knowledge of its behavior on different materials. There is often a sign difference in these two parameters.

TEMPERATURE-COMPENSATED GAGES

Gages attached to (say) steel and made from copper-nickel wire show a decrease in resistance when heated, while gages made from nickel-chromium alloy show an increase in resistance. Hence it should be possible to make self-temperature-compensating gages by combining, in the correct proportion, lengths of both wire in the same gage. Higson[42] and Barker[43] have described the characteristics of these types of gages, finding in general that a marked reduction in the magnitude of temperature coefficient can be achieved. Scott and Saleeba,[44] faced with the problem of using conventional gages $(\eta = -25 \times 10^{-6}/°C)$ in thermal stress measurement, were able to change the effective temperature coefficient by the use of auxiliary gages made of copper wire (Fig. 8). This technique is of course restricted in its application.

Compensated gages are generally hard to make because very small variations in wire properties can cause unacceptable variations in the tempera-

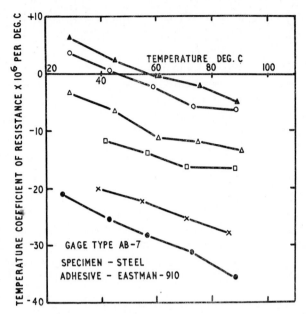

Fig. 8. Temperature compensation using auxiliary gages. —●—, uncompensated; —✕—, with 0.103-ohm copper auxiliary gage; —□—, with 0.329-ohm copper; —△—, with 0.504-ohm copper; —○—, with 0.729-ohm copper; —▲—, with 0.821-ohm copper.

ture-affected output. In addition, compensation is dependent on the thermal expansion coefficient, and this of course is strongly dependent on the previous treatment received by the specimen material. Also there is a restriction imposed on the usable temperature range.

Concluding Remarks

It can be seen that temperature effects on gages can produce quite serious errors, not only in precision work but in routine measurements. However, provided the possible occurrence of these errors is realized, it is not difficult to take the necessary steps to ensure that the effects are kept small.

Acknowledgment

The author is indebted to the Chief Scientist, Australian Defence Scientific Service, Department of Supply, Melbourne, Australia, for permission to publish this paper.

Appendix I. The Theoretical Determination of Temperature Coefficient

The increase in length L of the specimen due to temperature change $d\theta$ is $L\lambda_0 d\theta$, and the increase in length L of the gage wire due to a similar temperature change is $L\lambda d\theta$, where λ_0 is the thermal expansion coefficient for the material of the specimen, and λ is the thermal expansion coefficient for the material of the gage wire.

Similarly, the increase in length L of the specimen due to strain $d\epsilon_0$ is $Ld\epsilon_0$, and the increase in length L of the gage wire due to strain $d\epsilon$ is $Ld\epsilon$. Now if it is assumed that the wire is perfectly bonded to the specimen, then the total elongation of the specimen over length L is the same as the total elongation of the wire, i.e.,

$$\lambda_0 d\theta + d\epsilon_0 = \lambda d\theta + d\epsilon$$

or

$$d\epsilon = d\epsilon_0 + d\theta(\lambda_0 - \lambda).$$

Again the decrease dA_1 in the cross-sectional area A of the gage wire due to strain is $-2A\nu d\epsilon$ where ν is Poisson's ratio for the material of the wire and the increase dA_2 in the cross-sectional area of the gage wire due to the temperature change is $2A\lambda d\theta$, the total change in area dA being given by

$$dA = 2A(\lambda d\theta - \nu d\epsilon)$$

or

$$\frac{dA}{A} = 2(\lambda d\theta - \nu d\epsilon),$$

some minor approximations having been made.

Finally, write $R = sL/A$ where R is the resistance of the gage wire and s is its resistivity, and from which follows

$$\frac{dR}{R} = \frac{ds}{s} + \frac{dL}{L} - \frac{dA}{A}.$$

Now if this change in resistance was brought about by temperature change $d\theta$, it follows that

$$\frac{1}{R}\frac{\partial R}{\partial \theta}d\theta = \frac{1}{s}\frac{\partial s}{\partial \theta}d\theta + \frac{1}{L}\frac{\partial L}{\partial \theta}d\theta - \frac{1}{A}\frac{\partial A}{\partial \theta}d\theta.$$

But $\dfrac{1}{R}\dfrac{\partial R}{\partial \theta} = \eta_0$, the temperature coefficient of resistance;

$\dfrac{1}{s}\dfrac{\partial s}{\partial \theta} = \chi$, the temperature coefficient of resistivity, while

$\dfrac{1}{A}\dfrac{\partial A}{\partial \theta} = 2\lambda$ and $\dfrac{1}{L}\dfrac{\partial L}{\partial \theta} = \lambda$, the thermal expansion coefficient.

Now consider once more $R = sL/A$ and follow Gayman to write for simultaneous temperature and strain changes

$$\frac{dR}{R} = \frac{1}{s}\left(\frac{\partial s}{\partial \theta}\right)_\epsilon d\theta + \frac{1}{s}\left(\frac{\partial s}{\partial \epsilon}\right)_\theta d\epsilon$$

$$+ \frac{1}{L}\left(\frac{\partial L}{\partial \theta}\right)_\epsilon d\theta + \frac{1}{L}\left(\frac{\partial L}{\partial \epsilon}\right)_\theta d\epsilon$$

$$- \frac{1}{A}\left(\frac{\partial A}{\partial \theta}\right)_\epsilon d\theta - \frac{1}{A}\left(\frac{\partial A}{\partial \epsilon}\right)_\theta d\epsilon.$$

Substituting and rearranging it follows that

$$\frac{dR}{R} = \left(\frac{1}{s}\frac{\partial s}{\partial \theta} + \frac{1}{L}\frac{\partial L}{\partial \theta}\right) d\theta + \left(\frac{1}{s}\frac{\partial s}{\partial \epsilon} + \frac{1}{L}\frac{\partial L}{\partial \epsilon}\right) d\epsilon$$

$$- 2(\lambda d\theta - \nu d\epsilon)$$

$$= \left(\frac{1}{s}\frac{\partial s}{\partial \theta} + \frac{1}{L}\frac{\partial L}{\partial \theta} - 2\lambda\right) d\theta + \left(\frac{1}{s}\frac{\partial s}{\partial \epsilon} + \frac{1}{L}\frac{\partial L}{\partial \epsilon} + 2\nu\right) d\epsilon$$

and

$$\frac{dR}{R} = \left(\frac{1}{s}\frac{\partial s}{\partial \theta} + \frac{1}{L}\frac{\partial L}{\partial \theta} - 2\lambda\right) d\theta$$

$$+ \left(\frac{1}{s}\frac{\partial s}{\partial \epsilon} + \frac{1}{L}\frac{\partial L}{\partial \epsilon} + 2\nu\right)(d\epsilon_0 + d\theta\overline{\lambda_0 - \lambda})$$

$$= (\chi + \lambda - 2\lambda)d\theta + G(d\epsilon_0 + \overline{\lambda_0 - \lambda})$$

where

$$G = \frac{1}{s}\frac{\partial s}{\partial \epsilon} + \frac{1}{L}\frac{\partial L}{\partial \epsilon} + 2\nu = \frac{1}{s}\frac{\partial s}{\partial \epsilon} + 1 + 2\nu$$

is the gage factor of the wire. Now for $d\epsilon_0 = 0$ it follows that

$$\frac{dR}{R} = (\eta_0 + G\overline{\lambda_0 - \lambda})d\theta$$

from which the temperature coefficient of resistance of the attached gage can be defined as

$$\eta = \eta_0 + G\overline{\lambda_0 - \lambda}.$$

If it is assumed that the wire is not perfectly bonded to the specimen, a factor $k < 1$ can be introduced so that

$$\eta = \eta_0 + Gk\overline{\lambda_0 - \lambda}.$$

Note that for an unattached gage the temperature coefficient $\eta \neq \eta_0$ which applies only to the wire, but

$$\eta' = \eta_0 + Gk\overline{\lambda_0' - \lambda}$$

where λ_0' is now the expansion coefficient for the base material.

APPENDIX II. ANALYSIS OF TEMPERATURE COEFFICIENT NETWORK

The basic circuit for resistance measurement is shown in Fig. 5, from which it can be seen that the use of three wires to the test gage should help to minimize the effects of lead resistance changes with temperature.

Consider the star network comprising X together with the two parts of p, i.e., q and $(p - q)$. This star network is transformed to the delta form to give two resistances, Y and Z, in parallel with the P and R arms, respectively.

With the oven at temperature θ_1, bridge balance is obtained when

$$\frac{Y_1(P + x)}{Y_1 + P + x} = \frac{Z_1(R + x)}{Z_1 + R + x}$$

from which

$$P = \frac{R - k_1 x(R + x)}{1 + k_1(R + x)}$$

where

$$k_1 = \frac{Y_1 - Z_1}{Y_1 Z_1}.$$

With the oven at temperature θ_2 whence $\theta_2 - \theta_1 = \theta$, bridge balance is obtained when

$$\frac{Y_2\{P(1 + \eta\theta) + x(1 + \eta_x\theta)\}}{Y_2 + P(1 + \eta\theta) + x(1 + \eta_x\theta)} = \frac{Z_2\{R + x(1 + \eta_x\theta)\}}{Z_2 + R + x(1 + \eta_x\theta)}$$

where η is the temperature coefficient of resistance of the test gage and η_x is the temperature coefficient of resistance of the lead wire. By eliminating P an expression for η results which without serious error and having regard to the various circuit values used and expected reduces to

$$\eta = (k_1 - k_2)\frac{R}{\theta}.$$

Now

$$k = \frac{Y - Z}{YZ} = \frac{2q - p}{Xp + q(p - q)}$$

hence

$$k_1 - k_2 = \frac{2q_1 - p}{Xp + q_1(p - q_1)} - \frac{2q_2 - p}{Xp + q_2(p - q_2)}$$

and provided that $0.4p \leqslant q \leqslant 0.6p$, the denominator may be written as $Xp + 0.25p^2$ without serious error. Hence

$$\eta = \frac{R}{\theta} \cdot \frac{2(q_1 - q_2)}{Xp + 0.25p^2},$$

a result which is essentially independent of lead resistance and not dependent on a highly accurate knowledge of the gage resistance.

REFERENCES

1. Campbell, W. R., *Natl. Advisory Comm. Aeronaut. Tech. Note No.* 1456 (1948).
2. Day, E. E., *Testing Topics* **11**, No. 1, 6 (1956).
3. Day, E. E., and Sevand, A. H., *Proc. Soc. Exptl. Stress Anal.* **8**, 133 (1950).
4. Majors, H., *Proc. Soc. Exptl. Stress Anal.* **9**, 123 (1951).
5. Gustafsson, G. V. A., *Natl. Bur. Standards (U. S.) Circ. No.* 528, p. 79 (1954).
6. Hines, F. F., *Testing Topics* **11**, No. 1, 7 (1956).
7. Day, E. E., *Proc. Soc. Exptl. Stress Anal.* **9**, 141 (1951).
8. Campbell, W. R., *Natl. Advisory Comm. Aeronaut. Tech. Note No.* 1656 (1948).
9. Maslen, K. R., and Scott, I. G., Ministry of Supply, R. A. E., *Tech. Note* INSTN 134 (August, 1953).
10. Maslen, K. R., Ministry of Supply, R. A. E., *Tech. Memo* INSTN 283 (November, 1957).
11. Saleeba, G. J., and Scott, I. G., Dept. Supply, Aeronaut. Research Labs., *Tech. Memo* ARL/SM 80 (March, 1959).
12. Scott, I. G., Dept. Supply, Aeronaut. Research Labs., *Tech. Memo* ARL/SM 83 (February, 1960).
13. Jones, E., and Maslen, K. R., Ministry of Supply, R. A. E., *Rept.* INSTN 2 (November, 1948).
14. Maslen, K. R., Ministry of Supply, R. A. E., *Tech. Note* INSTN 160 (April, 1957).
15. Anderson, J. R., Ministry of Supply, Aeronaut. Research Council, Current Papers, *C.P. No.* 415 (20,554); Aeronaut. Research Council Tech. Rept. (1959).
16. Scott, I. G., Dept. Supply, Aeronaut. Research Labs., *Rept.* ARL/SM 276 (August, 1960).
17. Bassiere, M., *AGARD Rept.* 14 (1956), translated by W. F. Fielding, Ministry of Supply, R. A. E., *Trans.* 666 (June, 1957).
18. Hansen, R. M., *AGARD Rept.* 9 (1956).
19. Anderson, J. R., Ministry of Supply, R. A. E., *Tech. Note* AERO 2290 (January, 1954).
20. McFarland, K. H., and Dimeff, J., *AGARD Rept.* 12 (1956).
21. Anderson, J. R., Ministry of Supply, R. A. E., *Tech. Note* AERO 2434 (January, 1956).
22. Statham, L., *Statham Labs. Inst. Notes* (October and November, 1948).
23. Jackson, P., *Instr. Practice* **7**, 775 (1953).
24. Tate, D. R., *Natl. Bur. Standards (U. S.) Circ. No.* 528, p. 121 (1954).

25. Sanders, N. D., and Brodie, G. H., *Natl. Advisory Comm. Aeronaut. Research Memo.* E54 B08 (1954).
26. Maslen, K. R., and Coulter, M., Ministry of Supply, R. A. E., *Tech. Note* INSTN 150 (November, 1955).
27. Gustafsson, G. V. A., *Aeronaut. Inst. Sweden, Rept. No.* 22 (1947).
28. Gayman, W. H., *Statham Labs. Inst. Notes* (March and April, 1949).
29. Champetier, L., *Machines et métaux* **31**, 39 (1947).
30. Tiffany, A., and Wood, J., *Electronic Eng.* **30**, 528 (1958).
31. Saleeba, G. J., and Scott, I. G., *Dept. Supply, Aeronaut. Research Labs., Tech. Memo* ARL/SM 92 (August, 1960).
32. Boyer, A. G., and Scott, I. G., *Dept. Supply, Aeronaut. Research Labs., Tech. Memo* ARL/SM 46 (October, 1955).
33. Scott, I. G., *Dept. Supply, Aeronaut. Research Labs., Tech. Memo* ARL/SM 70 (May, 1958).
34. Geiger, R. C., and Sherlock, I., *Proc. Soc. Exptl. Stress Anal.* **14**, 117 (1957).
35. Ball, L. M., *Proc. Soc. Exptl. Stress Anal.* **3**, 1 (1945).
36. Barker, R. S., *Proc. Soc. Exptl. Stress Anal.* **11**, 119 (1953).
37. Campbell, W. R., *Natl. Advisory Comm. Aeronaut. Tech. Note* 1011 (1946).
38. Saleeba, G. J., and Scott, I. G., *Dept. Supply, Aeronaut. Research Labs., Tech. Memo* ARL/SM 81 (March, 1959).
39. Johnson Matthey & Co. Ltd., Electrical Resistance Materials, *Data Sheet* 1440 (May, 1949).
40. Wiebe, W., *Natl. Research Council Can. N.A.E., Mech. Eng. Rept.* MS-100 (1959).
41. Saleeba, G. J., and Scott, I. G., *Dept. Supply, Aeronaut. Research Labs. Tech. Note* ARL/SM 260 (October, 1959).
42. Higson, G. R., *J. Sci. Instr.* **36**, 157 (1959).
43. Barker, R. S., *Proc. Soc. Exptl. Stress Anal.* **11**, 119 (1953).
44. Scott, I. G., and Saleeba, G. J., *Dept. Supply, Aeronaut. Research Labs., Tech. Memo* ARL/SM 90 (August, 1960).

DIGITAL POTENTIOMETER FOR PRECISION MEASUREMENTS WITH STRAIN GAGES

WALTER ENGL

Siemens & Halske Aktiengesellschaft Wernerwerk für Messtechnik, Karlsruhe, West Germany

ABSTRACT

A digital potentiometer for measurements with strain gages with an accuracy of 0.01% of full scale is described. It is built up of inductive voltage dividers due to the fact that the symmetry of an inductive divider equals the ohmic symmetry of its windings divided by the Q-factor. The null detector is fully transistorized, it discriminates voltage differences between 0.5 and 10000 μv without having any recovery time. An electronic crane scale with wireless telemetry by pulse-code-modulation is described.

INTRODUCTION

It has been possible for a considerable period of time to produce transducers with bonded strain gages with an accuracy better than 0.1% of full scale. The transducer output levels are normally of the order of 10 mv and it is established usage to measure and record them by analog electronic potentiometers in the industrial applications field. The accuracy of these potentiometers is of the order of 0.25% of full scale and is therefore not in keeping with the accuracy of the strain gages. The main sources of error of self-balancing potentiometers are: setting uncertainty of the servomechanism, nonlinearity of the slide-wire, and the presence of random noise at the input terminals. For DC operation the presence of thermal voltages is an additional source of error. Partial suppression of these errors is possible with the "extended range recorder" a self-balancing potentiometer which automatically divides the total range into subranges. Usually five subranges are provided, thereby reducing the relative error of the servomechanism (normally 0.05–0.1%) and nonlinearity of the potentiometer (normally 0.05–0.1%) each by a factor of 5. The number of subranges is limited in that the end of one subrange extremely accurately coincides with the beginning of the next. This in turn depends on the accuracy and stability with which voltage dividers can be built up from ohmic resistors In the Federal Republic of Germany, the "Physikalisch Technische Bundesanstalt," an equivalent of the U. S. National Bureau of Standards, certifies a long time accuracy of 0.02% for such resistive dividers. Finally, for DC operation, the presence of a chopper drift voltage of about 1 μv and an unavoidable thermal voltage of at least 1 μv (if measurements are made outside the laboratory) set a limit for the sensitivity of the null detector.

The use of an instrument with extended range is in fact a first step towards a digital measuring device. It is a hybrid measuring instrument, the range being characterized by digits and the reading within the range by a moving analog indicator. Indeed, this method has neither the advantage of an analog measuring device (in other words, to allow the approximate position of the value within the range to be seen at a glance) nor of a digital measuring device (to enable the reading of the exact value to be made without reading error). Therefore the next step seems to be to go one step further and to design an instrument entirely digital. The subject of this paper is to describe a four decade digital potentiometer, designed especially to be used with strain gages with an accuracy of 0.01% and a sensitivity of 0.005% both of full scale.

PRINCIPLES OF STRAIN GAGE TRANSDUCER MEASURING CIRCUITS

Most of the electronic potentiometers are operated with direct current and necessitate the provision of two galvanically independent DC sources of a constant voltage ratio for feeding transducer and potentiometer (Fig. 1). To circumvent this problem, the transducer output is often not

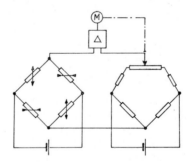

FIG. 1. Two-source measuring circuit by compensating the transducer output voltage.

compensated but the transducer bridge is balanced by means of an auxiliary branch circuit of variable resistors (Fig. 2). To compensate the dead weight, additional branch circuits are often added. This method has the advantage of being simple but it is not suitable for precision measurements because of the change in the transducer sensitivity as well as the resulting lack of linearity due to the addition of auxiliary branch circuits to the bridge and because of the transducer terminals not being identical with the corners of the bridge. There are additional resistors connected between the corners of the bridge and the terminals for compensating the effects of temperature on sensitivity and for balancing the output levels (Fig. 3). Therefore, the operation of the compensation is affected in a manner not easy to see through. Precision measurements are only possible if the transducer is regarded as a two-port[1] and only two-port parameters are allowed to enter

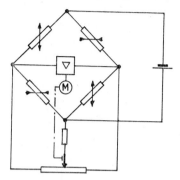

Fig. 2. One-source measuring circuit by rebalancing the bridge.

the measurement. In particular, no additional connections are allowed between the output and the input of the two-port. This means that the transducer and the potentiometer must be fed by separate sources. It is worthwhile mentioning how this is realized in the DC electronic potentiom-

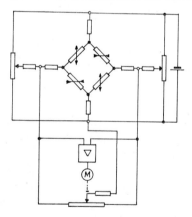

Fig. 3. Completed circuit for one-source measuring device.

eter of the Siemens & Halske Company because the basic principle of this instrument is of general applicability to precision measurement and can hence also be used in a digital potentiometer (Fig. 4). The null motor M can alternatively be connected to the measuring slide-wire or an auxiliary slide-wire by a magnetic clutch. The auxiliary slide-wire is part of a voltage divider which feeds the potentiometer. The difference between the two source voltages is periodically applied to the input of the null detector by a switch and is balanced to zero by the auxiliary slide-wire. Moreover, by doing so, the influence of the resistance of the lead wires (drawn thick in Fig. 4) and its changes with temperature are eliminated when connecting additional voltage measuring leads directly to the input terminals of the strain gage bridge. In an AC potentiometer, a transformer with a common primary but separate secondaries provides independent potential sources of a constant voltage ratio for both the transducer and the potentiometer.

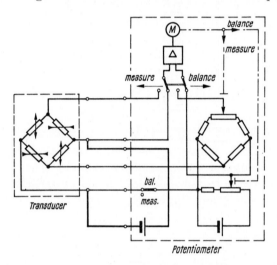

FIG. 4. Measuring circuit using automatic lead wire resistance compensation (Siemens & Halske).

But the elimination of the lead wire effects alone is sufficient reason to introduce the above-mentioned compensation. However, we shall not enter a philosophical discussion on the merits and demerits of AC and DC feeding. The reason is that for a measuring range of 10 mv and a demanded sensitivity of 0.005% the limit of detection of the differential voltage between transducer and potentiometer must be as low as 0.5 μv and this can only be achieved with an AC amplifier at the present state of the art. It is tacitly assumed that strain gages under load give no rise to phase displacements to a degree which would render measurements impossible at an accuracy of 0.01%. Investigations have subsequently shown that this assumption is justified.

PRINCIPLES OF THE AC DIGITAL POTENTIOMETER

The function of a digital potentiometer is to subdivide its input voltage into a maximum possible number of discrete parts. This number is restricted either by the accuracy with which the ratio of the divider can be realized or by the sensitivity with which the null detector can discriminate a voltage-difference of the smallest digit from noise, or both combined. As already mentioned, the limit for certification of DC potentiometers by the Physikalische Technische Bundesanstalt is 0.02%. One is therefore induced to

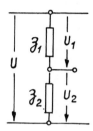

FIG. 5. Voltage divider with complex resistors.

examine the possibility of making inductive voltage dividers. The voltage ratio in this case depends mainly on the turns ratio which does not change with either temperature or time. To understand the principles involved, let us consider a voltage divider of two complex resistors which are nearly equal (Fig. 5). The symmetry Σ_z of a voltage divider shall be defined as:

$$\Sigma_z = \frac{U_1 - (U/2)}{U} = \frac{1}{2} \cdot \frac{z_1 - z_2}{z_1 + z_2}. \tag{1}$$

For a voltage divider made of ohmic resistors, Σ_R runs as follows:

$$\Sigma_R = \frac{1}{2} \cdot \frac{R_1 - R_2}{R_1 + R_2}. \tag{2}$$

To compute the symmetry of an inductive voltage divider (Fig. 6a) we make use of the fact that two coupled inductances can be represented by a simple equivalent circuit (Fig. 6b). The flux through L_1 and L_2, respec-

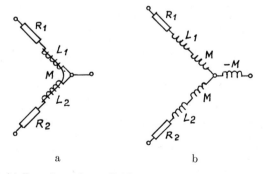

a   b

FIG. 6. (a) Reactive voltage divider and (b) its equivalent T-circuit.

tively, may be written as the sum of a part which is linked with M and a part which represents the leakage flux:

$$L_1 = \ddot{u}M(1 + \sigma_1); \qquad L_2 = \frac{1}{\ddot{u}}M(1 + \sigma_2). \tag{3}$$

Here

$$\ddot{u} = w_1/w_2 \tag{4}$$

is the ratio. σ_1 and σ_2 are stray coefficients defined as:

$$\sigma_1 = \frac{L_{\sigma_1}}{\ddot{u}M}; \qquad \sigma_2 = \frac{L_{\sigma_2}}{(1/\ddot{u})M}, \tag{5}$$

where L_{σ_1} and L_{σ_2} are leakage inductances. The total stray coefficient is given by:

$$\sigma = 1 - \frac{M^2}{L_1 L_2} = \sigma_1 + \sigma_2. \tag{6}$$

From this the equivalent circuit for a 1:1 divider follows (Fig. 7a). Defining

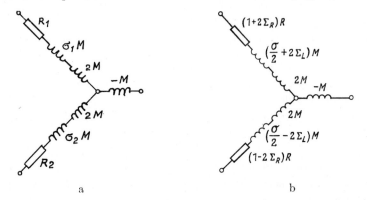

FIG. 7. (a) Inductive voltage divider, equivalent T-circuit with primary and secondary stray coefficients. (b) Inductive voltage divider, equivalent T-circuit with total stray coefficient and symmetry parameters.

again a symmetry parameter Σ_L, as in Eqs. (1) and (2), we obtain:

$$\Sigma_L = \frac{1}{2} \cdot \frac{L_1 - L_2}{L_1 + L_2} = \frac{\sigma_1 - \sigma_2}{4}. \tag{7}$$

Using Eqs. (6) and (7) we can further write:

$$R_{1,2} = R(1 \pm 2\Sigma_R); \tag{8}$$

$$\sigma_{1,2} = \frac{\sigma}{2} \pm 2\Sigma_L,$$

where R is defined by the equation:

$$R = \frac{R_1 + R_2}{2}.$$ (9)

The final equivalent T-circuit is shown in Fig. 7b. The symmetry of the inductive divider hence is:

$$\Sigma_i = \frac{1}{2}\left(\Sigma_L + \Sigma_R \cdot \frac{R}{j\omega M}\right).$$ (10)

If the inductive divider is made by winding on a toroidal core the partial windings in the form of two twisted bifilar wires, experience teaches that the sum of primary and secondary stray coefficients $\sigma = \sigma_1 + \sigma_2$ is so low that their difference $(\sigma_1 - \sigma_2)/4 = \Sigma_L$ is negligible compared with $\Sigma_R \cdot (R/j\omega M)$. For the frequency range in question the following equation holds:

$$\Sigma_i \approx \Sigma_R \cdot \frac{R}{2\omega M}.$$ (11)

This equation proves the advantage of an inductive divider over an ohmic divider: The symmetry of an inductive divider equals the ohmic symmetry

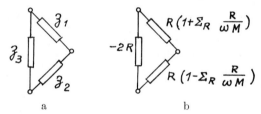

FIG. 8. Inductive voltage divider, (a) general and (b) approximate π-circuit.

of its windings divided by the Q-factor. To explain another advantage of the inductive divider, we convert the equivalent T-circuit into the equivalent π-circuit (Fig. 8a):

$$z_{1,2} \approx \left(R + \frac{\sigma}{2}j\omega M\right) \cdot \left[1 \pm \left(\Sigma_L + \Sigma_R \cdot \frac{R}{j\omega M}\right)\right];$$

$$z_3 = -2\left(R + \frac{\sigma}{2}j\omega M\right) - \frac{(R + (\sigma/2)j\omega M)^2}{j\omega M}.$$ (12)

Tolerating the same degree of approximation as in Eq. (11), Eq. (12) can be simplified with the result of Fig. 8b. Hence we see that the internal resistance of an inductive divider is determined only by its ohmic winding resistance, i.e., it is possible to construct a potentiometer of very low impedance. The output power of the strain gages therefore is transmitted almost entirely to the null detector and is dissipated in the potentiometer only to a negligible extent. In addition, the inductive potentiometer due to its low internal resistance is considerably less affected by a capacitive load than an ohmic potentiometer. A final advantage is concerned with the summation of the partial voltages in the potentiometer. Every switch has finite contact resistance which usually varies to some extent. Therefore an ohmic potentiometer has to be laid out as high-ohmic as required to minimize the effects of contact resistance. In an ohmic potentiometer, there is always a current flow through the compensating circuit and therefore also through the switch contacts. In the case of the inductive potentiometer, however, it is possible to total the voltages through contacts without current flowing under compensated conditions and thus the problem of contact resistance does not arise. On the other hand, the use of AC entails some disadvantages: The strain gage bridge has also to be balanced for capacitance; the phase shift between the output of the strain gage bridge and the potentiometer has to be adjusted to zero, and finally the permissible length of the lead wires is always shorter for AC operation than for DC operation. This is, however, no serious disadvantage because the digital information can be transmitted by means of pulse-code-modulation over any required distance.

Construction of Digital Potentiometer

The potentiometer voltage is built up in a binary-decade manner. For each decade an inductive divider is provided consisting of 10 strands and on the same core with one primary winding (Fig. 9). The numbers between 1 and 9 are binary produced as shown in Fig. 10. Among the several possibilities to build up powers of 2, we chose the one needing the smallest possible number of switches. Contrary to an ohmic potentiometer, it is possible to add the single decades independent of potential on the input side. Therefore, we are permitted to add up the compensation voltages of the single decades by galvanically connecting them in series. Further, it can be seen from Fig. 10 that the method applied is a true compensating method. All measurements with strain gages are ratio measurements. In terms of the network theory, the open circuit voltage ratio is measured. Therefore the potentiometer does not need to be fed from a source of stable voltage. Its input voltage can be derived from the transducer supply at a fixed ratio and which needs not to be stabilized. This is achieved by two transformers. The ratio is such that the voltage at the first decade is 10 mv identical with the full scale transducer output when fed with 6 volts. Voltages from 0 to 9999 μv in steps of 1 μv can be produced in the potentiometer as required to balance the output voltages of the transducer. The difference between the two voltages is taken to a null detector, at the output of which a decision is made as to which of these two voltages is

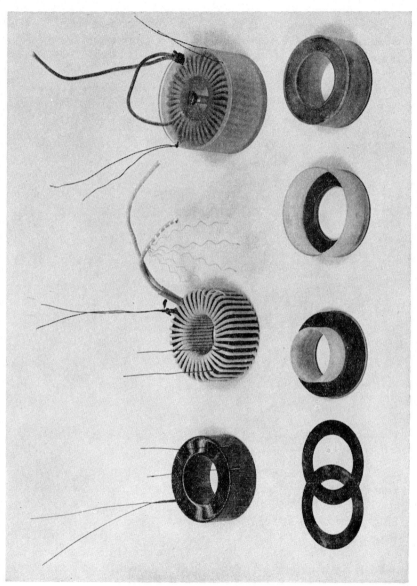

Fig. 9. View of an inductive decade voltage divider.

larger, dependent on the relative phase position of the voltage difference. Finally, I ig. 10 shows the balancing circuits for ohmic and capacitive unbalance and also a phase shifter provided to adjust to zero the phase displacement between transducer and potentiometer. This balancing operation is made only once with the transducer fully loaded. The phase shifter is arranged in such a way as to render the 90°-voltage independent of frequency drift as a first-order approximation. The potentiometer is operated at a frequency of 311 cps. Siemens ES-relays or Siemens dry reed relays were used. Semiconductor switches were found to be inadequate at the

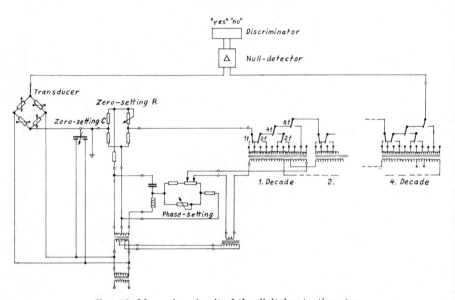

Fig. 10. Measuring circuit of the digital potentiometer.

present state of art. The complete balance of the 4 decades requires 16 switching operations each lasting 10 msec. Even if transistors would serve the purpose, the speed could not be appreciably increased as the delaytime in the amplifier is as high as about 4 msec at the given frequency. If an attempt were made to shorten the delay time by increasing the bandwidth of the amplifier, the signal-to-noise ratio would get worse and the sensitivity of the null detector would decrease accordingly. It seems unreasonable to increase the operating frequency considerably because capacitive effects in the transducer and in the potentiometer would adversely affect the accuracy. Figure 11 shows the digital potentiometer with ES-relays. In Fig. 12 the (a) front and (b) rear sides of the whole measuring device with dry reed relays can be seen.

Fig. 11. View of a digital potentiometer using Siemens ES-relays.

FIG. 12a. Front view of total measuring device (dry reed relay device).

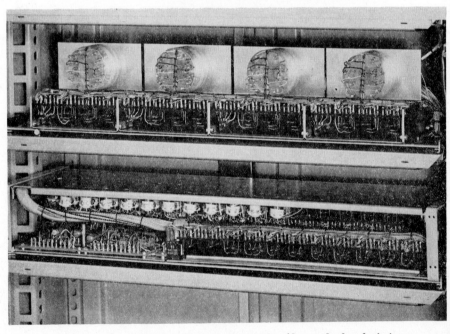

FIG. 12b. Rear view of total measuring device (dry reed relay device).

Null Detector

The null detector amplifies the resultant of transducer and potentiometer voltages and discriminates on the phase position. The amount the voltages to be discriminated can be between the limits of 0.5 and 10,000 μv and a large signal may be followed by a small one after one step. For this reason the amplifier recovery time must be of the order of 2 msec even after an overload as high as $10^4:1$. This was essentially achieved by the introduction of a strong negative DC feedback over two stages each. This prevents the shift of the operating points. The amplifier consists of four stages and is fully transistorized. The input is floating. This is achieved through an input transformer, transducer as well as potentiometer being grounded on one side. The output voltage is phase-sensitively rectified by a ring demodulator and controls a Schmitt-trigger after being filtered by a low-pass filter. As mentioned above, the amplifier delay time for a signal of a frequency of 311 cps is shorter than 5 msec. An emf of 0.5 μv from a source of 300 Ω internal resistance is required to trigger the Schmitt-trigger. The signal-to-noise ratio is 3:1, the input power 2×10^{-16} watt. By extending the balancing time, the sensitivity can be improved by a factor of 10.

Potentiometer Drive

The potentiometer drive can be compared with an operator manipulating a potentiometer (Fig. 13). It consists of a multivibrator, a relay selector, and a discriminator for the output of the null detector. The code of the

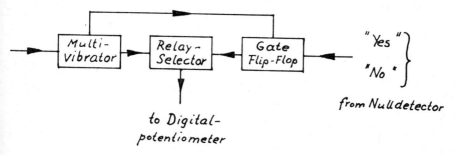

Fig. 13. Block diagram of the potentiometer drive.

potentiometer is binary-decade as explained earlier. That means that for each decade four weights 8, 4, 2, and 1 are available from which all values from 0 to 9 can be composed. Meaningless combinations of the sum larger than 9 are excluded. The drive mechanism follows a fixed program. After the starting signal, it commences in the first decade on the "8" unit by energizing the corresponding "8" relay in the potentiometer. Thus the

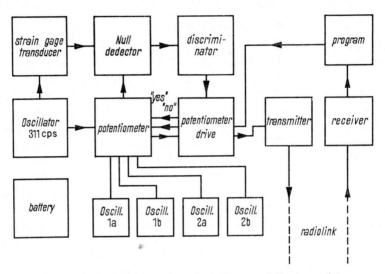

FIG. 14. Electronic crane scale, block diagram of the transmitter.

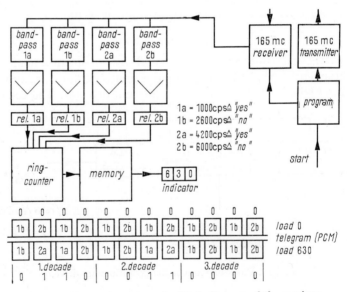

FIG. 15. Electronic crane scale, block diagram of the receiver.

decision is made by the null detector as to whether the transducer bridge is out of balance by more than 80%. In the case larger than 80% the "8" relay remains energized, otherwise it drops. The same play is repeated with the "4" unit in the same decade, thereafter for the "2" unit and the "1" unit. After these four steps the first decade is dealt with. Now the drive mechanism switches over to the next lower decade probing again the units 8, 4, 2, 1, and so on. To complete the four decades, the potentiometer drive has to take $4 \times 4 = 16$ steps, the accuracy being 0.01%.

CRANE SCALE WITH WIRELESS TELEMETRY

An electronic crane scale with wireless telemetry is an example of the application of the digital potentiometer demonstrating the progress in this field. The function is shown by the block-diagrams of Figs. 14 and 15.

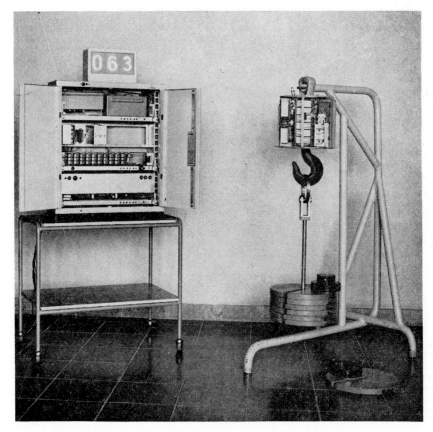

FIG. 16. View of the electronic crane scale with wireless telemetry.

Telemetry works on pulse-code modulation. The method is based on two pairs of frequencies 1 and 2. Pair 1 indicates all odd steps, pair 2 all even steps. This frequency sequence controls a ring counter in the receiver and which maintains synchronism of the digits in both the transmitter and the receiver. It still has to be decided wheter 0 or 1 applies at the digit in question. Both frequency pairs are split into the frequencies 1a and 1b, respectively, 2a and 2b, where a means "yes" means "1" and b means "no" means "0." These four frequencies are modulated with a transmitter frequency of 165 mc. This procedure gives the maximum possible velocity of transmission because the delay between receiver and transmitter is only 1 bit. The procedure also provides a considerable safety of transmission; for the width of the pulses can be distorted up to 50% before the transmission fails. Figure 16 shows the complete device.

Acknowledgments

The author wishes to acknowledge the help which was extended to him by E. Deeken, K. Peter, and E. Weber, Siemens & Halske AG, Wernerwerk für Messtechnik, Karlsruhe, West Germany.

Reference

1. Engl, W., Vierpoleigenschaften von Dehnungsmesssstreifen-Gebern, in preparation.

Bibliography

Wirk, A., and Thilo, H. G., "Niederfrequenz-Mittelfrequenz-Messtechnik." Hirzel-Verlag, Stuttgart, 1956.

RECENT DEVELOPMENTS IN SEMICONDUCTOR STRAIN TRANSDUCERS

W. P. Mason, J. J. Forst, and L. M. Tornillo

Bell Telephone Laboratories, Incorporated, Murray Hill, New Jersey

Abstract

In this paper it is shown that some of the defects of lightly doped semiconductor strain gages can be removed by going to considerably higher doping levels than have previously been employed. Measurements in the range 5×10^{18} to 10^{20} boron atoms per cubic centimeter in silicon result in a somewhat reduced gage factor but one which is more constant with temperature and with strain. It is shown that there is a nonlinearity inherent in lightly doped semiconductor strain gages. While various circuits can be used to take advantage of this effect and alleviate its deleterious effect, the higher linearity of highly doped material is a decided advantage.

Fluctuation noise is also less for a highly doped material and strains in the order of 3×10^{-10} have been measured by using such gages.

I. Introduction

Semiconductor strain gages have been in general use since about 1958 and they have been applied to various pressure, force, and acceleration measuring devices.[1-4] The original type gages were an outgrowth of research[5-7] on the physical properties of semiconductors which showed that there was a connection between applied stress and the flow of electrons in specified directions in the semiconductor crystal. This line of research first established the multivalley nature of the energy surfaces in silicon and germanium. The original data indicated gage factors, i.e., change in resistance due to strain divided by the product of the original resistance times the strain, as high as 175 for p-type silicon. These factors were allmeasured for lightly doped materials having resistivities above 1 ohm-cm.

Such high gage factors obtained in lightly doped material are accompanied by a number of rather undesirable features. These are a gage factor that varies inversely as the absolute temperature, an initial resistance that changes a considerable amount with temperature, a rather fragile structure which does not allow extensions of more than 1000 microinches/inch, and a nonlinearity of response which can amount to as high as 50% increase or decrease from the linear value for strains of 1000×10^{-6}. As discussed in reference 4, a number of these defects can be eliminated by incorporating the transducers in special circuits. However, these tend to limit the sensitivity and versatility of the gages and considerable improvements can be effected if the stability of the effect can be improved and the material made stronger.

It is the purpose of the present paper to discuss recent research directed at improving the performance properties of these semiconductor strain gages. It is shown that by doping the crystals to much higher values than those commonly used, the unstrained resistance, the gage factor, and the linearity of the devices are all greatly improved. The densities of the majority carriers are so high with respect to the minority carriers that a source of fluctuation noise present in lightly doped semiconductors is practically eliminated and the only noise source is that due to thermal fluctuations.

The work of Pearson et al.[8] on the elastic properties and strength of silicon material shows that the stress-strain curve is linear up to the fracture point for temperatures under 500°C. For sizes of rods greater than 3×10^{-5} square inches in cross section, the fracture stress is about 3×10^9 dynes/cm^2 giving a limiting value of 1600 microinches/inch. Safe values should be limited to around 1000 microinches/inch. The radius of curvature that a strain gage can be bent around is given by the equation

$$R = \frac{t}{2(\Delta L/L)} \tag{1}$$

where t is the thickness in the same units used for the radius of curvature and $\Delta L/L$ is the limiting extension or compression divided by the length of the specimen. For example, for a strain gage 0.006 inch in thickness, the radius of curvature is 3 inches for a limiting strain of 1000 microinches/inch.

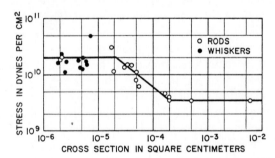

FIG. 1. Effect of size on room temperature fracture stress for silicon rods.

This calculation indicates the advantage of going to smaller gages of the "whisker" type. Furthermore, the measurements of Pearson et al. show that the limiting stress becomes larger (see Fig. 1) and for diameters of 0.002 inch or less, the limiting breaking stress approaches 2×10^{10} dynes/cm², although with a somewhat larger variation than for the larger size rods. Taking 10^{10} dynes/cm² as a safe value, small gages can be safely stressed up to 5000 microinches/inch. For gages 0.001 inch in diameter, radii of curvature of 0.1 inch can be obtained, which makes the gages considerably less fragile. They can also be applied to curved surfaces.

The measurements of Pearson *et al.* show that the same strength results whether the silicon is grown as a whisker from a vapor solution or is obtained by etching a small rod down to the desired dimensions by means of a slow etch. The latter method is much to be preferred since the doping can be closely controlled and, moreover, by protecting the ends from the etching solution, larger sized end sections can be obtained. These increased end areas facilitate the attachment of leads and the attaching of the strain gages to the surface whose strain is to be measured. The larger surface area of contact compared to the cross-sectional area of the strain sensitive part prevents creep in the glue from being a determining part of the hysteresis effect.

II. Effect of Doping on the Stability with Temperature of the Gage Factor and the Initial Resistance

The first measurements which indicated that a heavily doped silicon sample had a piezoresistance constant which differed in magnitude and temperature effect from a lightly doped material, were given in reference 4, Fig. 19. For a doping of about 5×10^{18} boron atoms per cubic centimeter the gage factor was 121 at room temperature compared to 175[5] for lightly doped samples. Furthermore, over a temperature range the variation was less than half that for a lightly doped sample. These observations show that the simple energy surface theory begins to break down for these highly doped, degenerate samples.

In order to evaluate and map the effect of a continuous range of doping, measurements were made on a series of samples which varied in impurity content from 5×10^{18} to 10^{20} boron atoms per cubic centimeter. These resulted in *p*-type specimens. Rods cut along a [111] axis were etched over a center section of 1.25 cm to a thickness of about 0.0053 cm and a width of 0.00965 cm. The end sections were larger and were supported and contact was made to the silicon by two gold wires fused on each end. The sample was completely surrounded by a metal can to ensure temperature stability of the sample. A small hole was bored in the can through which passed a wire for attaching weights to the sample. The gage factor was determined from the known weight, the accurately measured cross section, and the measured values of the elastic moduli of silicon determined[9] over a temperature range.

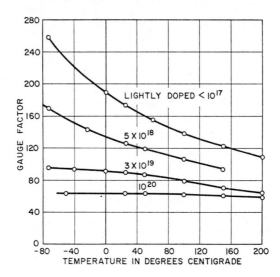

FIG. 2. Effect of doping levels on the value and temperature variation of p-type silicon strain gages.

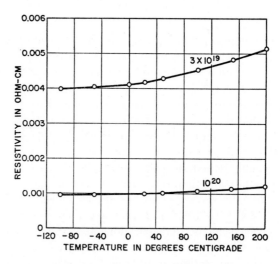

FIG. 3. Unstrained resistivities of p-type silicon plotted as a function of temperature and doping levels.

The gage factors, i.e., the change in resistance divided by the product of the unstrained resistance times the strain, are shown plotted against the temperature on Fig. 2 for four doping ranges. The gage factor decreases as the impurity content increases, but the temperature stability increases very markedly. For dopings as high as 10^{20}, the gage factor is about one-third that for a lightly doped crystal, but the variation with temperature is practically absent. Lower dopings give higher gage factors but more variation with temperature. The resistivity values for these four degrees of doping are shown by Fig. 3. These measurements are in fair agreement with the values given in reference 10.

It is evident from these measurements that the degree of doping should be fitted to the uses for which the gages are intended. Gages operating at high temperatures will obviously benefit by using the highest doping shown. For a more moderate temperature range, a lower doping value will probably be preferable.

III. Nonlinearity of Semiconductor Strain Gages

It is easily shown from the simple, many-valley theory of semiconductors, as shown in the appendix, that there is a nonlinearity inherent in the change in resistance as a function of the strain. For a semiconductor with its maximum sensitivity along the [111] axis, the change in resistance, divided by the resistance, can be expressed in the form

$$\frac{\Delta R}{R} = AS + BS^2. \tag{2}$$

This equation holds for n-type germanium with the constants

$$A = -149; \qquad B = 52,600.$$

For an n-type silicon semiconductor with its length along a [100] axis, the theory indicates an equation of the form

$$\frac{\Delta R}{R} = -125S + 26,000S^2. \tag{3}$$

p-Type silicon and germanium have a symmetry similar to that for n-type germanium but the many-valley energy surface is not applicable. For p-type, constant A is positive. The linearity for p-type silicon has been measured over wide strain and doping ranges and the deviation is much smaller than for n-type material. The change in resistance follows a formula of the type

$$\frac{\Delta R}{R} = AS + BS^4. \tag{4}$$

For low doping, B is negative, but it changes to a positive value for high doping.

Since one of the largest uses of these gages may be in replacing an expensive amplifier by utilizing the large signal that can be obtained from a highly strained semiconductor, the linearity of these gages is a matter of interest.

Equation (2) indicates that the departure from linearity is 42% for a lightly doped n-type germanium strained to 1000 microinches per inch, while Eq. (3) indicates that the nonlinearity for an n-type silicon is 20.8% for the same strain.

This nonlinearity for n-type semiconductors can be made use of in increasing the gage factor. This can be done by putting the n-type gage under compression. If we introduce a compression having a strain value $-S_0$, and superpose on this a strain of S_1, Eq. (3) can be written in the form

$$R = R_0[1 - 125(-S_0 + S_1) + (26,000)(S_0{}^2 - 2S_0S_1 + S_1{}^2)]$$
$$= R_0[1 + 125S_0 - S_1(125 + 52,000S_0) + (26,000)S_1{}^2]. \qquad (5)$$

Hence for a compressional strain of 2.4×10^{-3} the gage factor will be increased to -250 or twice that of the unstrained gage. At the same time the nonlinearity factor involving the square of S_1 will be smaller in comparison to the linear term. This compression of the gage might be accomplished by cementing every point onto a metal strip which has been

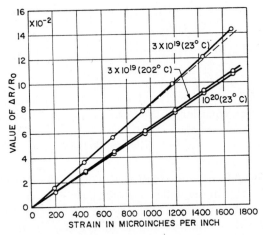

FIG. 4. Change in resistance as a function of the strain for a p-type semiconductor strain gage measured at room temperatures.

extended by the amount S_0. When the tension is taken off, the metal will return to its normal length, putting a compressional strain of $-S_0$ on the gage.

When two similar gages are used, one in tension and the other in compression, and are put in conjugate arms of a strain gage bridge, the nonlinear terms cancels out since they raise the resistance by the same amount in each arm. The linear terms are of opposite sign and add their effects. For a strain of one sign, the nonlinear effect can be reduced by using both a *p*- and an *n*-type gage in conjugate arms of the bridge. For this case the linear terms add but the nonlinear square law terms tend to cancel.

Measurements of the more highly doped material show that the nonlinear term is considerably smaller than in the more lightly doped material. Figure 4 shows the change in resistance plotted against strain for the most heavily doped material having 10^{20} boron atoms per cubic centimeter. The nonlinear term is much smaller than that indicated by Eq. (2). These measurements were made at room temperature. For equal signals out of two differently doped materials, the higher doped sample has the lowest nonlinearity. When highly doped materials are made in the form of extra strong thin specimens, they provide the most linear and temperature free materials.

IV. THERMAL AND FLUCTUATION NOISE IN SEMICONDUCTOR STRAIN GAGES

When very small strains are to be measured, the inherent noise present in the gage is a source of concern. It is well known that semiconductor materials, in addition to the thermal resistance noise common to all resistive materials, have a fluctuation type noise whose power increases approximately as the square of the current passing through the semiconductor. This type of noise has a power spectrum which increases inversely proportional to the frequency down to very low frequencies. This type of noise has been studied by Montgomery[11] who finds that it is connected with the lifetime of the minority carrier, i.e., for a *p*-type material, the noise will be connected with how long an electron can last before it combines with a hole to produce phonons, i.e., heat in the material. Combinations of holes and electrons occur at surfaces and imperfections in the crystals such as vacancies and interstitial atoms. The form of a strain gage with a large ratio of surface to volume is a good one for suppressing fluctuation noise.

Measurements were made by Montgomery on these gages doped with 5×10^{18} boron atoms per cubic centimeter. These were in the form of rods 0.006 inch on a side and $\frac{1}{4}$ inch long. For a one cycle band located at 30 cycles, the results indicated that the fluctuation noise was about equal to the resistance noise for a current of 0.012 amp through the gage and was larger than the resistance noise for larger currents. A current of 0.010 amp produces a temperature rise of 10°C for a unit in air and is about the limiting useful value. When the semiconductor is more highly doped, the ratio of the fluctuation noise to the thermal noise decreases since a larger share of the current is carried by holes, rather than short lived electrons and hence for the more highly doped material, the thermal noise exceeds the fluctuation noise down to very low frequencies.

The thermal voltage is given by a formula of the type

$$e_T = \sqrt{4kTR(\Delta f)} \tag{6a}$$

where k is the Boltzmann's constant (1.38×10^{-23} joules/°K), T is the absolute temperature, R the resistance of the circuit, and Δf the bandwidth in cycles over which the noise is measured. For $T = 300°K$, i.e., room temperature, this voltage becomes

$$e_T = 1.29 \times 10^{-10} \sqrt{(\Delta f)R} \text{ volt.} \tag{6b}$$

To determine how small a strain can be measured by a semiconductor strain gage, let us suppose that the galvanometer responds to fluctuations up to 1 cps, but that its inertia and spring constant are in the right ratio to suppress faster variations than this. For a semiconductor strain gage having a resistance of 100 ohms, the noise voltage is, from (6b),

$$e_T = 1.29 \times 10^{-9} \text{ volt.} \tag{7}$$

The signal from the same strain gage is

$$e_S = \Delta Ri = iRGS \tag{8}$$

where G is the gage factor and S the strain. For a resistance of 100 ohms and a current of 0.010 amp, the signal voltage is

$$e_S = GS. \tag{9}$$

In order to obtain a definite reading it is usually assumed that the signal voltage should be 10 times the noise voltage. Hence the strain that can be measured is

$$S = \frac{1.29 \times 10^{-8}}{G} \doteq 2.6 \times 10^{-10} \tag{10}$$

for a gage factor of 50.

Strains of this order of magnitude have been measured by using the weight of the device itself to load the gage. From the elastic moduli (1.87×10^{12} dynes/cm²) and density (2.33 for silicon) it can be shown that the difference in strain between the top and bottom halves of the gage is 3×10^{-10}. By turning the device over, a measurable difference was obtained between the two positions. To measure such small strains a very good balance has to be obtained and held in the bridge. Ordinarily this may be the limiting factor rather than the noise output of the semiconductor.

APPENDIX: CALCULATION OF THE NONLINEARITY OF LIGHTLY DOPED SEMICONDUCTOR STRAIN GAGES

For n-type silicon, there are six positions along the crystallographic axes for which the energies of the conduction bands reach a minimum. If constant energy surfaces are plotted on a momentum diagram, ellipses of the form shown by the solid lines of Fig. 5 result. The corresponding mobilities $\mu_\perp$ and $\mu_\parallel$ perpendicular and along the direction of an applied field are determined by the shape of the ellipsoid and in silicon $\mu_\perp$ is 5 times as large as $\mu_\parallel$. The effect of a tension along the x-axis, i.e., a tension T_{11}, is to raise the energy level for those valleys lying along x and to lower the energy levels for those valleys perpendicular to x. Hence the same energy will

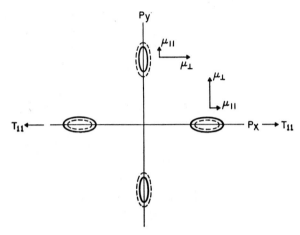

FIG. 5. Position of energy valleys with reference to crystallographic axes for n-type silicon.

occur in the form of a smaller ellipse along the x-axis (as shown by the dashed line) and in the form of a larger ellipse for directions perpendicular to x. The principle effect of this energy change is to cause the populations of electrons to be larger in the valleys perpendicular to the direction of the stress and to be smaller in those parallel to the stress. If the energy levels in the parallel valleys [100] are raised by an amount $\alpha_1 T_{11}$ and those in the [010] valleys are lowered by an amount $-\alpha_2 T_{11}$, the relative numbers of electrons in the two type valleys will be, by Boltzmann's principle,

$$\frac{N_{[010]}}{N_{[100]}} = \frac{e^{[V_0 + \alpha_1 T_{11}]/RT}}{e^{[V_0 - \alpha_2 T_{11}]/RT}} = e^{(\alpha_1 + \alpha_2) T_{11}/RT} \tag{11}$$

where V_0 is the energy level for no stress, R the gas constant equal to 2 cal/mole/°K, and T is the absolute temperature. A second equation is that the total number of electrons N_0 must remain constant. Hence

$$N_0 = 2N_{[100]} + 4N_{[010]}. \tag{12}$$

The total conductivity σ is determined by the charge on the electron, e, the mobility of each component and the number of electrons, according to the equation

$$\sigma = e[2N_{[100]}\mu_{\|} + 4N_{[010]}\mu_{\perp}]. \tag{13}$$

Solving Eqs. (11)–(13), we find for the resistivity $\rho = 1/\sigma$, the value

$$\rho = \frac{1}{\sigma} = \frac{1 + 2e^{(\alpha_1+\alpha_2)T_{11}/RT}}{N_0 e[\mu_{\|} + 2\mu_{\perp}e^{(\alpha_1+\alpha_2)T_{11}/RT}]}. \tag{14}$$

For a stress $T_{11} = 0$, this reduces to

$$\rho = \frac{3}{N_0 e[\mu_{\|} + 2\mu_{\perp}]}. \tag{15}$$

Hence we find that the change in resistivity $\Delta\rho$ divided by the initial resistivity is

$$\frac{\Delta\rho}{\rho_0} = \frac{\rho - \rho_0}{\rho_0} = \frac{2}{3}\frac{(\mu_{\perp} - \mu_{\|})(1 - e^{(\alpha_1+\alpha_2)T_{11}/RT})}{\mu_{\|} + 2\mu_{\perp}e^{(\alpha_1+\alpha_2)T_{11}/RT}}. \tag{16}$$

If we expand this expression in powers of the applied stress T_{11}, we have

$$\frac{\Delta\rho}{\rho_0} = -\frac{2}{3}\frac{(\mu_{\perp} - \mu_{\|})}{(\mu_{\|} + 2\mu_{\perp})}\frac{(\alpha_1 + \alpha_2)T_{11}}{RT}$$
$$\left[1 - \left(\frac{2\mu_{\perp}}{\mu_{\|} + 2\mu_{\perp}} - \frac{1}{2}\right)\frac{(\alpha_1 + \alpha_2)T_{11}}{RT} + \cdots\right]. \tag{17}$$

For n silicon, $\mu_{\perp} = 5\mu_{\|}$ and $\Delta\rho/\rho_0 T_{11} = -0.95 \times 10^{-10}$ cm^2/dyne from measurements for small stresses. Hence we evaluate $(\alpha_1 + \alpha_2)/RT$ as being equal to 3.92×10^{-10} at room temperature. The numerical expression becomes

$$\frac{\Delta\rho}{\rho_0} = -0.95 \times 10^{-10}T_{11}[1 - 1.6 \times 10^{-10}T_{11}]. \tag{18}$$

Using the value of 1.3×10^{12} dynes/cm^2 for the value of Young's modulus for n-type silicon measured along a crystallographic axis, one obtains

$$\frac{\Delta\rho}{\rho_0} = 125S_1 - 26{,}000S_1^2, \tag{3}$$

in agreement with Eq. (3).

A similar expression can be derived for n-type germanium. For this case it is believed that there are four potential minima lying along the [111] cube diagonals. Since the resistance decreases for a tensional stress, the effect of such a stress along the [111] axis is to populate the valleys in the direction perpendicular to the tension. Hence

$$\frac{N_{[1\bar{1}1]}}{N_{[111]}} = e^{-(\alpha_1+\alpha_2)T_{111}/RT} \tag{19}$$

where $(\alpha_1 + \alpha_2)/RT$ turns out to be negative. $N_{[1\bar{1}1]}$ designates the number of electrons lying in the nearly perpendicular valleys and $N_{[111]}$ the number lying in the valley in the stress direction. The conservation of charge equation becomes

$$N_0 = N_{[111]} + 3N_{[1\bar{1}1]}. \tag{20}$$

The $[1\bar{1}1]$ valleys lie at an angle of $70°30'$ from the $[111]$ valley. Since the mobility for the $[1\bar{1}1]$ valleys along the $[111]$ direction is determined by the equation

$$\mu = \mu_\perp \sin^2 (70°30') + \mu_\| \cos^2 (70°30')$$

$$= \tfrac{8}{9}\mu_\perp + \tfrac{1}{9}\mu_\|, \tag{21}$$

the equation for the conductivity becomes

$$\sigma = e[N_{[111]}\mu_\| + 3N_{[1\bar{1}1]}[\tfrac{8}{9}\mu_\perp + \tfrac{1}{9}\mu_\|]]. \tag{22}$$

Solving for the resistivity $\rho = 1/\sigma$ from Eqs. (19)–(22),

$$\rho = \frac{1 + 3e^{-(\alpha_1 + \alpha_2)T_{111}/RT}}{N_0 e[\mu_\|(1 + \tfrac{1}{3}e^{-(\alpha_1 + \alpha_2)T_{111}/RT})] + \tfrac{8}{3}\mu_\perp e^{-(\alpha_1 + \alpha_2)T_{111}/RT}} \tag{23}$$

For zero stress, the resistivity is

$$\rho_0 = \frac{3}{N_0 e[\mu_\| + 2\mu_\perp]} \tag{24}$$

in agreement with Eq. (15). Subtracting this from ρ, the change in resistivity $\Delta\rho/\rho_0$ is

$$\frac{\Delta\rho}{\rho_0} = \frac{\tfrac{2}{3}(\mu_\perp - \mu_\|)(1 - e^{-(\alpha_1 + \alpha_2)T_{111}/RT})}{\mu_\|(1 + \tfrac{1}{3}e^{-(\alpha_1 + \alpha_2)T_{111}/RT}) + \tfrac{8}{3}\mu_\perp e^{-(\alpha_1 + \alpha_2)T_{111}/RT}}. \tag{25}$$

If we expand this in powers of T_{111}, as before, we have

$$\frac{\Delta\rho}{\rho_0} = \left(\frac{\mu_\perp - \mu_\|}{2\mu_\| + 4\mu_\perp}\right)\left(\frac{\alpha_1 + \alpha_2}{RT} T_{111}\right)$$

$$= 1 + \left[\frac{\mu_\| + 8\mu_\perp}{4\mu_\| + 8\mu_\perp} - \frac{1}{2}\right]\left(\frac{\alpha_1 + \alpha_2}{RT} T_{111}\right) + \ldots\,]. \tag{26}$$

Using $\mu_\perp \doteq 5\mu_\|$ and utilizing the measured value

$$\frac{\Delta\rho}{\rho_0} = -96 \times 10^{-12} \text{ cm}^2/\text{dyne at } T = 300°K \tag{27}$$

for small stresses, this equation becomes

$$\frac{\Delta\rho}{\rho_0} = -96 \times 10^{-12}T_{111}(1 - 2.28 \times 10^{-10}T_{111}). \tag{28}$$

By inserting the value

$$T_{111} = Y_0 S_{111} \text{ where } Y_0 = 1.55 \times 10^{12} \text{ dynes/cm}^2 \tag{29}$$

along a [111] axis, this equation reduces to the numerical Eq. (2),

$$\frac{\Delta\rho}{\rho_0} = -149 S_1 + 52,600 S_1^2. \tag{2}$$

For p-type silicon and germanium, this simplified model does not hold and one cannot calculate the constants.

REFERENCES

1. Mason, W. P., and Thurston, R. N., Use of piezoresistive materials in the measurement of displacement, force, and torque, *J. Acoust. Soc. Am.* **29,** 1096 (1957).
2. Mason, W. P., "Physical Acoustics and the Properties of Solids." Van Nostrand, Princeton, New Jersey, 1958.
3. Mason, W. P., Semiconductors in strain gages, *Bell Labs. Record* **37,** 7 (1959).
4. Geyling, F. T., and Forst, J. J., Semiconductor strain transducers, *Bell System Tech. J.* **39,** 705 (1960).
5. Smith, C. S., Piezoresistive effect in silicon and germanium, *Phys. Rev.* **94,** 42 (1954).
6. Morin, F. J., Geballe, T. H., and Herring, C., *Phys. Rev.* **105,** 525 (1957).
7. Herring, C., Transport properties of many valley semiconductors, *Bell System Tech. J.* **34,** 237 (1955).
8. Pearson, G. L., Read, W. T., and Feldmann, W. L., Deformation and fracture of small silicon crystals, *Acta Met.* **5,** 181 (1957).
9. McSkimin, H. J., *J. Appl. Phys.* **24,** 988 (1953).
10. Shockley, W., "Electrons and Holes in Semiconductors," p. 284, Fig. 11.7. Van Nostrand, Princeton, New Jersey, 1950.
11. Montgomery, H. C., *Bell System Tech. J.* **31,** 950 (1952).

STRAIN GAGES WITH SHORT DRYING TIME AND FREEDOM FROM TRANSVERSE SENSITIVITY

ARNOLD U. HUGGENBERGER

Physical Instruments Huggenberger, Zurich, Switzerland

ABSTRACT

A brief description of a strain gage without cross sensitivity for the stress analysis field is discussed.

INTRODUCTION

Quick readiness for measurements is in many cases of greatest importance and very often it is indispensable that the cementing and drying time is as short as possible. If a short drying time for quick readiness is achieved it will be possible that measurements can be carried out on the very same day. This allows in many cases to save considerable traveling expenses. In many conditions the measuring problem requires a prompt and quick measuring readiness. Faultless measuring results when testing bridges are depending very often from the temporal crossing of the trains. The free-load time of a railway bridge is sometimes only a fraction of an hour during which the strain measurements must be done.

GENERAL DISCUSSION

The strain gage TEPIC K meets these requirements for quick measuring readiness which is attained within about half an hour. The carrier of the strain gage is of synthetical material with first-class electrical insulation and water repulsive. The carrier is transparent so that air bubbles between cementing surface and carrier can be noticed at once. Such enclosures influence the measuring accuracy. The electric lead wires are embedded in the finest miniature tubes of the same material, which on the gage side give a perfect boundary with the carrier foil. These small tubes assure the lead wires besides the eminent high electrical insulation, a great flexible firmness and at the same time a good flexibility. A breakage of these terminal lead wires is therefore practically impossible.

The strain gage type K is extremely flexible. The strain sensitive wires are parallel without loops contrary to the well-known grid wire types. The cross connections are of large cross sections, so that the influence of transverse strain is of no practical influence. The TEPIC strain gage indicates, therefore, the true value of the longitudinal strain, not influenced by transverse strain (Fig. 1).

121

The Tepicolle KA59 is a special two-component polymerizing cement. The properties of this adhesive show a high electrical insulation and insensitivity to moisture. As the strain gage foil and adhesive consist of the same material and as the drying process does not take place by evaporation of

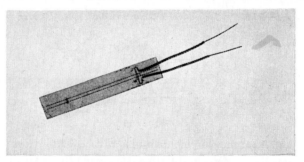

Fig. 1. TEPIC strain gage.

a solvent, a perfect boundary is assured. This cement is of the cold setting type. The strain gage is ready for measurement within half an hour.

The standard TEPIC strain gages, type K, are available with gage lengths of $\frac{2}{16}$, $\frac{25}{64}$, $\frac{3}{4}$, and $7\frac{1}{8}$ inch and with a resistance of 120, 500, and 600 ohms (Table I).

TABLE I

TEPIC Strain Gage, Type K, Gage Factor about 2.2

No.	Type	Gage length l mm	Active width a mm	Total length c mm	Total width b mm	resist- ance ohms	Cable code for a standard package
1	BK $\frac{1}{2}$/120	5	2.8	12	8	120	kuhal
2	BK 1/120	10	1.2	17	7	120	kuone
3	BK 2/120	20	0.5	28	6	120	kutwo
4	BK 2/600	20	3.6	28	10	600	kusec
5	BK 18/500[a]	150	1.5	188	10	500	kuaci

[a] The Type BK 18/500 has an extra long gage length and is therefore preferred for strain measurements on concrete and stone structures.

CHARACTERISTICS OF RESISTANCE STRAIN GAGES

Roscoe L. Bloss

National Bureau of Standards, Washington, D. C.

Although resistance strain gages are very useful devices for many applications, their characteristics and limitations must be examined closely when use in a new situation is contemplated. The characteristics and factors which may limit the usefulness of these gages include (1) strain sensitivity, (2) temperature sensitivity, (3) resistance instability, (4) shelf life of components, (5) effects of moisture, (6) incompatibility of components, (7) fatigue life, (8) frequency range, (9) magnetostrictive effects, and (10) incompatibility with environment. These factors are discussed and illustrated.

Introduction

The electrical resistance strain gage is, without doubt, one of the most useful tools available to the structural engineer of today. These gages are also being used extensively in transducer and research applications where the accurate measurement of small material deformations is necessary. The use of these gages has been so successful that, for many applications, the results obtained with them are accepted without question. Perhaps it is due to these successful applications that there is an unfortunate tendency to use these gages in other situations involving different conditions without fully considering the characteristics of the gages. In some cases these applications may be successful. In others, the time and expense of attempting to use the gages may be lost as it becomes evident that they are not suited for the particular application, or erroneous gage readings may be obtained which may lead to wrong conclusions and disastrous results. It is therefore important to understand the gage characteristics and the limitations that they impose under various test conditions. This is especially important when the gages are to be exposed to new environmental conditions, such as elevated temperatures and nuclear radiation, two environments that are currently receiving great attention.

The various types of resistance strain gages are adequately described in the literature,[1-9] and the development of the mathematical relationships describing their performance has been carried out.[1-3] There is also considerable information available on the performance of some of the gage types as well as descriptions of equipment used to determine this behavior.[5,10-13] It is therefore neither necessary nor appropriate to repeat this information

123

at this time. However, a discussion of some of the general characteristics of these gages and the limitations that these characteristics impose on the utilization of the gages may be useful. The results used as illustrations were obtained from a number of types of gages from various manufacturers by several investigators, and they should not be considered to be indicative of the performances of any one type of gage. It should be noted that in some cases gages having very undesirable characteristics are used as examples in order to provide dramatic illustrations. It should also be pointed out that a gage type used to show undesirable performance in one example may be very valuable when used under the appropriate test conditions.

Strain Sensitivity

The strain sensitivity of a resistance strain gage, expressed quantitatively by the gage factor, is the relationship between the change of resistance of the gage and the strain to which the gage is subjected. It is this relationship

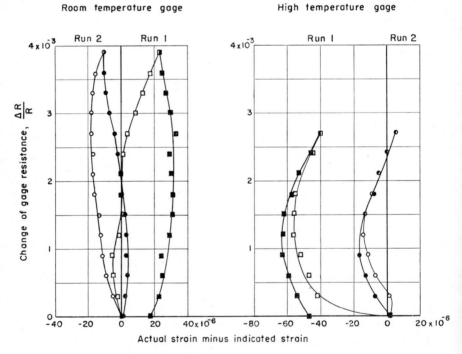

Fig. 1. Nonlinearity of two gages at room temperature.

between a measurable resistance and an unknown strain that makes the gage useful. If reliable results are to be obtained, this relationship must be known for all conditions under which the gages are to be used.

In general, a gage factor value is supplied by the manufacturer with each gage or small group of gages. Usually a single gage factor value is given. This implies that the relationship between gage resistance and strain is linear; that the sensitivities of all gages of the group are the same; that the gage factor is independent of direction of loading and strain level; and that the strain sensitivity is not affected by conditions normally encountered in use.

It has been shown experimentally that the gage resistance is not an exact linear function of strain at room temperature[10] and that the non-linearity may become even greater at elevated temperatures.[5] Also, in general, the resistance of the gage while the strain is increasing will not be exactly the same at the same strain as when the strain is decreasing. Examples of the nonlinearity and hysteresis are shown in Fig. 1.

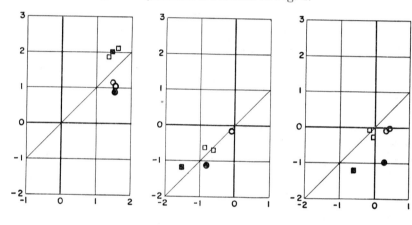

Percent departure of gage factor from
manufacturer's value, tension loading

Fig. 2. Gage factor deviation for three types of room temperature gages. Filled symbols are for first strain cycles.

When gage factor values have been determined for several gages for tension and compression loading, considerable information about the repeatability of the gage factor can be obtained by plotting the values for compression loading on one axis of a graph and values for tension loading on the other axis. Such a plot is shown in Fig. 2. In this figure the per cent departures of experimental values from the manufacturers' nominal gage factor values are plotted. Of course, ideally all points should fall on the origin. Even though there may be differences between gages, if each gage has the same sensitivity for tension and compression loading all points would fall on the diagonal line. The frequent difference between the point for the first strain cycle and subsequent loadings indicates a sensitivity to strain history. Figure 3 shows that the gage factors of gages which are designed for use at elevated temperatures are, in general, less well behaved than the more widely used room temperature gages.

When gages are to be used over a considerable temperature range, the variation of gage factor with temperature becomes important. Gage factor

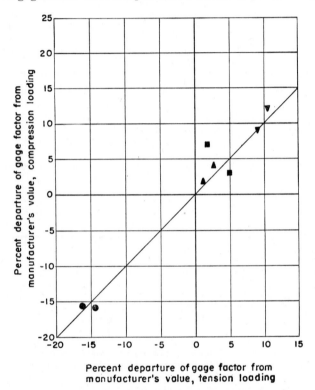

FIG. 3. Gage factor deviation for four types of high temperature gages at room temperature.

values at very low temperatures must be determined when use under cyrogenic conditions is contemplated. The results of at least two such investigations, with the methods of determination, have been reported.[14,15] Figure 4 shows the variation of gage factor over the temperature range −320° to 70°F for one type of gage as determined by a dynamic method similar to the one described by Bloss.[16] Figure 5 shows the variation of gage factor of one gage type between room temperature and 1000°F.[16] As can be seen, the gage factor of this gage type is affected by temperature and also by the history of the gage.

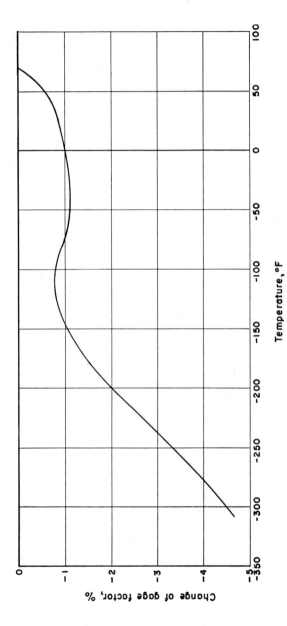

Fig. 4. Variation of gage factor with temperature for one gage type.

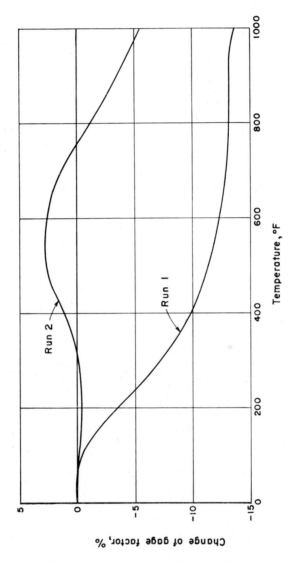

FIG. 5. Variation of gage factor with temperature for one gage type.

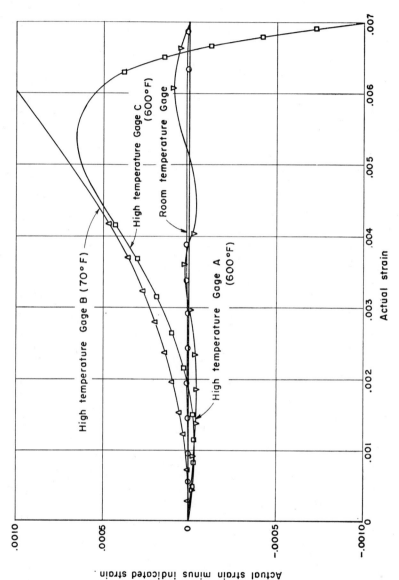

Fig. 6. Behavior of gages at high strains.

Gage factor determinations are generally carried out at relatively low strain levels, usually 0.001 or less. Therefore the ability of the gages to withstand higher strains and the stability of the gage factor at the higher strain levels are not determined by these tests. Behaviors of a number of room temperature resistance gages at high tensile strains were determined by Campbell in 1945.[17] More recently, similar tests of post-yield and high temperature gages were conducted at the National Bureau of Standards. Results of tests carried out at the National Bureau of Standards on one room temperature gage and three high temperature gages are shown in Fig. 6. An upward curvature indicates that the cement is not transmitting strain properly or that the gage factor is becoming smaller with increasing strain.[18] A steep downward trend probably indicates a gage element failure.

TEMPERATURE SENSITIVITY

In addition to being cognizant of the effects of the various foregoing factors on strain sensitivity, a constant alert must be kept for resistance changes caused by factors other than strain. Since any change of resistance will appear as a strain, accurate measurements require that other contributing factors be known so that their effects can be reduced or eliminated by compensating or correcting techniques.

The effect that has received the most attention is that due to temperature changes. The resistance change of an installed gage due to temperature is a function of the coefficient of resistance of the strain sensitive element, the coefficients of linear expansion of the gage element and base material, and the strain sensitivity of the gage. The change of resistance of the leads to the gage must also be considered. Several methods have been used to reduce or eliminate the effects of temperature changes on the gages. The most commonly used methods are:

(1) The use of self-temperature-compensating gages (gages with nearly zero temperature sensitivity when used on a given material),

(2) the use of a "dummy" gage for compensation, and

(3) the correction of the strain readings by accurately measuring the temperature at the gage location and using the known temperature sensitivity of the gage installation.

Each of these methods is useful, but each has limitations which must be recognized.

Self-temperature-compensating gages of two general types are available. The newer of these are gages produced from material which has been selected or treated, before or after gage fabrication, to have properties such that negligible resistance changes will be caused by temperature changes when the gage is attached to a given material. These attempts have been reasonably successful, even over a considerable temperature

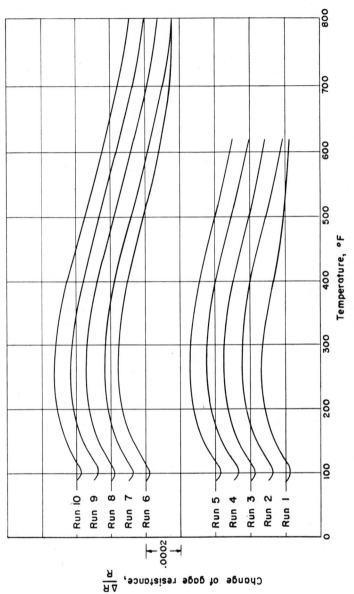

Fig. 7. Variation of resistance of one gage type with temperature.

range, as shown by Fig. 7. The older, and still popular, temperature-compensated gage has a sensitive element of two materials having different characteristics and combined in the proper proportion to produce a negligible temperature sensitivity when attached to a given material. The apparent strain due to temperature of eight gages of one type as determined by Hinze et al.[19] is shown in Fig. 8. Since the resistance change of a self-compensating gage resulting from a temperature change is due to a combination of one or more characteristics of two or more materials, all of which are usually nonlinear, complete compensation cannot be expected. However, these gages do have the advantage of requiring neither an accurate measurement of temperature nor that two pieces of material be maintained at the same temperature.

A frequently used method of temperature compensation is to mount a gage of the same type and from the same lot on a piece of material the same as the "active" gage is mounted on. If the material on which the "dummy" gage is mounted remains stress-free and undergoes the same temperature fluctuations as the test specimen, compensation for temperature effects should result if the gages are connected as adjacent arms of a bridge circuit. Although this method is capable of excellent results under ideal conditions, it is frequently impracticable to provide a stress-free piece of material which will undergo the same temperature changes as the test specimen. This method also ignores the effect of strain on the coefficients of expansion and resistivity of the materials involved, and, in general, temperature changes due to loading[20] are ignored. Although these effects may be small, their existence should be recognized.

Although it is undesirable from data accumulation and reduction considerations, it is sometimes necessary to measure the temperature of the gage installations and apply corrections to the test data by utilizing temperature sensitivity information for the particular gage type and specimen material involved. Besides complicating the data handling process, this method requires that accurate temperature measurements be made and that the temperature sensitivity of the gage installation be known. Gross errors might result from small percentage errors in these two factors when a high, rapidly changing temperature sensitivity such as that shown in Fig. 9 is involved.

All of the above compensation and correction techniques are based on there being a definite, reproducible relationship between the temperatures of the gage element and the material on which it is mounted. The assumption of such a relationship may not be justified, especially when high gage currents, transient heating conditions, materials with poor thermal conductivity, large heat sinks, or combinations of these factors are involved.

Any change in the resistance of the leads used to connect the gage into a

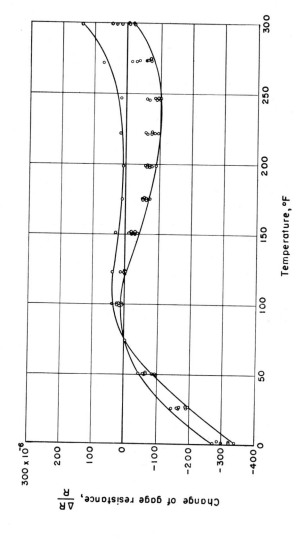

FIG. 8. Variation of resistance of self-compensating gages with temperature.

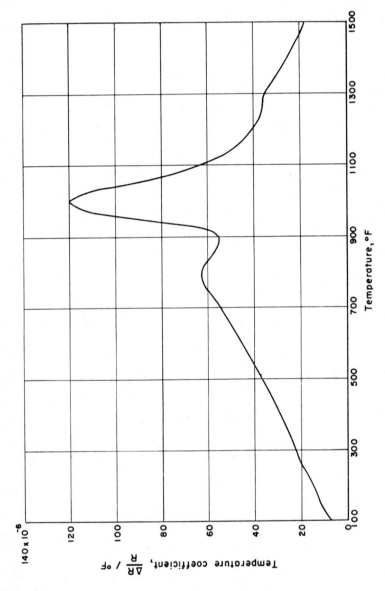

FIG. 9. Temperature sensitivity of one type of gage.

bridge circuit may be indistinguishable from changes in gage resistance. Therefore precautions must be taken to reduce the magnitude of such effects. The use of as large a diameter lead wire as practicable, thereby keeping the total resistance of the leads small, is of considerable advantage. Further improvement can be obtained by using the three-wire-compensating lead configuration described by Ruge.[21] Applications which require the use of leads of small diameter or alloys having high resistivity should, if possible, utilize this three-wire system or some other means for compensating for lead wire effects.

It is not always possible to ignore the effects of the thermocouples formed where dissimilar materials are joined within the gage and at the connection of leads to the gage. If instrumentation that is sensitive to DC voltages is used, care must be used to reduce the thermal emf of the gage circuit to a negligibly small value. It may be possible to accomplish this

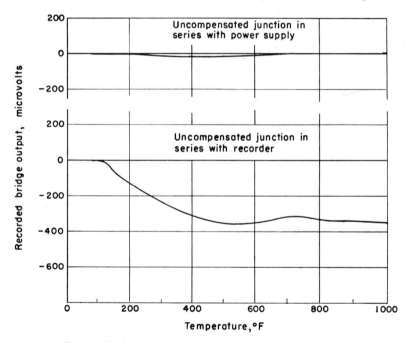

FIG. 10. Bridge circuit output due to thermocouple effects.

by providing pairs of opposing thermocouples that are always at the same temperature or by connecting the gage into its circuit in such a way that uncompensated thermocouples are in series with the power source rather than being in series with the read-out instruments. The difference in apparent output voltage of one gage installation for the two methods of connection is shown in Fig. 10. In any case the possible existence of such thermally induced signals must be considered.

RESISTANCE INSTABILITY

The instability of gage resistance with time has become increasingly important as the temperature at which strain gages are used has risen. In most cases this effect can be neglected at room temperature and, for some

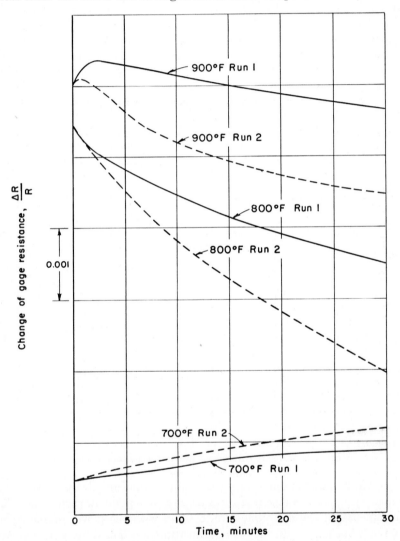

FIG. 11. Drift behavior of one gage.

gage types, it is low at temperatures as high as 700°F. However, to the present time, no gage type has been found to be free of this instability at elevated temperatures. The cause of the "drift" is not fully understood, but it seems certain that it is a complex combination of effects including corrosion, selective oxidation, relief of residual stresses, dimensional changes of cements, and other factors with time. Because of the complex nature of this drift, it is not surprising that it may vary greatly with temperature and also be strongly affected by gage history. This is shown in Fig. 11. These results were obtained by holding an installed gage for 30 minutes at temperatures of 600°, 700°, 800°, 900°, and 1000°F in that order, and

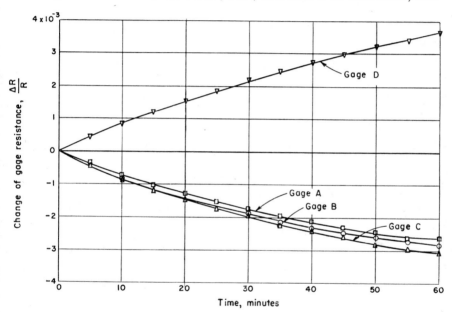

Fig. 12. Drift behavior of one type of gage at 900°F.

then repeating the test. It is seen that the drift may be either positive or negative, depending upon temperature and in some cases upon time at temperature. During the first run this gage was held at 1000°F for about 30 minutes. Although it has frequently been suggested that such treatment should stabilize a gage for use at a lower temperature, the drifts were actually greater during the second run. The effect of gage history on the stability of another gage type is shown in Fig. 12. Gages A, B, and C had not been above 900°F before the results shown were obtained, although they may have been held at lower temperatures (as high as 800°F) for 1 hour. Gage D had been held at 1000°, 700°, and 800°F in that order, 1 hour at each temperature, before the results shown were obtained. In this

case the direction as well as the magnitude of the resistance change was
affected by the gage history. Figure 13 shows the variation of the average
drift rate for another gage type during the first 10 minutes at a test temperature. Such behavior would, of course, make useful results difficult to

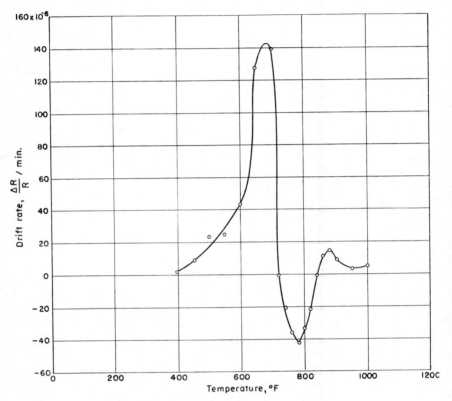

FIG. 13. Initial drift rate of one type of gage.

obtain over a considerable temperature range except under very special
conditions. It should be pointed out that the temperatures at which the
results shown in Figs. 11–13 were obtained do not exceed the temperatures
for which these gages were recommended for use.

DYNAMIC EFFECTS

When dynamic strains are to be measured, there are additional characteristics which may become important. It has been reported that at a
strain level of ±0.001 the fatigue life of different wire gages may differ
by a factor of at least 62, depending upon the strain sensitive material,
and that the introduction of an intermediate size wire between the strain

sensitive element and the gage lead (dual lead gages) increases the fatigue life by at least 30 times.[22] Tests of some gages made of thin foils have shown them to have a fatigue life of more than 1,250,000 cycles at a strain level of ±0.0015.[23] There is, of course, the possibility that the bonding agent will fail in fatigue or will not be able to withstand the high rates of loading encountered in impact testing. The upper frequency limit of resistance gages has not been established, but it has been shown that the gage output depends upon the ratio of strain wavelength to gage length[24] and that installation techniques, especially those determining the cement thickness, may affect the gage response significantly.[25] When suitable care was taken, the static gage factor was found to be reliable within 5% at frequencies up to 20 kc/second.[25] It has also been pointed out that some gage types generate an emf that is proportional to strain rate.[26,27] These self-generated voltages, generally attributed to magnetostrictive effects within the gage wire, may introduce significant errors, especially under impact loading conditions.

Environment

Reliable results cannot be expected from a gage installation unless all of the components used are in good condition at the time of use. Some of the cements commonly used, such as phenolic and cyanoacrylate cements, may have limited shelf life and should be stored under refrigeration or other special conditions. Such special precautions are usually specified by the vendor, and expiration dates are sometimes given.

Considerable difficulty with gages can be caused by moisture. Gages which have been installed may deteriorate or even become inoperative if they are subjected to an atmosphere of high humidity. This may be due to deterioration of the bonding properties of the cement; reduced electrical resistivity of the cement, carrier, etc., so that the gage is effectively shunted with a resistance of relatively low value; corrosion of the base material resulting in reduced bond strength; or reaction between the gage element and the cement in the presence of moisture. Techniques have been described for protecting gage installations from moisture, even when the gages are submerged in water at pressures up to 1000 psi.[28-30] The use of suitable protective procedures for gages that will be exposed to normal atmospheres is now a common and worthwhile practice.

It is not so well recognized that there may be instances where, in a high humidity atmosphere, the strain sensitive element is not compatible with some component of its carrier or other material with which it makes contact. One such instance is demonstrated by Fig. 14 which shows that one gage type, before being installed, increased in resistance very rapidly when exposed to high humidity. As would be expected, erratic results were

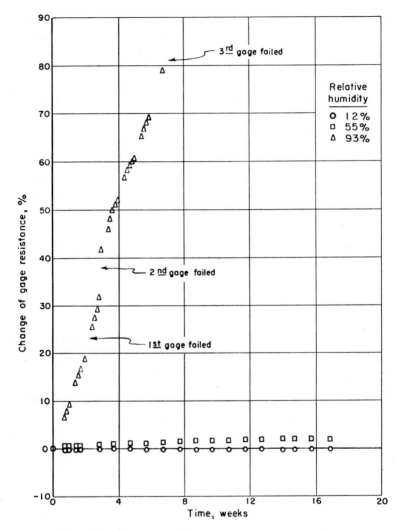

FIG. 14. Effect of humidity on shelf life on one type of gage. Average values for three gages.

obtained in tests of this gage type when no precautions were taken in storing the gages prior to use.

Other test conditions must receive careful study, and often evaluation tests must be conducted to determine if reliable results can be obtained with the available resistance strain gages and associated materials. For example, the reliability of gage performance in strong electrostatic or magnetic fields or in areas of intense nuclear radiation cannot be assumed because of possible effects such as the deterioration of electrical properties of cements which has been shown to occur in fields of reactor radiation.[31]

SUMMARY

Although resistance strain gages have been found to give reliable results under a wide variety of conditions, it cannot be assumed that they are suitable for use in any given situation unless an examination of their known characteristics or the results of evaluation tests show that they will operate satisfactorily under the conditions that will be encountered. Sometimes a slight modification of test set up or procedure will permit the use of these gages where erroneous results would have been obtained under the original conditions. The reduction of undesirable effects by use of suitable electrical and electronic circuitry, compensating techniques, and test planning based upon an understanding of gage characteristics can also make the difference between meaningful results and wasted effort.

REFERENCES

1. Perry, C. C., and Lissner, H. R., "The Strain Gage Primer." McGraw-Hill, New York, 1955.
2. Dobie, W. B., and Isaac, P. C. G., "Electric Resistance Strain Gauges." The English Univ. Press, London, 1948.
3. Murray, W. M., and Stein, P. K., "Strain Gage Techniques." Society for Experimental Stress Analysis, Cambridge, Massachusetts, 1957.
4. Characteristics and applications of resistance strain gages, *Natl. Bur. Standards (U. S.) Circ. No.* 528 (1954).
5. Symposium on elevated temperature strain gages, Am. Soc. Testing Materials Spec. Tech. Publ. No. 230 (1958).
6. *Strain Gage Readings*, Stein Engineering Services, Phoenix, Arizona.
7. deForest, A. V., and Leaderman, H., The development of electrical strain gages, *Natl. Advisory Comm. Aeronaut. Tech. Note No.* 744 (1940).
8. Simmons, E. E., Jr., Materials testing apparatus, U. S. Patent 2,292,549 (1942).
9. Kearns, C. M., and Guerke, R. M., Vibration stress measurements in strong centrifugal fields, *J. Appl. Mechanics* **4,** A-156 (1937).
10. Campbell, W. R., Performance tests of wire strain gages, *Natl. Advisory Comm. Aeronaut. Tech. Notes Nos.* 954, 978, 997, 1042, 1318, and 1456 (1944–1948).
11. Day, E. E., Characteristics of electric strain gages at elevated temperatures, *Proc. Soc. Exptl. Stress Anal.* **9,** 141 (1951).
12. Brosius, G. F., and Hartley, D., Evaluation of high temperature strain gages, *Proc. Soc. Exptl. Stress Anal.* **17,** 67 (1959).
13. Anonymous, Baldwin-Lima-Hamilton Corporation, *Tech. Data Bulls. Nos.* 4310-3, 4310-4, 4310-6, 4310-7, 4320-5 (1958–1959).
14. Day, E. E., and Sevand, A. H., Characteristics of electric strain gages at low temperatures, *Proc. Soc. Exptl. Stress Anal.* **8,** 133 (1950).
15. McClintock, R. M., Strain gauge calibration device for extreme temperatures, *Rev. Sci. Instr.* **30,** 715 (1959).
16. Bloss, R. L., The evaluation of resistance strain gages at elevated temperatures, *Materials Research and Standards* **1,** No. 1, 9 (1961).

17. Campbell, W. R., Performance tests of wire strain gages III—Calibrations at high strains, *Natl. Advisory Comm. Aeronaut. Tech. Note No.* 997 (1945).
18. Kuczynski, G. C., Effect of elastic strain on the electrical resistance of metals, *Phys. Rev.* **94,** 61 (1954).
19. Hinze, D. W., Namkoong, D., and Campbell, W. R., unpublished work.
20. Champion, F. C., and Davy, N., "Properties of Matter," 3rd ed., pp. 82–83. Philosophical Library, New York, 1959.
21. Ruge, A. C., Elimination of lead wire errors in the SR-4 temperature-compensated strain gages, *Testing Topics* **6,** No. 3, 6 (1951).
22. Stephens, R. W., Fatigue life of SR-4 strain gages, *Testing Topics* **8,** No. 3, 1 (1953).
23. Anonymous, Baldwin-Lima-Hamilton Corporation, *Tech. Data Bull.* 4310-6 (1958).
24. Brennan, J. N., and Nisbet, J. S., Direct method of accelerometer calibration, *J. Acoust. Soc. Am.* **30,** 41 (1958).
25. Nisbet, J. S., Brennan, J. N., and Tarpley, H. I., High frequency strain gauge and accelerometer calibration, *J. Acoust. Soc. Am.* **32,** 75 (1960).
26. Meitzler, A. H., Effect of strain rate on the behavior of iso-elastic wire strain gauges, *Rev. Sci. Instr.* **27,** 56 (1956).
27. Vigness, I., Magnetostrictive electricity in strain gauges, *Rev. Sci. Instr.* **27,** 1012 (1956).
28. Boiten, R. G., Cementing and waterproofing of resistance strain gages, *Natl. Bur. Standards (U. S.) Circ. No.* 528, p. 11 (1954).
29. Dean, M., III, Techniques for protecting and waterproofing resistance wire strain gages, David Taylor Model Basin, *Research and Develop. Rept. No.* 797 (1956).
30. Crowe, W. D., Waterproofing strain gages submerged in pressure vessels, *Testing Topics* **12,** No. 1, 4 (1957).
31. Smith, R. C., and Rendler, N. J., Transducers for strain measurement in intense radiation fields, *Proc. Soc. Exptl. Stress Anal.* **16,** 73 (1959).

PRACTICAL ASPECTS OF TEMPERATURE EFFECTS ON RESISTANCE STRAIN GAGES

Frank F. Hines and Leon J. Weymouth

Baldwin-Lima-Hamilton Corporation, Electronics Division, Waltham, Massachusetts

Abstract

This paper discusses the effects of temperature changes on bonded resistance type strain gages with particular emphasis on the subject of temperature compensation. Basic theory and strain sensing materials are considered prior to a detailed description of five methods of compensation. The relative effectiveness of each method is discussed from the viewpoint of both user and manufacturer.

Introduction

The accuracy of strain indication obtained from bonded electrical resistance type strain gages is influenced by several factors involving environment, materials, time, and instrumentation. One of the more important environmental factors in the measurement of static strain is the change in temperature of the gage and test specimen during the measuring operation. The effects of such changes in temperature and the effectiveness of various temperature compensation techniques is the subject of this discussion. Gages designed specifically for dynamic measurement, in which high strain sensitivity is the major objective, will not be considered.

One of the greatest problems faced by the experimental stress analyst is the measurement of strain under transient temperature conditions, particularly under adverse temperature environments well above or below normal ambient conditions. In such cases the deformation in a structure or component can be caused by external loads, by thermal stresses set up by unequal temperature changes or differential expansion, and by simple thermal expansion. The components of such deformation may be defined as (a) mechanical strain, ϵ_m, the unit deformation which, within the elastic limit of the specimen, is proportional to the stress in the specimen, and (b) thermal strain, ϵ_α, the unit deformation of the specimen which would occur if it was unrestrained and subjected to a uniform change in temperature. Mechanical strain, as defined, includes strain caused by both applied loads and thermal stress.

The stress analyst, because design criteria are based primarily on stress, is interested in measuring only the mechanical strain. The ideal strain gage for stress analysis, then, should be insensitive to deformations in the specimen caused by simple thermal expansion, ϵ_α. This can be accomplished, with varying degrees of success, through the use of simple techniques or the use of one of several types of strain gages made specifically for the purpose.

BASIC CONSIDERATIONS

A simplified explanation of what happens within a bonded strain gage when subjected to a temperature change must consider four properties of the materials involved.[1] These are:

C_f The thermal coefficient of resistivity of the gage filament in the free, unbonded state (ohms/ohm/degree).

α_f The thermal coefficient of expansion of the gage filament (inches/inch/degree).

G.F.   Strain sensitivity of the gage filament (ohms/ohm/inch/inch).

α_s The thermal coefficient of expansion of the test specimen to which the gage is bonded (inches/inch/degree).

Both the thermal coefficient of resistivity and the thermal coefficient of expansion are nonlinear functions and exact expressions for both involve second or higher order terms. Handbook data are usually expressed as chord (straight line) slopes over a specified temperature range. Although the nonlinear characteristics of both thermal expansion and resistance coefficient functions have considerable significance as related to temperature compensation of strain gages, for the purpose of this explanation it is simpler to consider them as simple linear relationships.

For a free, unbonded filament subjected to a change in temperature ΔT, the unit change in resistance is

$$\left(\frac{\Delta R}{R}\right) = C_f \cdot \Delta T \tag{1}$$

where R is the original resistance and ΔR is the change in resistance. At the same time the unit change in length of the filament will be

$$\left(\frac{\Delta L}{L}\right)_f = \alpha_f \cdot \Delta T \tag{2}$$

where L is the original length and ΔL is the change in length.

Now consider the filament bonded to a test specimen in such a manner that the filament is constrained to follow the dimensional changes of the specimen regardless of the cause of such change. This is, in fact, the criterion of a bonded strain gage since, if it were not so constrained, the filament would not act as a strain gage. The specimen, when subjected to a temperature change, will undergo a unit change in length of

$$\left(\frac{\Delta L}{L}\right)_s = \alpha_s \cdot \Delta T. \tag{3}$$

The bonded filament will undergo a mechanical strain equal to the difference between the change in dimension of the specimen and the change in dimension of the filament that would occur if the filament were not constrained. Then the imposed strain on the filament is

$$\epsilon_t = \left(\frac{\Delta L}{L}\right)_s - \left(\frac{\Delta L}{L}\right)_f$$

$$= \alpha_s \cdot \Delta T - \alpha_f \cdot \Delta T. \tag{4}$$

The imposed strain will, because of the strain sensitivity of the filament, produce a change in resistance equal to $\epsilon_t \cdot G.F.$

The total unit change in resistance of the bonded gage when exposed to a temperature change, may then be expressed as

$$\left(\frac{\Delta R}{R}\right)_t = C_f \cdot \Delta T + \epsilon_t \cdot G.F.$$

$$= C_f \cdot \Delta T + (\alpha_s - \alpha_f)G.F. \cdot \Delta T. \tag{5}$$

As indicated by Eq. (5), the temperature response of a bonded gage depends upon certain properties of both the gage filament material and of the test specimen. The temperature response of any given gage can vary broadly, depending upon the α_s of the specimen material to which it is bonded. Nominal values of α_s for some common materials are:

Quartz	$+ 0.5$ ppm/°F
Mild steel	$+ 6.5$ ppm/°F
Stainless steel	$+ 6$ to $+9$ ppm/°F
Aluminum alloys	$+ 13$ ppm/°F
Magnesium alloys	$+ 15$ ppm/°F.

A strain gage that has zero temperature response on quartz, for instance, would have a response of $+6$ microinches/inch/°F when placed on steel due to the difference in thermal expansion characteristics of the specimen materials.

If $(\Delta R/R)_t$ of the installed gage is sensibly zero over a given temperature range, we say the gage is self-temperature compensated for the particular material to which it is bonded over the designated temperature range. Within certain limits, then, a change in temperature of the unstressed specimen will produce a negligible resistance change in the bonded strain gage. Hence no spurious indications of mechanical strain will be produced.

SENSING MATERIALS

The resistance of all electrical conductors and semiconductors is dependent on temperature, some to a greater and some to a lesser degree. The temperature coefficient of resistivity is quite large in some materials, particularly the pure metals, and is frequently used as a means of measuring temperature, as in the well-known platinum resistance thermometers. Many alloys, including some semiconductors, have also been developed for the express purpose of measuring temperature. On the other end of the scale are alloys that have been developed and are used primarily for their low temperature coefficients of resistivity. Such low coefficient alloys include Manganin, Constantan, Karma,* Evenohm,* 1000 Alloy,* Kanthal DR* and others. It is from this group of alloys that the manufacturer of strain gages usually selects his sensing material.

Manufacturers of these various alloys state temperature coefficient of resistivity tolerances ranging from ± 0.00001 to ± 0.00004 ppm/°C, usually over the range of either 0° to 100°C or 20° to 100°C. Some manufacturers publish the actual temperature versus change in resistance curves that apply to the tolerance limits and to typical melts. The curves are much more informative than numbers because none of the low coefficient alloys have a linear relationship between temperature and resistance. Material manufacturers usually determine their values of C_f on samples of soft annealed wire of approximately 0.005 inch in diameter, loosely coiled. The manufacturer's value of C_f rarely agrees with the C_f of the same material after it has been processed for strain gage use, either into fine wire or foil. In fact, the temperature coefficient of resistivity is subject to considerable control through the processing technique.

A common use for the low temperature coefficient alloys is in wire-wound resistors where stable, constant resistance values are required. The resultant effect of temperature changes on the resistance is regarded as negligible over normal temperature ranges. However, the temperature coefficient of these same "low coefficient" alloys can be quite serious in strain gage applications and a change in temperature can sometimes produce a resistance change larger than that caused by the strain to be measured. Hence the importance of considering and understanding the temperature coefficient characteristics of common strain gage sensing alloys and the temperature compensation techniques that may be applied to strain gages.

The strain gage producer must control the temperature characteristics of gages through the C_f factor in Eq. (5). To provide gages having self-compensating characteristics to fit the many structural materials in use

* Trade marks: Driver-Harris Company, Wilbur B. Driver Company, C. O. Jelliff Manufacturing Corporation, and the Kanthal Corporation, respectively.

today would require the availability of a broad, almost infinite, selection of C_f values. Fortunately, the vagaries of some alloys result in every melt having a slightly different temperature coefficient. Hence, "selection" of melts can provide a variety of values in an otherwise uniform alloy. In addition, the final temperature coefficient of many alloys can be adjusted by altering the processing procedure by which the material is reduced to final size or by heat treatment after processing to final size. These various methods are all used by producers of strain gages to get material that is more or less accurately adjusted to the desired temperature coefficient. The control of the actual temperature coefficient and the manner in which such materials are used in the strain gage determines the degree of temperature compensation that is obtained.

TEMPERATURE COMPENSATION METHODS

Strain gage temperature compensation methods can be divided into two groups: circuit compensation, and self-compensation. Circuit compensation is a system in which a resistance change or voltage change external to the strain sensing gage is used to effectively cancel the response of the strain sensing gage to thermal strains. Self-compensation is the control of the temperature coefficient of resistivity of the strain sensing gage itself so that the actual response of the strain sensing gage to thermal strains is minimized.

CIRCUIT COMPENSATION

Dummy Gage

The "dummy" compensating gage was the original method used to obtain temperature compensation of bonded resistance strain gages. Although the oldest in concept and use, the dummy gage method still offers many advantages that cannot be matched by newer methods.[3]

The principle of the dummy compensating gage method of temperature compensation is quite basic. In its simplest practice an "active" gage is bonded to the test specimen and a second identical gage (dummy, or compensating gage) is bonded to a separate tab or small block of the same material as that of the test specimen. The dummy, or compensating, gage is then physically arranged so that it is exposed to the same temperature environment as the active gage but isolated from mechanical strain. In the unstressed state both gages will then have the same response to temperature changes. The active and dummy gages are connected into adjacent arms of the measuring (Wheatstone) bridge. In this configuration the dummy gage cancels the effect of temperature changes upon the resistance of the active gage and the bridge balance will be responsive only to mechanical strain imposed on the active gage.

To explain the advantages of the dummy gage method of compensation, we must consider the thermal coefficient of electrical resistance characteristics of the strain sensing materials commonly used in bonded electrical gages. Constantan alloy is typical. Each melt, or heat, of Constantan has a different thermal coefficient of resistance. Normal commercial tolerances for this low coefficient alloy are ±0.000011 ohm/ohm/°F between 68° and 212°F (±0.000020 ohm/ohm/°C between 20° and 100°C). Typical resistance change vs. temperature curves for the temperature range of −100° to +500°F are shown in Fig. 1. The characteristic shape of the curve is

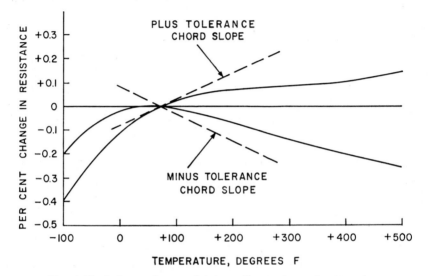

FIG. 1. Typical manufacturers' data on Constantan melts, free wire.

that of a flat reversed S, with positive coefficients appearing in the subzero region. Both positive and negative coefficients are available only in the intermediate temperature region. At no place in the entire temperature range is there a linear region.

Through selection of both the proper melts and processing techniques Constantan can be obtained having positive, negative, and essentially zero temperature coefficients when bonded to any given specimen material. Typical examples are shown in Fig. 2. Note that the curves are plotted to a scale applicable to strain gage work. It is quite evident that even the best fitted Constantan shows substantial nonlinearity and deviation from zero slope. Thus, even a best fitted material has a zero temperature coefficient only over a limited temperature range. To fit all normally encountered temperature ranges and specimen materials would require an extremely large number of sensing materials covering a broad range of temperature coefficients. In addition, a "lot" of strain sensing material having a temperature coefficient perfectly matched to any given specimen material is difficult to obtain. Practical considerations usually force us to settle for a coefficient with a tolerance equivalent to ± 1 microinch/inch/°F.

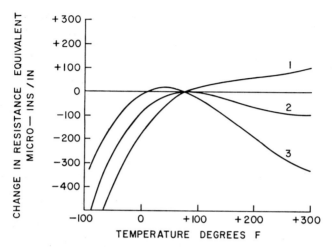

Fig. 2. Typical resistance vs. temperature curves of gages having various coefficients at room temperature. Curve 1, $+1$ microinch/inch/°F at 75°F; curve 2, zero at 75°F; curve 3, -1 microinch/inch/°F at 75°F.

The dummy compensating method has three advantages that cannot be obtained with a single gage having a selected best-fit temperature coefficient. These are:

1. the absence of nonlinearity in temperature response;
2. effective compensation over a broad temperature range; and
3. effective compensation on all test specimen materials.

The absence of nonlinearity is obtained by canceling the nonlinear characteristics of the active gage with identical nonlinear characteristics of the dummy compensating gage. Even if the temperature response characteristics of the active and dummy gages are not exactly and precisely identical, the over-all response will be linear and much smaller than can be had with a single selected gage.

The same characteristics that provide for cancellation of nonlinearity, i.e., identical temperature response of active and dummy gages, also make this method effective over large temperature ranges. For instance, dummy gages have been used successfully over the range of room temperature to -320°F where the temperature response of both gages taken separately is more than the equivalent of 10,000 microinches/inch. The method has also been used to 1200°F. In addition, the "zero" or starting temperature may be anywhere within the operating range of the gages.

As shown previously, the thermal expansion characteristics of the test specimens is a contributing factor to the temperature coefficient of a gage bonded to it. Again, since the active and dummy gages are both bonded to the same type of material, the effect of the thermal expansion of the test specimen is effectively canceled. It is, then, unnecessary to stock or wait for gages having a particular temperature coefficient to fit a given specimen material.

It should be emphasized that the active and dummy gages must have the same temperature characteristics. A "lot number" is generally used to distinguish gages having the same basic temperature characteristics. It is necessary only to be sure that both active and dummy gages bear the same manufacturer's lot number.

There are, of course, some situations in which the dummy gage will not work effectively. Where environmental temperatures are changing rapidly, there can be a large temperature difference between the dummy and active gages. It is sometimes difficult to balance the heating effects caused by radiant energy, of which the practice of obtaining high heating rates by means of quartz tube lamps is an extreme case. There are also other physical reasons, such as lack of space or other environmental conditions, that make the use of a dummy gage impractical. It should be remembered, though, that a difference of 5 or 10 degrees between the active and dummy gages will seldom cause a significant error.

Circuit Compensation

Integral Resistance Thermometry

A recent development which combines the features of self-compensation with circuit compensation provides the unique ability to compensate for temperature effects on materials with a wide range of expansion coefficients by varying the parameters of a simple external circuit.[4]

This dual element grid combines a thermometer grade platinum wire element symmetrically located within the boundaries of a nickel-chromium alloy foil grid to produce a half-Wheatstone bridge as shown in Fig. 3.

An adjustable ballast resistor, R_B, placed in series with the low resistance (approximately 3.5 ohms) platinum element, R_T, is used to control the percentage change in resistance of the dummy compensating bridge arm caused by variations in temperature and thus cancels the unwanted temperature-induced resistance change in the 120-ohm Nichrome, R_G, active bridge arm. The simple bridge completion network is shown in Fig. 4.

The Nichrome and platinum combination was selected for two reasons.

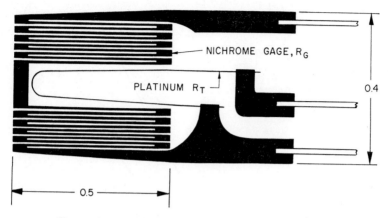

FIG. 3. Configuration of the Baldwin FNH-50-12E gage.

In order to reduce the nonlinear temperature response characteristics experienced with most strain sensing materials, it was necessary to match two materials with similar temperature response linearity and polarity for use in the half-bridge configuration. It was also desirable to select a material for the dummy arm which would be highly sensitive to temperature and relatively insensitive to strain so that the over-all gage factor would not be adversely affected. See Fig. 5 showing the nearly linear response of the

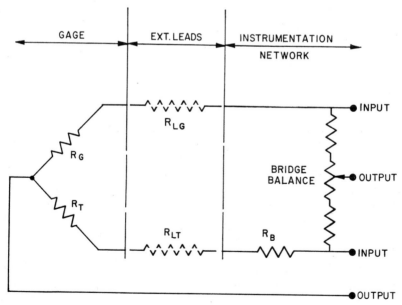

FIG. 4. Typical installation circuit.

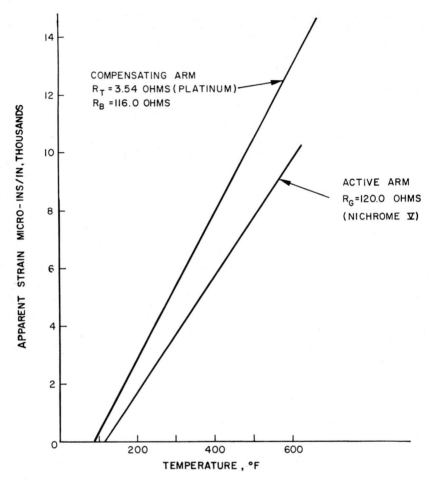

FIG. 5. Apparent strain vs. temperature of active bridge arm and compensating bridge arm on 316 stainless steel.

apparent strain vs. temperature characteristics for Nichrome V and for platinum in series with a fixed resistance which represents a typical value of R_B.

Calculation of the Resistance Value R_B

With the nearly linear temperature response of Nichrome V and platinum as bonded to 316 stainless steel, the calculation for the required value of R_B to accomplish temperature compensation can be made using the following formula developed with the circuit parameters defined by Fig. 4.

The percentage change in resistance of the active Nichrome arms must be equal to the percentage change in resistance of the dummy platinum arm; therefore,

$$\frac{\Delta R_G}{R_G + R_{LG}} = \frac{\Delta R_T}{R_T + R_{LT} + R_\mathrm{B}}. \tag{6}$$

For simplification let

$$\frac{\Delta R_G}{R_G} = \Delta G \qquad \frac{\Delta R_T}{R_T} = \Delta T, \tag{7}$$

then

$$\frac{\Delta R_G \cdot R_G}{R_G(R_G + R_{LG})} = \frac{\Delta R_T \cdot R_T}{R_T(R_T + R_{LT} + R_\mathrm{B})} \tag{8}$$

and

$$\frac{\Delta G \cdot R_G}{R_G + R_{LG}} = \frac{\Delta T R_T}{R_T + R_{LT} + R_\mathrm{B}}; \tag{9}$$

solving for R_B

$$R_\mathrm{B} = \frac{\Delta T}{\Delta G}\left[R_T \left(1 + \frac{R_{LG}}{R_G}\right)\right] - R_T - R_{LT}. \tag{10}$$

In order to perfectly compensate the unwanted temperature induced errors the ratio $\Delta T/\Delta G$ indicated by Eq. (10), would have to remain constant over the entire operational temperature of the gage. This condition would require absolute temperature coefficient of resistance linearity for

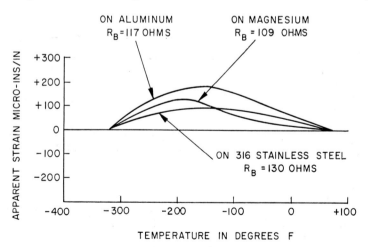

FIG. 6. Typical temperature response curves of compensated gage in cryogenic region using best-fit R_B values.

both the Nichrome and platinum as well as a linear difference between the thermal coefficients of expansion of the test material, the Nichrome, and the platinum.

Since the above coefficients are rarely constant except over very narrow temperature ranges, some apparent strain will be observed depending upon the test material and the operating temperature range even when the "best-fit" R_B value has been determined experimentally. Figure 6 shows typical temperature response characteristics in the cryogenic temperature range on several test materials.

Compensation Control with Changes in R_B

In order to analyze the degree of temperature compensation control that can be exercised by altering the value of the ballast resistor, R_B, we must make some assumptions concerning the conditions of test. Assume that the test material is a variety of stainless steel on which the temperature coeffi-

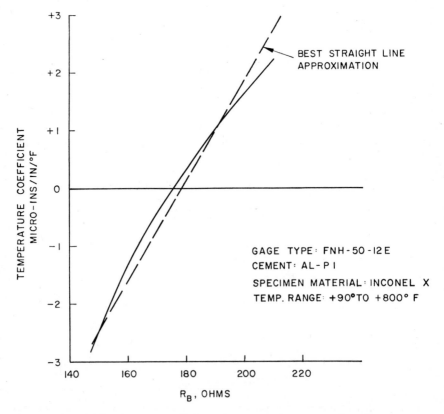

FIG. 7. Temperature coefficient of compensating arm vs. R_B value.

cient for Nichrome V will be $+20$ ppm/°F without the influence of the platinum compensating arm. The compensating arm would then be required to alter the temperature coefficient by $\frac{1}{20}$th or 5% to accomplish a slope change of 1 ppm/°F. If we further assume that the ratio of $\Delta T/\Delta G$ is essentially constant, then the temperature coefficient of the combined active and dummy arms can only be altered by a resistive change in R_B. It will be approximately true that a 5% change in the value of R_B will result in a 1 microinch/inch/°F change in the temperature coefficient. In order to accomplish temperature compensation within ±0.1 micro-inch/inch/°F, the value of R_B must be set within 0.6 ohm for an average R_B value of 120 ohms. In actual practice where the effect of changes in R_B have been observed experimentally, this approximation has been verified as shown in Fig. 7.

Strain Sensitivity Effect of R_T

The effect of the strain sensitivity of the platinum on the over-all gage factor may be shown as follows.

Assume no resistance in series with the platinum element, R_T. The known gage factor at room temperature for platinum is approximately 6; therefore,

$$G.F._{R_T} = \frac{\Delta R_T}{R_T/\epsilon} \cong 6.0. \tag{11}$$

Using the typical values of R_B and R_T shown in Fig. 5, $R_B = 116$ ohms in series with $R_T = 3.54$ ohms, the effective gage factor of the platinum arm would be:

$$G.F._{R_T+R_B} = \frac{\Delta R_T}{(R_T + R_B)/\epsilon} = \frac{\Delta R_T}{R_T/\epsilon} \cdot \frac{1}{1 + (R_B/R_T)}; \tag{12}$$

substituting (1),

$$\frac{6}{1 + (116/3.54)} \cong 0.2. \tag{13}$$

Given: $G.F._{R_G} \cong 2.2$ known for Nichrome V at room temperature,

$$G.F._{total} = G.F._{R_G} - G.F._{R_T+R_B} \tag{14}$$

$$G.F._{total} \cong 2.2 - 0.2 = 2.0 \cong 10\% \text{ loss in sensitivity.} \tag{15}$$

Strain Sensitivity Variations Caused by Changes in R_B

It can be seen from Eq. (12) that the over-all gage factor depends not only upon the platinum resistance, R_T, but upon the value of the ballast resistor, R_B. Normally the values of R_B are in the range between 90 and

170 ohms which produces a maximum error of about 3% as shown in Fig. 8. These values were observed during a shunt calibration of the circuit utilizing a six-wire system shown in Fig. 9.

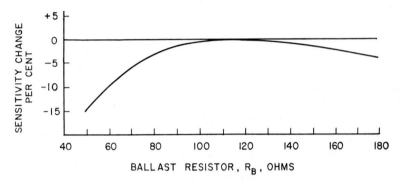

FIG. 8. Effect of ballast resistor, R_B, on bridge sensitivity. $R_S = 10,000$ ohms, $R_G = 119.6$ ohms, $R_T = 3.33$ ohms.

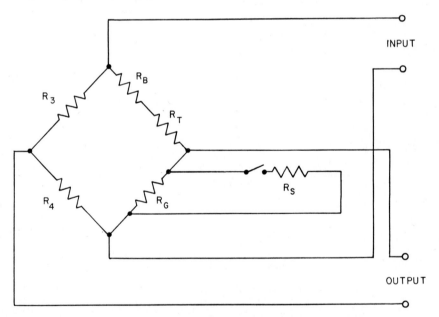

FIG. 9. Six-wire calibration circuit.

This type of compensation yields the most accurate solution to the problem of minimizing the effects of temperature where a conventional dummy compensating system cannot be employed. A single gage type can be adjusted to fit most engineering materials at a specific operating temperature or over a broad temperature range within a practical temperature coefficient slope tolerance of ± 0.1 microinch/inch/°F.

There are some obvious disadvantages which also must be considered. Each gage requires a completion network including the ballast resistor and bridge balancing resistors. The circuit parameters must be calculated with care and in most cases determined experimentally for at least one gage of a particular "lot" as bonded to a given material. The correction factor may be applied to all gages of the "lot" bonded to the same material as that tested. Although the symmetrical three-wire lead wire system employed with this gage type normally cancels temperature effects on the leads, the system is valid only when the two bridge arms are of equal resistance. Since the ohmic value of R_G is seldom equal to the value of $R_T + R_B$, any change of resistance of R_{LG} and R_{LT} created by changes in temperature will create a signal error. This effect may be minimized by use of low resistance, low temperature coefficient of resistance lead wires.

CIRCUIT COMPENSATION

Added Thermocouple[2,3]

An uncompensated bonded strain gage in a bridge circuit will, when exposed to a temperature change, produce a change in the bridge unbalance. The change in the bridge unbalance will be a function of the gage temperature and, for a fixed bridge excitation voltage, the output voltage of the bridge can be expressed in terms of millivolts per degree change in temperature. A change in the bridge excitation voltage will produce a proportional change in the slope of the millivolt per degree output curve. If the bridge excitation voltage is DC, the change in bridge output vs. temperature has the same units and character as a thermocouple output. It is evident, then, that a thermocouple can be used to produce an equal and opposite voltage for cancellation purposes if the proper bridge excitation voltage is selected.

Variable bridge excitation voltages are undesirable and it is more practical to provide an excess of thermocouple voltage and then reduce it to the desired level. Figure 10 shows one type of bridge network with adjustable thermocouple compensation. Other arrangements are also possible. The resistors, R_1 and R_2, provide a divider network for reduction of the generated thermocouple voltage to the desired correction voltage E_{TC}. For perfect compensation the correction voltage E_{TC} should be equal and opposite to the bridge output E_O that is generated by a temperature change in the strain gage R_G. The sum of the voltages E_{TC} and E_O will then be responsive only to strain in the gage.

Thermocouple compensation is a simple and effective way to reduce the apparent thermal strain indication of a gage. External adjustment of the degree of compensation permits use of the gage on materials having various thermal expansion coefficients as well as the experimental adjustment of any particular gage installation to a best-fit compensation. A limitation is

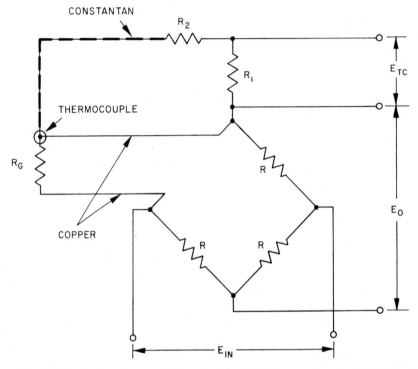

FIG. 10. Typical strain gage bridge network with thermocouple compensation.

that the bridge must be DC excited. The linearity of a thermocouple output is usually better than the apparent thermal strain indication of a gage, therefore, the compensated output always shows some residual nonlinearity.

SELF-TEMPERATURE COMPENSATION

Combining Plus and Minus Temperature Coefficient Materials

The combining of positive and negative temperature coefficient materials is a method of achieving a single sensing grid having a best fit temperature coefficient when bonded to a given specimen material.[3] As is self-evident, this method requires two different strain sensing materials, one of which has a positive temperature coefficient over some specific temperature range when bonded to a specific specimen material and the other having a negative coefficient under the same conditions. Typical curves of equivalent strain vs. temperature for two such materials are shown in Fig. 11. The two sensing materials are combined into a single composite gage grid so that the over-all result is a single gage having a minimum temperature coefficient.

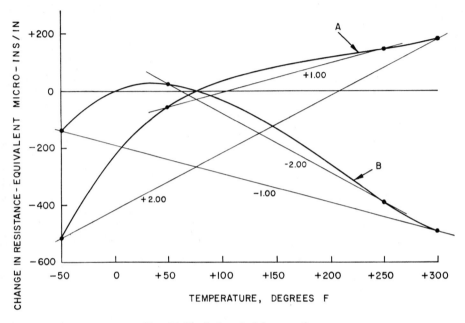

FIG. 11. Typical material properties.

A typical gage configuration in wire is shown in Fig. 12. The ratio of the resistance of the two sensing materials is normally inversely proportional to the chord slope of the temperature coefficient curves of the individual materials over the desired temperature range.

The advantage of this method of obtaining temperature compensation is that the resultant coefficient is accurately and continuously controllable over a reasonably wide temperature coefficient range. Varying the number and length of the strands in each portion of the gage grid provides a continuous and unbroken adjustment of the over-all temperature coefficient over 80% or more of the total temperature coefficient range between the two individual materials. It is this "adjustability" that permits the manufacture of gages having a chord slope tolerance of better than $\pm\frac{1}{4}$ microinch/inch/°F over any desired temperature range. This tolerance is in sharp contrast to the normally accepted ± 1 microinch/inch/°F associated with single element gages made of selected or heat treated sensing materials.

Figure 13 shows typical curves and tolerance limits for self-compensated gages having a minimum temperature response over the temperature ranges of $+50°$ to $+250°$ and $-50°$ to $+300°F$. The close tolerance held on this type of gage requires that a temperature range be specified. In fact, the use of the term "self-compensated" for a gage using a sensing material having a nonlinear temperature response is without meaning unless the temperature range is also mentioned.

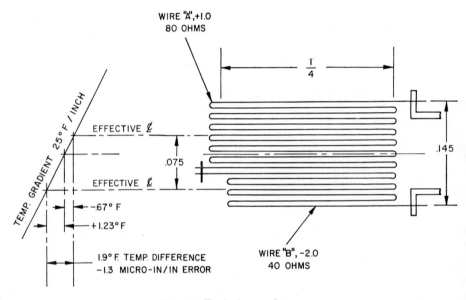

Fɪɢ. 12. Typical gage element.

From a manufacturing standpoint, the composite gage provides excellent versatility. The possession of a few sensing materials having selected temperature coefficients enables one to produce self-compensated gages to fit practically any structural material over any temperature increment between $-50°$ and $+300°F$. During production the proportions of the two sensing materials can be adjusted as required to compensate for normal variations in the basic materials, thus permitting the manufacture of lot after lot of gages having the same temperature characteristics within narrow limits.

The outcome of combining two known materials in any given proportion is quite predictable, thus the manufacture of gages to fit special materials of special temperature ranges can be done with a minimum of experimental work.

The composite grid gage acts the same as a single element gage and thus has the advantage of being able to follow rapid temperature changes. Knowledge of the approximate temperature of the test specimen at the gage location permits correction of the strain readings during temperature changes through use of the curve furnished with the gages.

Self-temperature compensated gages made of plus and minus coefficient materials have been criticized because of a possible error in reading due to test specimen temperature gradients in a sideway direction across the gage grid. A look at the physical dimensions of a typical gage grid will show that

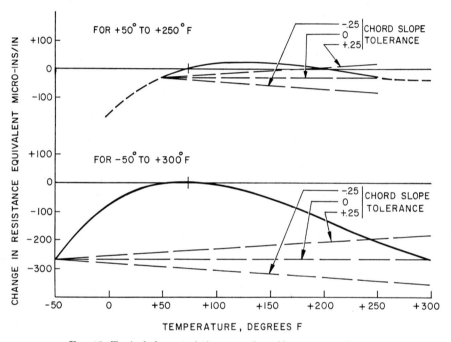

FIG. 13. Typical characteristic curves for self-compensated gages.

it is nearly impossible to get a noticeable error from this cause. Figure 12 shows the dimensions of a typical 120-ohm, ¼-inch-gage-length gage. The distance between the effective centers of the two grid parts, 0.075 inch, remains the same regardless of how the grid is proportioned between the two wires. Assume a temperature gradient across the gage as shown in Fig. 12. At first glance it appears that such a gradient might produce a noticeable error. However, by figuring the change in resistance in each part of the grid and adding them to get the total change, we find that the actual error is −1.3 microinches/inch. Thus, a gradient as large as 100°F per inch would produce errors in the range of only 5 microinches/inch, an inconsequential strain in any stress analysis problem. Obviously, such high temperature gradients take very special effort to produce and are never encountered in ordinary service.

One disadvantage that is not overcome in the composite type self-compensated gage is the nonlinearity characteristics of the temperature response. This is a fundamental characteristic of Constantan and other low coefficient alloys that cannot be eliminated in this way. The ability to set the absolute temperature coefficient of this gage to a close tolerance best fit over any desired temperature range overcomes some of the nonlinearity disadvantage.

Selection or Processing of Strain Sensing Materials

As stated in the section concerning temperature compensation by use of a dummy gage, many strain sensing alloys such as Constantan display temperature coefficient of resistances indicative of the particular melt or heat of the material. The manufacturers of the raw materials can control this characteristic within specified limits but even under the most ideal conditions cannot control the limits to within the tolerance required for strain gage alloys. A very careful search for a particular melt must be made so that when processed into wire or foil and manufactured as a strain gage, the system will exhibit a minimum temperature response over a specified temperature range on a test material having a specific thermal coefficient of expansion. Some typical temperature response characteristics for Constantan are shown in Fig. 14.

Consider that the apparent strain measurement was made with gages manufactured from the indicated "lot" of Constantan and bonded to AISI 1020 annealed steel. This particular steel has a handbook value for the linear coefficient of thermal expansion of 6.5×10^{-6} inches/inch over the temperature range 68°–212°F. Theoretically, any of the gages from a particular "lot" bonded to a material having a different coefficient of expansion than the steel, would have a temperature coefficient variation of exactly the difference between the coefficients of expansion of the two test specimens. If we plot this difference in coefficient of expansion between the test steel and other materials, we can observe the approximate temperature response behavior of these various Constantan gage "lots" with respect to materials other than the test steel.

For example, 302 stainless steel has a handbook value for the linear temperature coefficient of expansion of 9.6×10^{-6} inches/inch/°F over a temperature range 32°–212°F. The expansion coefficient difference between 1020 and 302 would be $(6.5 - 9.6)10^{-6}$ inches/inch/°F equivalent to an apparent strain of -310 microinches/inch for a 100°F temperature rise between 75° and 175°F. If the difference in coefficients of expansion is linear, a straight line may be connected between the zero apparent strain reference at room temperature (75°F), and −310 microinches/inch apparent strain at 175°F. An identical procedure was used to establish the dashed lines indicating magnesium, 2024-T4 aluminum, and titanium. It is now obvious that gages showing minimum deviation from a dashed line representing a particular test material will have minimum temperature response on that material. This is the basis for "Selected Melt" type self-temperature compensation.

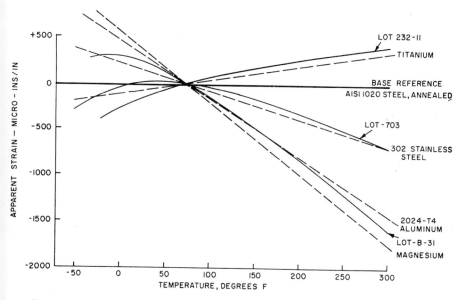

FIG. 14. Typical apparent strain vs. temperature characteristics for strain gages manufactured from various lot numbered Constantan alloy. Gages bonded to 1020 steel.

In addition to the selection of materials with a specific temperature response, it is possible to process the raw materials by cold work or heat treatment to arrive at the desired minimum apparent strain characteristic. The metallurgical changes in some strain sensing alloys created by temperature increases above their normal stable operating range alters the temperature coefficient as shown for the more common strain gage alloys in Figs. 15 and 16.

These plots are typical for relatively short-term temperature excursions and do not indicate the effect of time at temperature on the phenomenon. The particular melt of Karma shown is not indicative of a satisfactory melt for strain gage use but demonstrates the control which might be exercised by careful heat treatment. Karma can be selected in the raw material state with temperature coefficient of resistance values in the range of Constantan. The Nichrome V could not be considered a controllable

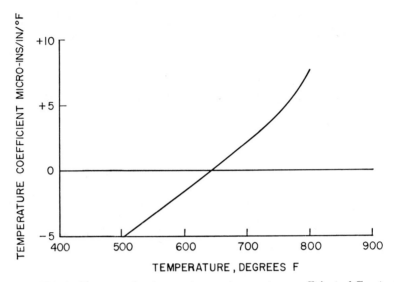

FIG. 15. Effect of heat treating temperature on temperature coefficient of Constantan foil.

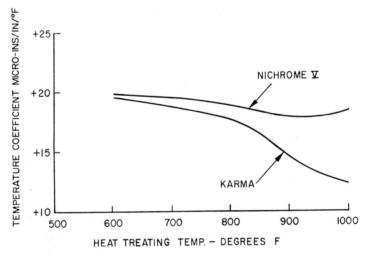

FIG. 16. Effect of heat treating temperature on temperature coefficient of Karma and Nichrome V foils.

material showing less than a 2-microinch/inch/°F change over the entire test temperature range.

The combination of proper selection of raw material and process control results in self-temperature-compensated strain gages with a practical temperature coefficient tolerance of ±1 microinch/inch/°F for a specific

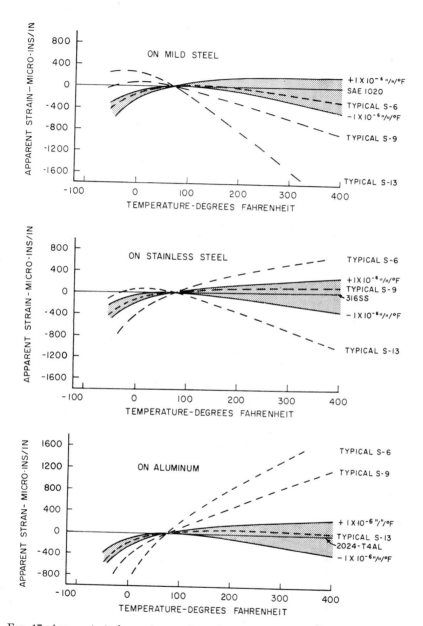

Fig. 17. Apparent strain vs. temperature characteristics. SR-4® selected melt Constantan bonded filament strain gages.

temperature range on a particular material. The disadvantages of this system are nonlinearity of temperature response and deviation over large temperature ranges.

Some degree of judgment must be exercised by the user in the selection of a particular gage for minimum response to temperature depending not only on the test material but the temperature range. For example, a Constantan of the "Selected Melt" type suitable for use on mild steel in the elevated temperature range above room temperature will in general not be self-compensated on the same material in the very low temperature range below room temperature. A gage normally selected for use on stainless steel in the elevated temperature region would display a minimum temperature response on mild steel in the low temperature region below 50°F. Similarly, a gage normally used on aluminum at elevated temperature will be more suitable for use on stainless steel in the very low temperature range. Typical temperature response characteristics for Constantan "Selected Melt" gages are shown in Fig. 17.

Conclusion

A fairly comprehensive study of the problems of temperature compensation by various methods has been undertaken in this paper without regard to other ramifications of temperature induced errors. A mention of these other considerations is felt necessary in view of the effects not only on the apparent strain characteristic but on the stability and strain sensitivity as well. Details of these considerations may be found in the Bibliography at the end of the paper.

It is possible to destroy or permanently alter the normal performance characteristics of the gage system by exceeding the temperature limitations of the grid carrier materials, strain sensing alloys and by poor selection of accessory items such as bonding cements and lead wire materials, insulation, and solder.

Consider that the metallurgical changes in the strain sensing alloys which alter the temperature coefficient of resistance may also alter the specific resistivity. These phenomena will result in a change in resistance of the gage appearing as zero drift with time at constant temperature. Under proper temperature conditions, the "dummy" gage system of apparent strain compensation will compensate to a fair degree for this condition but any self-temperature-compensated gage signal must be corrected for zero drift. Corrections require an accurate temperature-time measurement at the strain gage location and a knowledge of the drift behavior of the gage system employed.

In the case of the gages supplied with an integral carrier for direct bonding to the specimen, the combination of the carrier and bonding cement must be considered. The strain gage performance regardless of the strain sensing alloy employed depends upon the ability of the carrier and bonding cement to faithfully transmit the surface strains to the grid as well as provide electrical insulation between the grid and the specimen. Carrier and bonding cements may suffer a loss in shear strength at elevated temperature, resulting in a reduction of gage sensitivity and excessive creep, or become brittle at very low temperatures, reducing the normal strain range of the system. The combination of carrier and bonding cement in general become electrically conductive to varying degrees at elevated temperature allowing a shunting action of adjacent grid filaments and the grid to the specimen. This shunt action will create zero drift problems as the gage resistance to ground approaches the original gage resistance. Ceramic cements are notably poor in this respect at very high temperatures, and organic cements break down electrically and mechanically at even lower temperatures.

It is also possible to alter the true strain gage characteristics by poor selection of lead wire materials and insulation which are actually part of the strain gage system within the conventional Wheatstone bridge circuit. A symmetrical three-wire lead system using low resistance and low temperature coefficient of resistance materials should always be employed in areas of high temperature or large thermal gradients. Any inactive resistance in series with the gage reduces the system strain sensitivity and the same zero drift and apparent strain problems that create errors in the gage itself may be present in the lead system effecting the over-all errors. The insulating quality of the insulation used on the lead wires should be at least equivalent to that of the carrier and bonding cement.

The above are but a few of the many factors to be considered in the selection of the strain gage system. Each application will have its own unique environmental problems. Strain gage manufacturers cannot urge strongly enough that the users consider and understand the limitations of the gage and associated accessories and to use this knowledge in the planning and conduct of test to yield accurate and reliable information.

References

1. Manson, S. S., Thermal stresses in design, *Machine Design* **31,** 109–116 (1959).
2. Bodner, M., and Brewer, W. B., Temperature compensated strain gage, U. S. Patent No. 2,930,224 (to Lockheed Aircraft Corporation).
3. "Proceedings of Western Regional Strain Gage Committee," Oct. 15, 1959.
4. Harris, C. R., and Davis, J. E., A new strain gage for use at cryogenic temperatures, The Martin Company, republished by Baldwin-Lima-Hamilton Corporation, Electronics Division, TD4320-7 (January, 1960).

BIBLIOGRAPHY

SR-4® strain gage waterproofing investigation report, Tech. Data Rept. 4310-1, Baldwin-Lima-Hamilton Corporation, Electronics Division (February, 1958).

SR-4® strain gage bonding cement evaluation report, Tech. Data Rept. 4310-2, Baldwin-Lima-Hamilton Corporation, Electronics Division (March, 1958).

SR-4® strain gage performance report, Tech. Data Rept. 4310-4, Baldwin-Lima-Hamilton Corporation, Electronics Division (October, 1958).

SR-4® strain gage performance summary, Tech. Data Rept. 4310-6, Baldwin-Lima-Hamilton Corporation, Electronics Division (October, 1958).

SR-4® strain gage evaluation, Tech. Data Rept. 4310-7, Baldwin-Lima-Hamilton Corporation, Electronics Division (May, 1959).

High temperature cement evaluation, Tech. Data Rept. 4310-9, Baldwin-Lima-Hamilton Corporation, Electronics Division (January, 1960).

Stability of alloys for high temperature foil gages, Tech. Data Rept. 4320-3, Baldwin-Lima-Hamilton Corporation, Electronics Division (October, 1958).

Summary high temperature foil gage alloy evaluation, Tech. Data Rept. 4320-4, Baldwin-Lima-Hamilton Corporation, Electronics Division (August, 1958).

SR-4® high temperature foil gage performance report, Tech. Data Rept. 4320-5, Baldwin-Lima-Hamilton Corporation, Electronics Division (October, 1958).

SR-4® Type FNH-50-12E temperature compensated high temperature strain gage typical installation and test history, Tech. Data Rept. 4320-6, Baldwin-Lima-Hamilton Corporation, Electronics Division (February, 1959).

L. J. Weymouth, Current day state of the strain gage art, Strain Gage Applications, Baldwin-Lima-Hamilton Corporation, Electronics Division, presented at Cleveland IRE Meeting (February, 1960).

C. C. Perry and H. R. Lissner, "The Strain Gage Primer." McGraw-Hill, New York, 1955.

Strain Gage Readings, **1**, No. 1 (1958) through **3**, No. 3 (1960).

W. M. Murray and P. K. Stein, "Strain Gage Techniques." Society for Experimental Stress Analysis, Cambridge, Massachusetts, 1960.

CHARACTERISTICS AND APPLICATIONS OF A SEMICONDUCTOR STRAIN GAGE*

M. A. Xavier and C. O. Vogt

Century Electronics & Instruments, Inc., Tulsa, Oklahoma

Abstract

The piezoresistive effect in properly prepared semiconductors makes possible strain gages with gage factors exceeding 100. This paper describes the basic properties of a line of silicon strain gages that have been developed. Particular emphasis is placed on temperature characteristics. Also included is information on mounting techniques, typical circuitry and temperature compensation techniques. Several applications to transducing devices are cited.

I. Introduction

The development of a family of silicon strain gages has been discussed previously in several publications.[1,2] These devices are based on the now well-known piezoresistive effects pioneered by Bell Telephone Laboratories.[3-5] The purpose of this paper is to present more characteristics of the family of strain gages and to discuss the effect of these characteristics on applications of the Strainistor, as the commercial item is called. Of primary interest will be the effects of temperature upon the behavior of these semiconductor devices.

II. Characteristics

Physical

The Strainistor consists of a small rectangular bar of single crystal silicon with a metal tab attached at each end (see Fig. 1). The tabs provide electrical connections to the bar and serve as large surface area anchors to permit the Strainistor to be bonded securely to the surface of the specimen under test. The silicon bar has a cross section of 0.006 by 0.006 inch. The active length of the element is 0.350 inch with an over-all length including tabs of 0.650 inch. The fabricating technique results in a bar with good uniformity of cross section and flat smooth surfaces. Production units are inspected to ensure that they are free from pits, necking, and other irregularities.

---

* Presented at Instrument Society of America, Fifteenth Annual Instrumented Automation Conference, September 26–30, 1960, New York, New York.

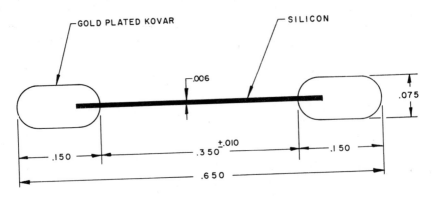

FIG. 1. Strainistor dimension drawing.

Mounting Techniques

The Strainistor can be bonded to the surface of a test specimen in the same manner as ordinary strain gages. They are uninsulated, much as are unbacked foil gages, so as not to limit the temperature range by the characteristics of the carrier material. To aid in handling and mounting, the

FIG. 2. Handling and installation fixture.

units are supplied attached to a holder. A photograph of a holder with attached Strainistor is shown in Fig. 2. The mounting procedure is briefly as follows:

The area is first cleaned, using the normal strain gage procedures and precautions. Next, a thin insulating coat of cement is applied to the test area and at least partially cured. Another layer of cement is added and the Strainistor pressed into the cement by means of the holder. After the cement has fully cured, the holder may be removed with a slight pull. The holder has been coated with a release agent to prevent adhesion of the cement. Leads can then be connected by soldering or spot welding to the exposed portions of the end tabs. These steps are indicated in Fig. 3.

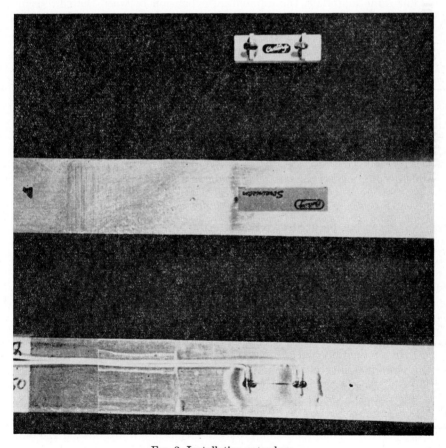

FIG. 3. Installation procedure.

A considerable number of cements have been evaluated or are currently under test. Eastman 910, EPY-150, and Mithra No. 200 have proven very satisfactory. The technique for using Eastman 910 requires care but can be easily mastered by most strain gage technicians. Ceramic cements have not yet been fully evaluated for proper mounting techniques with the Strainistor.

In most installations using cements that are cured at elevated temperature, the sensor will be found to be in compression when cooled to room temperature. This occurs because most materials expand at a faster rate than silicon (expansion coefficient 1.3 ppm/°F). At the temperature at which the cement hardens, the test bar has expanded more than the silicon. Upon cooling, the bar contracts, carrying the sensor with it. This can be used to an advantage as outlined below.

For some materials, the differential expansion between the silicon and the test specimen can be sufficient to introduce considerable strain. This will limit the magnitude of the strain level which can be used. By using a cement that cures at a temperature near the middle of the range to be encountered, the temperature-induced strain will be only one-half as much as would result from use of a cement that cured at one end of the temperature range. Since most high-temperature cements require elevated temperature cure, this condition is ordinarily easily achieved. This phenomenon can also be used to advantage in room temperature tests that are known to involve only tensile strains; the strain range can be extended by the precompression resulting from elevated temperature cure. The magnitude of this precompression can easily be made as high as 1400 microstrain.

Resistance

Units can be produced with the same dimensions having resistances from a few ohms to several megohms by adjusting the doping level of the silicon during crystal growth. Standard units with resistances of 50, 120, and 300 ohms have been developed and tested to conform to present industry accepted values. Since many of the properties of silicon vary with doping level, sample units were fabricated from material with a wide range of resistivity and thoroughly tested during development. The final resistivity range selected represents a compromise of the over-all properties.

Pilot production runs of several hundred units were completed to check the reproducibility of these units and to determine production tolerances. For the 50- and 120-ohm units it was found that a resistance tolerance of $\pm 5\%$ could be maintained with a very high percentage yield. The mean resistance values for these pilot lots were 50.0 and 120.1 ohms. These tolerances have been maintained in production runs of a few thousand 120-ohm units. The resistance of production units is measured on a 100% basis and matched to within 0.5%. For the 300-ohm units, it was necessary to increase the resistance spread to ±10% to maintain a high yield.

It is difficult to eliminate entirely the possibility of a small rectifying junction in some of the units at the connection between the silicon and end tab. Based on measurements of the pilot units, a tolerance of 0.3 ohm maximum was established for the difference in resistance of a unit with reversed polarity. This will introduce a maximum error of 20 microstrain if the polarity is reversed during a test. If polarity is maintained, no error will result.

Strain Sensitivity

The strain sensitivity of the Strainistor is defined in the same manner as the gage factor of conventional wire and foil strain gages; that is, strain sensitivity is equal to the unit change in resistance divided by the unit change in strain.

The strain sensitivity of silicon is a function of the resistivity, being a maximum of approximately 175 for high-resistivity material. The resistivities used in the 50-, 120-, and 300-ohm sensors result in nominal sensitivities of 119, 123, and 132, respectively. This variation is in general agreement with theoretical curves[6] although the absolute values are somewhat lower. The sensitivity of the 120-ohm unit agrees quite well with the experimental results of a similarly doped unit reported by Mason et al.[7] Within a production lot, the sensitivity of individual units falls within a range of ±5% of the nominal value for that lot.

Theoretical considerations indicate that the transverse sensitivity of the Strainistor should be quite small. Actual measurements reveal a value less than one percent of the axial sensitivity.

Tests on a number of units show that nearly all will safely withstand a strain of 2000 microstrain in tension. Some units have been used at strains exceeding 3000 microstrain without rupture. As indicated earlier, the tensile range can be extended by precompression. They are considerably stronger in compression than tension. The resistance change with strain in the 120-ohm units is linear to better than 1% for strains of 500 microstrain. The linearity at 2000 microstrain is within $2\frac{1}{2}$%. A curve of resistance vs. load for a unit mounted on a steel test strip is shown in Fig. 4. The maximum load corresponded to a strain of approximately 900 microstrain. The 50-ohm units have slightly less nonlinearity and the 300-ohm units somewhat more. The Wheatstone bridge circuits in which strain gages are commonly used can actually show greater nonlinearity than the Strainistor itself. However, with proper circuit design, the two effects can be made to cancel, resulting in very good linearity as will be pointed out later.

Tests on unmounted Strainistors (tested in tension) indicate no detect-

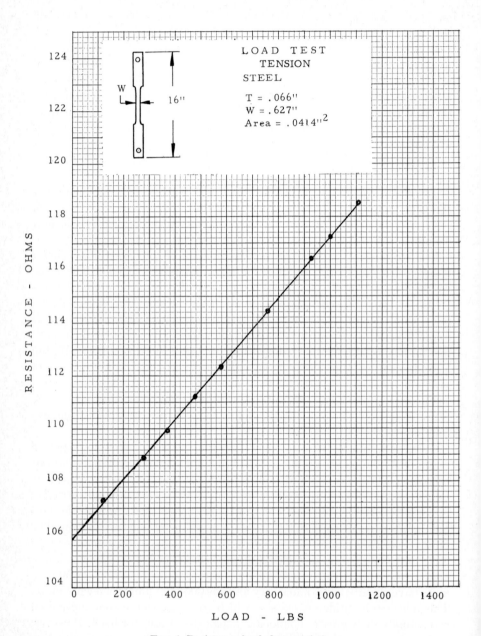

FIG. 4. Resistance-load characteristics.

able hysteresis within the unit itself. This is to be expected because of the single-crystal structure of the silicon and the fact that no dependence is made on an adhesive material to transmit the force. A poor installation can, of course, result in hysteresis in the cement as with conventional strain gages.

Photosensitivity

Tests have been conducted to determine the photosensitivity of the 120-ohm Strainistors. These tests were primarily qualitative in nature but do indicate the relative magnitude and the nature of the effects. A fluorescent light source and careful thermal insulation were employed to minimize temperature influences. Two effects are observed—a photoconductive effect and a photovoltaic effect.

The photoconductive effect is a bulk property and is noted in all parts of the semiconductor (i.e., center portion as well as end junctions). A light intensity of approximately 400 foot candles produced an effective resistance change of less than 0.008 ohm, equivalent to less than 0.6 microstrain.

The photovoltaic effect is a junction effect and is of opposite polarity at each junction. With uniform illumination, the effects at each junction cancel. With one junction covered and the other exposed to a light intensity of approximately 400 foot candles, an open circuit voltage of approximately 27 μv is generated. For an equal arm bridge with 10 ma per arm and one active gage, this would be equivalent to less than 0.4 microstrain. These values are for a unit with a polarity resistance difference of 0.3 ohm (the maximum production tolerance). A Strainistor with very little polarity sensitivity showed only one-fourth to one-third of the photovoltaic effect of the above unit.

The spectral sensitivity of the photoconductive and photovoltaic effect shows a maximum between 0.8 and 0.9 μ. The frequency spectrum from a fluorescent light has a maximum in the range of 0.58 μ. At this frequency, the photoconductive and photovoltaic effect are between 50 and 70% of maximum. If the maximum effects were both twice that measured, they would still be quite small and of no concern in normal usage. Opaque cements will reduce the effect even further.

Current

The current levels that can be used are limited by the self-heating effect in the silicon. Figure 5 shows the change in resistance with current for typical mounted units. To minimize heating effect, current should be limited to 60, 30, and 12 ma, respectively, for the 50-, 120-, and 300-ohm units. Considerably higher currents can, however, be used without damage to the elements.

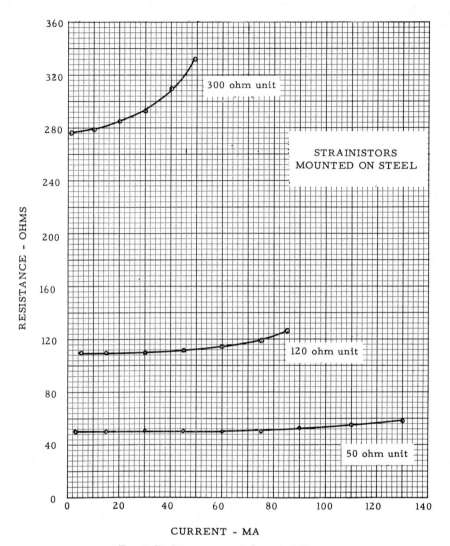

FIG. 5. Resistance-current characteristics.

Temperature Characteristics

The Strainistor can be used over a considerable temperature range without damage. There are, however, changes in the properties that must be taken into account. The primary effects of temperature change on an installed Strainistor are the following:

1. The resistance of the silicon changes.
2. The silicon changes in length.

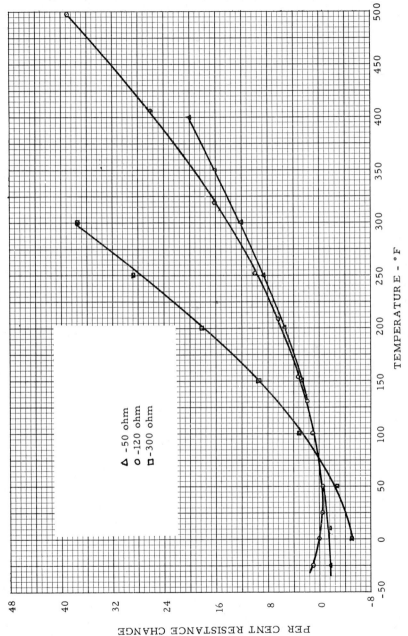

FIG. 6. Resistance change with temperature.

M. A. XAVIER AND C. O. VOGT

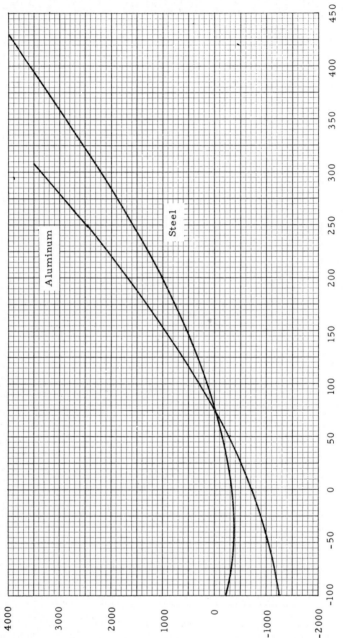

TEMPERATURE - ° F

Fig. 7. Apparent strain vs. temperature.

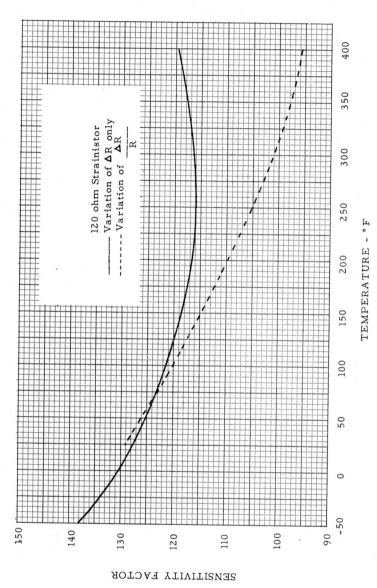

FIG. 8. Sensitivity change with temperature.

3. The test specimen changes in length.

4. The strain sensitivity changes.

While these effects are present to some degree in all strain gages, some of them are more significant in silicon. The resistivities used in these units have been selected to reduce these variations.

The change in resistance with temperature for typical 50-, 120-, and 300-ohm Strainistors are shown in Fig. 6. These are in good agreement with curves of the resistivity variation with temperature of silicon for various Boron doping concentrations published by Shockley.[8]

For a bonded strain gage, there is also a resistance change due to strain induced by the difference in expansion between the test material and the strain gage. This will, of course, be different for materials with different expansion coefficients. In Fig. 7 are shown curves of the total resistance change with temperature in terms of an equivalent strain for typical 120-ohm Strainistors mounted on steel and aluminum (this is commonly referred to as apparent strain). At room temperature there is an apparent strain of 6 microstrain/°F on steel and 12 microstrain/°F on aluminum. This is comparable to values for typical uncompensated wire and foil gages. Over the temperature range 50°F to below −100°F the unit is self temperature compensated on steel.

The strain sensitivity of high purity (high resistivity) silicon has been shown to vary as $1/T$ where T is the absolute temperature.[9] The variation of sensitivity with temperature of the Strainistor is somewhat less, due to the higher doping level. In Fig. 8 is shown a curve of sensitivity factor vs. temperature for a typical 120-ohm unit. This is in general agreement with the results published by Mason, Forst, and Tornillo. This strain sensitivity is defined as $\Delta R/R\epsilon$, where R is the unstrained resistance at that temperature. It hence includes the change in the unstrained resistance with temperature as well as the change in ΔR. The output of a properly designed circuit, as will be pointed out later, can be made proportional to ΔR rather than $\Delta R/R$. For such a circuit, the change in sensitivity with temperature will be only that represented by changes in $\Delta R/\epsilon$. A curve of the variation of sensitivity factor for a typical 120-ohm unit based on changes in $\Delta R/\epsilon$ only is shown in Fig. 8. Over the temperature range 50°–450°F, there is a variation of less than ±4%.

III. Applications

The Strainistor can be used in the measurement of very small strains and in the construction of sensitive transducers. Its high output permits simplification in the instrumentation for the measurement of higher level strains and makes possible high output transducers which can many times eliminate the need for expensive low level amplification. Besides these more obvious uses which involve substitutions for ordinary wire and foil gages, the properties of the Strainistor are applicable to devices for sensing and control for which wire and foil gages are not suitable. In this section, some of the considerations of temperature compensation and circuitry in the use of these units will be given, followed by brief descriptions of some actual applications.

Temperature Compensation

Of primary concern in applying the Strainistor are the effects of temperature which were given in Section II.

When they are used for the direct measurement of strain, there are several ways in which the zero shift or apparent strain due to temperature change can be compensated. The one most straightforward and simple is the use of a "dummy gage." This technique is employed quite extensively with wire and foil strain gages. A gage is mounted on the same material and near the active gage in such a manner that it is subjected to the same temperature as the active gage, but is not subjected to strain. Placing these two gages in adjacent arms of the Wheatstone bridge circuit will cause the resistance changes due to temperature to cancel at the output. This procedure is equally applicable to silicon strain sensors.

Other techniques that can be used include the following:

1. The use of a small thermistor mounted near the sensor to provide a resistance change with temperature that can be employed in the circuitry to balance out the resistance change in the sensor.

2. The use of a small thermocouple mounted near the sensor to provide a voltage that can be used to cancel the voltage at the output due to temperature-induced resistance changes in the sensor.

When measuring dynamic strains, the strain will ordinarily change more rapidly than the temperature. The resistance change due to temperature can be easily filtered out and no compensation for zero shift is necessary. One method for compensating the change in sensitivity due to temperature is to control the voltage applied to the circuit by the use of a temperature-sensitive device, such as a thermistor, mounted near the sensor. This control could also be introduced at the output of the bridge, but would have the disadvantage of changing the effective source impedance as seen by the indicating instrument.

In almost all instances a small thermocouple can, of course, be mounted near the sensor for recording temperature directly, simultaneously with strain; and, the appropriate corrections made for both zero shift and sensitivity change, using the proper curves. Typical temperature curves are furnished with each Strainistor.

The temperature characteristics are sufficiently repeatable between units to allow the use of general compensating schemes for standard units where only average accuracy is required. For closer compensation, it is necessary to measure the unmounted temperature characteristics of the units and apply individual compensation or match units. With ordinary wire and foil strain gages (except for the weldable gage manufactured by Micro-Test, Inc.) it is not possible to measure the unmounted temperature characteristics.

Some of the temperature effects that are important with wire and foil gages are almost insignificant with silicon strain sensors. The zero shift or bridge unbalance, due to resistance change with temperature of the lead wires of a wire or foil gage installation, can be considerable. The magnitude of these changes is usually insignificant compared to the resistance change in the silicon when measuring strains of average magnitude. This is also true of other parasitic resistances such as slip rings and switching boxes. With wire and foil strain gages, the leakage resistance of the cement may significantly affect readings at high temperatures. With silicon sensors, lower insulation resistance can be tolerated.

Circuits

It has been shown[10] that the maximum voltage sensitivity (open circuit) of a strain gage, regardless of the circuit in which it is used, is given by the following relationship:

$$S_{v_{max}} = R_g \times I_{g_{max}} \times G.F.$$

where $S_{v_{max}}$ = maximum voltage sensitivity in microvolts per microstrain
$\quad R_g$ = gage resistance in ohms
$\quad I_{g_{max}}$ = maximum gage current in amperes
$\quad G.F.$ = gage factor or sensitivity.

Using a current of 30 ma, the maximum voltage sensitivity of the Strainistor is 0.45 mv/microstrain. The actual sensitivity is always less than this maximum but can easily reach 90% with proper circuit design. For 2000 microstrain, the open circuit output is 0.81 volt. This can be read directly with a high impedance sensitive voltmeter without amplification.

Similarly, the maximum current sensitivity (short circuit) in microamperes per microstrain is given by

$$S_{I_{max}} = I_{g_{max}} \times G.F.$$

For the Strainistor, this quantity is 3.75. With a circuit efficiency of 90% and a strain level of 2000 microstrain, the short circuit output is 6.75 ma. This can be read directly on a simple inexpensive meter. In the case of dynamic strains, it is also large enough to drive many high frequency galvanometers.

In the measurement of dynamic strains, potentiometric circuits are recommended. This circuit allows a common ground connection between the strain gage and the measuring equipment. The output is normally connected through a capacitor or other filter to eliminate the DC level. The apparent strain or zero shift with temperature is ordinarily of sufficient low frequency to also be eliminated by this filtering. By making the series resistor (ballast) large compared to the Strainistor resistance, a circuit efficiency of 90% can be realized. This has the effect of providing a constant current source for the strain gage. A further advantage of using a large series resistor is the improvement in sensitivity variation with temperature. For this condition, the output variation with temperature will be determined by the variation of $\Delta R/\epsilon$ only, rather than $\Delta R/R\epsilon$. This variation is less than $\pm 4\%$ over the temperature range $50°–450°F$ as previously pointed out.

For the measurement of static strains, bridge circuits are required. For the most simple conditions in which high accuracy is not required and the temperature is relatively constant during the test, an ordinary resistance measuring Wheatstone bridge can be used to measure the resistance with and without the load, and the difference used to calculate strain.

Where bridge circuits are used, in which the unbalance output is read or recorded, some precautions must be observed. In the use of strain gages, it is ordinarily assumed that the output of a Wheatstone bridge circuit is linear with strain (that is, resistance change in the strain gage or gages). For the small resistance changes involved in wire and foil gages, this is ordinarily a fair assumption. For resistance changes of over 20%, which are possible with the Strainistor, this is not always true.

The output voltage of a Wheatstone bridge circuit (see Fig. 9A) that is initially balanced (i.e., $R_1 R_4 = R_2 R_3$), with one active gage, R_1, is given by

$$E_o = E_{in} \frac{R_4}{(R_1 + R_2)(R_3 + R_4)} \times \frac{\Delta R}{1 + [\Delta R/(R_1 + R_2)]}.$$

For equal arms (i.e., all R's equal) the nonlinearity can be as much as 10% for a 20% change in the active arm, R_1. If R_2 and R_4 are made large compared to R_1 and R_3, this nonlinearity is reduced. The output of this circuit is of the form shown in Fig. 9B. The nonlinearity of the change in resistance with strain previously mentioned is of the form $\Delta R = R \times G.F. \times \epsilon(1 + K\epsilon)$ [Mason et al.,[7] p. 6, Eq. (2)], where K is a constant that depends on the doping. This results in a curve of ΔR vs. strain as shown in Fig. 9C. By proper adjustment of the ratio of R_2 and R_4 to R_1 and R_3, the nonlinearity of the Wheatstone bridge circuit can be made to very nearly cancel that of the Strainistor. The additional advantages of improved circuit efficiency and sensitivity variation with temperature discussed under the potentiometric circuit are obtained with large R_2 and R_4. For zero shift temperature compensation, a dummy Strainistor should be used for R_3.

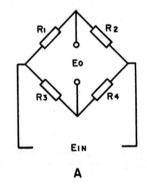

A

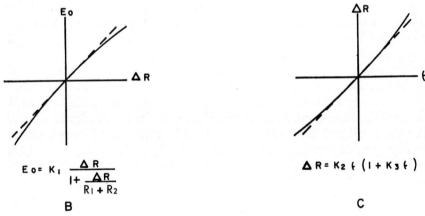

B

C

Fig. 9. A, Wheatstone bridge circuit; B, bridge nonlinearity; C, Strainistor nonlinearity.

In those cases in which bending modes of strain are to be measured or for use in transducers where both positive and negative strains can be produced at the same time, both R_1 and R_3 can be active. The output will be doubled and zero shift temperature compensation maintained. For this case, if the input and output connections in Fig. 9A are interchanged, the circuit will be linear even for equal resistances in all arms and for both constant current or constant voltage sources. The improvement in circuit efficiency and sensitivity variation with temperature, however, will not be realized with equal arms. The circuit efficiency of an equal arm Wheatstone bridge circuit is 50%.

When strains of both signs are available, all four arms of the Wheatstone bridge circuit can also be made active. In this case the output will be twice that of the similar two active arm bridge. In order to achieve very good temperature compensation for zero shift in both the two active arm and four active arm configurations, it is necessary to match the temperature curves of the Strainistors as was pointed out earlier.

Typical Applications

1. Accelerometers

Two simple acceleration sensing devices have been constructed to determine the basic characteristics of the Strainistor in accelerometers. No attempt was made to refine the units. In both models, cantilever beams were

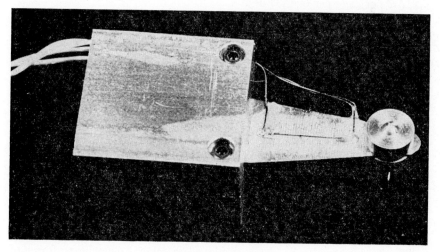

Fig. 10. Accelerometer.

employed. The first was a low frequency, high sensitivity unit utilizing a constant stress beam as shown in Fig. 10. Two active Strainistors were used providing zero shift temperature compensation. No attempt was made to match the Strainistors. The characteristics of this accelerometer are given below:

Beam: beryllium copper—0.005 inch thick
Resistance: 120 ohms
Mass element: 2.4 g
Natural frequency: 30 cps
ΔR per gage per G: 1.5 ohms
Full scale: at least 13 G

Open circuit output: 6.25 mv/volt/G at 30 ma/gage (7.2v) = 0.58 volt
full scale
Zero shift temperature coefficient: 0.03% F.S./°F from 70° to 130°F

The second model was a higher frequency, lower sensitivity unit. A glass
beam $\frac{1}{8}$ inch wide and $\frac{1}{4}$ inch thick was used. Two active gages, one on top
and one on the bottom, were used as before. The characteristics were determined with two different mass elements as tabulated below:

Beam: glass $\frac{1}{8}$ inch wide $\times$ $\frac{1}{4}$ inch thick
Resistance: 120 ohms
Mass element No. 1: 90 g
   Natural frequency: 250 cps
   ΔR per gage per G: 0.34 ohm
   Full scale: 60 G
   Open circuit output: 1.4 mv/volt/G
Mass element No. 2: 4.5 g
   Natural frequency: 2.5 kc
   ΔR per gage per G: 0.02 ohm
   Full scale: 1000 G
   Open circuit output: 0.083 mv/volt/G

These accelerometers have outputs several times that available from conventional unbonded strain gage types. The natural frequency of unbonded strain gage accelerometers are somewhat higher for the same full
scale G level. This difference is primarily the result of the additional force
required to strain the beam itself in the bonded configuration.

2. *Pressure Sensing Devices*

The Strainistor also has been employed in several elementary forms of
pressure sensing devices. In the first unit, the gage was cemented directly
to a diaphragm as shown in Fig. 11. A curve of resistance versus pressure
for this unit is shown in Fig. 12. As can be seen, the nonlinearity is quite
significant, making it unsuitable for a pressure transducer. The repeatability, however, for both increasing and decreasing pressure is quite good.
For use in a pressure switch, the actuation point and its repeatability are
the only critical characteristics, and linearity, for the most part, does not
enter into the performance. In order to make this into a completely solid
state pressure switching device, associated circuitry was developed using
silicon controlled rectifiers. The important parameters were:
   (1) the setting at which the switch actuated,
   (2) the setting at which the switch deactuated.
The difference between the above points is known as the dead band of the

switch. The circuitry developed could turn on and off the silicon controlled rectifiers with a dead band of approximately 2 ohms, corresponding to a pressure difference of approximately 2 psi. For a switch with a full scale

FIG. 11. Pressure sensor.

range of 50 psi, this corresponds to a dead band of less than 5%. By mounting the Strainistor in such a way as to precompress it heavily, considerable over-pressure can be tolerated without damage.

3. *Switching and Control*

The primary sensing device which provides strain to the Strainistor for use with the above switching circuit can take on any number of different forms. Devices can be constructed to provide for switching and/or control of a great variety of different phenomena, such as displacement, force, torque, and weight. In addition, completely contactorless toggle switches can be built. The advantages of the basic simplicity and reliability over other contactorless switching techniques is significant.

Only brief information is available on applications of the Strainistor by other users. In one, they were used to measure step functions of stress with very high rise times. The speed of response was quite good and the high

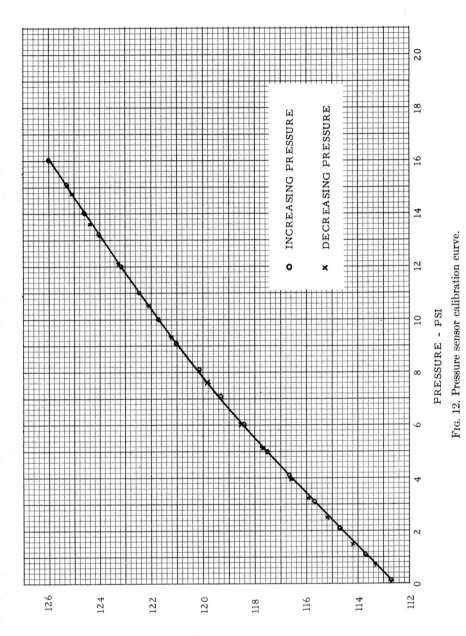

Fig. 12. Pressure sensor calibration curve.

output simplified read-out equipment and problems of signal-to-noise ratio. In another application, the Strainistor has been used to determine whether the propulsion system of a missile is functioning properly. A dummy gage is used to compensate for apparent strain due to temperature variation. The signal generated by the Strainistor is used to modulate a subcarrier oscillator directly, eliminating the need for voltage amplification. There have also been uses in several commercial applications such as go-no go indicators, limit switches, and static switching systems. However, full details of these applications cannot be presented until released by their respective users.

Conclusions

The characteristics of a semiconductor strain gage which has been developed were given, with particular emphasis on temperature effects. Some of the circuits in which the Strainistor can be used were discussed. Some actual applications in which these gages have been employed were described. Work is continuing on the development of improved gages, as well as on applications to sensing and measuring devices.

Acknowledgments

The authors are grateful to Esequiel Zarate, J. D. Schroeder, W. R. Holland, and Wilson Hummingbird for their assistance in the accumulation of the experimental results presented in this paper.

References

1. Vogt, C. O., The Strainistor—A semiconductor strain sensor, Sixth National Flight Test Instrumentation Symposium, San Diego, California, May 2–5, 1960.
2. Vogt, C. O., Semiconductor strain sensors, Thesis for Master of Science Degree, Oklahoma State University, Stillwater, Oklahoma, August, 1960.
3. Smith, Charles S., Piezoresistance effect in germanium and silicon, *Phys. Rev.* **94,** 42–49 (1954).
4. Mason, W. P., and Thurston, R. N., Piezoresistive materials in measuring displacement, force, and torque, *J. Acoust. Soc. Am.* **29,** 1096 (1957).
5. Geyling, F. T., and Forst, J. J., Semiconductor strain transducers, *Bell System Tech. J.* **39,** 705 (1960).
6. Mason, W. P., private communication.
7. Mason, W. P., Forst, J. J., and Tornillo, L. M., Recent developments in semiconductor strain transducers, see p. 109, this volume.
8. Shockley, W., "Electrons and Holes in Semiconductors," p. 284, Fig. 11.7. Van Nostrand, Princeton, New Jersey, 1950.
9. Morin, F. J., Geballe, T. H., and Herring, C., Temperature dependence of piezoresistance of high purity silicon, germanium, *Phys. Rev.* **105,** 525 (1957).
10. Murray, W. M., and Stein, P. K., "Strain Gage Techniques." Society for Experimental Stress Analysis, Cambridge, Massachusetts, 1959.

PRESSURE TRANSDUCER EVALUATION REPORT*

W. R. Humphrey

*General Electric Company, Aircraft Nuclear Propulsion Department,
Cincinnati, Ohio*

Abstract

This report describes the performance evaluation of 17 unbonded strain gage transducers which has been conducted to determine the suitability of these models to measure air pressures in an air cycle reactor system.

A change in temperature will *increase* or *decrease* the transducer millivolt output. The direction of this output is different for each individual transducer and it cannot be predicted before testing. The ± differential transducer will show large variations in the negative span excursion when there is a temperature differential between the transducer and the air pressure applied to the low side of the transducer. This condition is caused by the temperature of the applied air affecting the temperature of the strain gage, which is located on the low side of the transducer.

The zero shift of a transducer at constant temperature without vibration should be 0.5% or less. Vibration of 5 "g" 's or less had a negligible effect on the transducers. Any shutdown period where the excitation voltage or the temperature is turned off, can result in a permanent or temporary change in the zero pressure millivolt output.

These types of transducers can operate for 50 continuous hours with a sufficient warm-up period and still be within the ±2% error band for the specified operating conditions.

Introduction

Performance evaluation of 17 unbonded strain gage transducers has been conducted to determine the suitability of these models to measure air pressures in an air cycle reactor system.

Table I lists all of the original units and their range. The main part of the specification was that the total error band would be a maximum of ±2% for 50 hours of continuous operation with a transducer operating temperature between 150° and 250°F and a maximum vibration of 5 g's. See Fig. 1.

Objectives

The main objectives were to evaluate present-day transducers for total accuracy, span shift, and repeatability under the following conditions:

* Presented at Instrument Society of America, Fifteenth Annual Instrument-Automation Conference, September 26–30, 1960, New York, New York.

TABLE I
PRESSURE TRANSDUCERS PURCHASED FOR TESTING[a]

Transducer	Quantity	Pressure range	Low side
P and Q	2	0–185 psig	Chamber[b]
R and S	2	0–35 psig	Chamber
L	1	0–25 psig	Chamber
N	1	0–90 psig	Chamber
M	1	0–125 psig	Chamber
K	1	±1 psid	Vented[c]
J	1	0–4 psid	Vented
B	1	0–90 psig	Vented
H	1	0–125 psia	Chamber[b]
F	1	0–100 psig	Vented[c]
A and E	2	0–185 psig	Vented
C and D	2	0–35 psig	Vented
G	1	0–25 psig	Vented

[a] With 5-volts DC excitation all of the transducers will have approximately 20 mv output at full scale pressure.

[b] Chamber—one side of the transducer has a sealed chamber which contains an inert gas.

[c] Vented—vented to atmosphere.

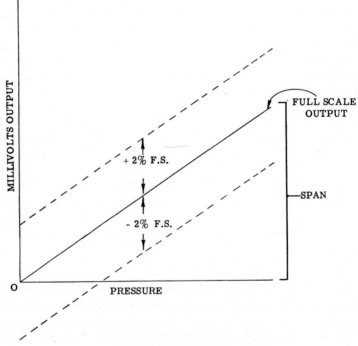

FIG. 1. Transducer error band.

1. 50 hours operation without resetting the zero;
2. vibration of 4 to 5 g's at 50 to 80 cps;
3. transducer operating temperature 150°–250°F.

Since the transducers are to be located on the power plant, normally, it would be necessary to run calibration air lines to each transducer necessitating installation of remote controlled air disconnects at each power plant disassembly point. From these tests, it will be determined if transducer calibration can be performed without calibration air.

If the span remains relatively constant with zero shift, calibration can be performed without calibration air by resetting the zero. The effects of radiation were considered by analyzing the materials in each transducer but it is not a part of this evaluation report.

The transducers used in this evaluation had a compensated temperature range of $-65°$ to $+250°F$.

Test Equipment

A general view of the test equipment is shown in Fig. 2. Figures 3 and 4 show more detail of the same equipment. All equipment used in these tests has been calibrated by General Electric's General Engineering Laboratory or on our Instrument Shop's dead weight tester. Heise gages were used for pressure readouts of 10 psig and higher. U-tubing manometers were used for readings below 4 psi. A power supply manufactured by Owens Laboratory was used for the transducer excitation voltage. Additional equipment included a Leeds and Northrup K-3 potentiometer, voltbox, MB shake table, Leeds and Northrup galvanometer, Rubicon millivolt box for reading T/C temperature, and a Hewlett-Packard voltmeter for measurement of the shake table displacement. An ice bath was used for the T/C reference. The over-all accuracy of the measurements is considered to be within 0.27% of full scale. See Fig. 5 which is the electrical schematic of the test setup. The transducers were heated by a wrap-around type heater during most of the tests. A wire cage kept the heater from directly touching the transducer.

Test Procedures

Transducer testing started with the following procedure:

Transducer Test I

I. *General*

Set the normal transducer balancing circuits for zero output using fixed precision resistors. This balancing network shall remain with its individual transducer during all tests. A reading as referred to below, means a millivolt output at zero or no pressure reading, 50% pressure, 100% pressure,

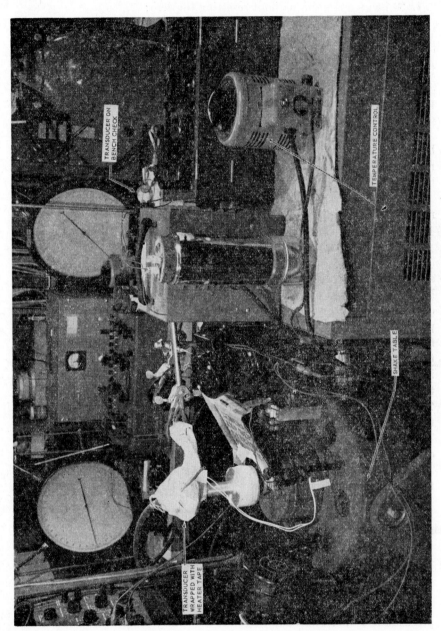

Fig. 2. ANPD pressure transducer evaluation test equipment.

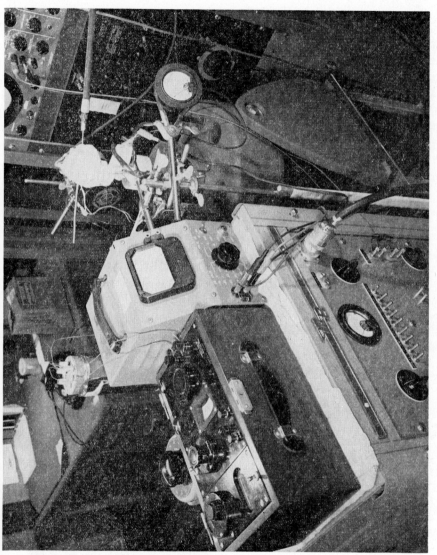

FIG. 3. Shake table and temperature read-out equipment.

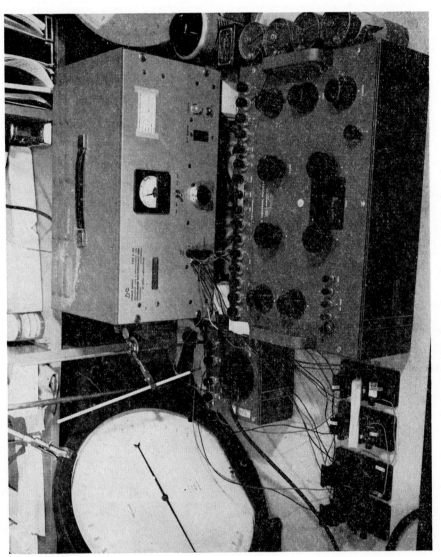

FIG. 4. Power supply and transducer read-out equipment.

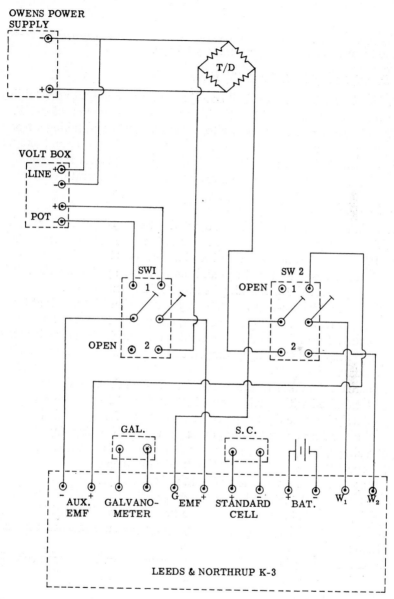

FIG. 5. Transducer test setup schematic. *Notes:* (1) Check power supply with switches in position No. 1. (2) Standardize with switches in position No. 2.

and the temperature of the balancing resistors. During the first half of any test, remove the pressure between readings. During the last half of any test, apply rated pressure between readings. Check on resonant frequencies of the transducer up to approximately 85 cps.

II. *Description of Tests for ±1% Error Band*

1. The balancing resistor shall be adjusted for zero output at a stabilized transducer temperature of 150°F with a maximum deviation of ±5°F.

2. Hold the above temperature for a period of 25 days, taking a reading every 2 hours during a normal working day. Keep the power and temperature applied to the transducer 24 hours a day, except over a weekend. On Monday, apply power and take a reading at room temperature.

III. *Description of Tests for ±2% Error Band*

1. Balancing resistors shall be adjusted for zero output at a stabilized transducer temperature of 200°F. After balancing, hold the temperature at 200°F ±5 for 120 hours. Record readings every 2 hours during a normal working day. Keep input voltage and temperature applied for the full 120 hours except over the weekend, when it should be turned off.

2. With the transducer at 200°F apply a vibration of ±6 mils at 80 cps, then take a reading. Decrease the temperature to $150°F^{+10}_{-0}$ for a period of 75 hours. Record a reading* every 2 hours during a normal working day, but keep input voltage, temperature, and vibration applied for 24 hours a day.

3. Increase the temperature to 200°F and when the transducer temperature is stabilized with a vibration of ±6 mils at 80 cps take a reading.* Immediately increase the temperature to $250°F^{+0}_{-10}$ for a period of 75 hours. Record a reading every 2 hours during a normal working day, but keep input voltage, temperature, and vibration applied for 24 hours a day.

4. Repeat 2 with a vibration of ±12 mils at 50 cps.

5. Repeat 3 with a vibration of ±12 mils at 50 cps.

6. (a) Repeat 2, 3, 4, and 5 for the other axis.

    (b) Repeat 2, 3, 4, and 5 with the transducer on its sensitive axis.

7. For differential type transducers, apply pressure in both directions and take readings on both sides of zero.

The earlier tests proved to be very time consuming. In order to complete the tests by the required date and as a result of newly gained experience, certain parts of test I were revised.

Transducer test II specifications outlined below were written to take care of these revisions.

---

* It may be necessary to install an electrical filter on the output of the transducer to eliminate vibration effects.

Transducer Test II

I. General

A reading, as referred to below, means a millivolt output at zero or no pressure reading, 50% pressure, and 100% pressure, except in paragraph III-1 record zero only. During the first half of any test, apply rated pressure between readings. Check on resonant frequencies of the transducer up to approximately 85 cps.

II. Description of Tests for ±1% Error Band

Apply a temperature of $150°F^{+10}_{-0}$ and hold for a period of 25 days taking a reading every 2 hours during the normal working day. Keep power and temperature applied to the transducer 24 hours a day, except over the weekend. On Monday, apply power and take a reading at room temperature.

III. Description of Tests for ±2% Error Band

1. Hold the temperature at 200°F ± 5 for 120 hours. Record readings every 2 hours during a normal working day. Keep input voltage and temperature applied for the full 120 hours except over a weekend when it should be turned off.

2. Starting at a stabilized temperature of $150°F^{+10}_{-0}$ take a reading. Increase the temperature to a stabilized 200°F ±5 and take another reading. Repeat this again for $250°F^{+0}_{-10}$. Apply a vibration of 80 cps at ±8 mils, still at 250°F for a period of 50 hours. Record a reading* every hour. Turn off the shake table, then take another reading at 250°F. Reduce the temperature to 200°F ±5 and $150°F^{+10}_{-0}$ and take a reading at each point. Keep the input voltage and temperature applied for the complete test.

3. For differential type transducers, apply pressure in both directions and take readings on both sides of zero.

Test Results

The following test results are recorded as case histories for each instrument just as they happened. This is done to point out the unexpected problems which can arise and also to emphasize the fact that each transducer has its own peculiar characteristics.

All error percentages are total errors, not ± errors, in per cent of full scale unless otherwise stated.

A complete history of each transducer follows:

* It may be necessary to install an electrical filter on the output of the transducer to eliminate vibration.

1. *Transducer A, Range 0–185 psig*

This transducer was tested as per test I. The balancing resistors were used for 75 hours as per par. III-1 (see upper part of graph on Fig. 6). This part of the test was run without balancing resistors. The zero error

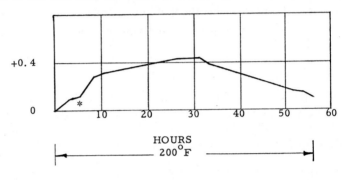

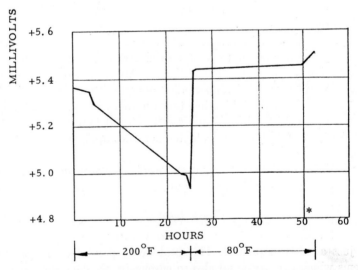

FIG. 6. Transducer A, 0–185 psig. *Upper:* Zero shift vs. time with balancing resistors. *Lower:* Zero shift vs. time without balancing resistors. *—off for weekend.

with a temperature change from 200° to 80°F was 2.4% which is excessive. During this time, other transducers were undergoing tests. Results show that some of these transducers had excessive errors. See later test results.

It was decided to pressure cycle (age) all transducers with abnormally

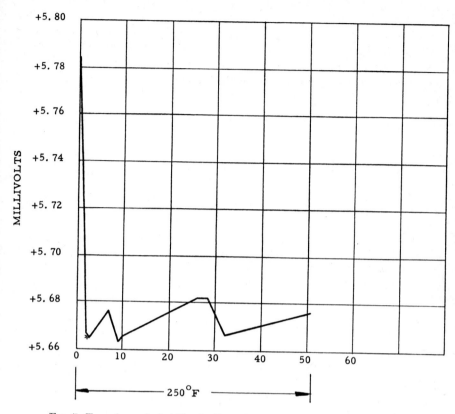

FIG. 7. Transducer A, 0–185 psig. Zero shift vs. time. *—off for weekend.

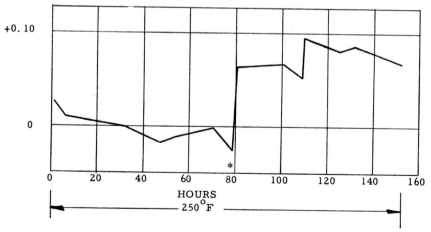

FIG. 8. Transducer A, 0–150 psig. Zero shift vs. time. *—off for weekend.

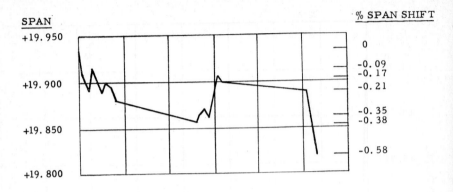

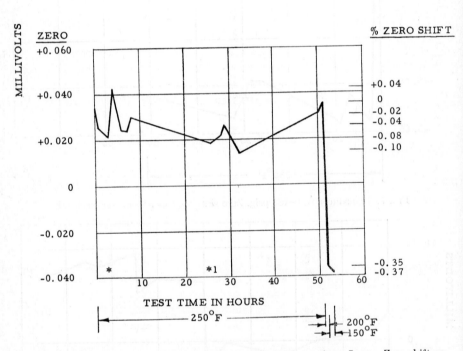

FIG. 9. Transducer A, 0–150 psig. *Upper:* Span shift vs. time. *Lower:* Zero shift vs. time. *—off for weekend. *1—vibration off overnight.

high zero shifts. At the conclusion of approximately 4200 pressure cycles, another 50-hour bench check at 250°F was run without balancing resistors. The aging or pressure cycling improved the zero shift to 0.6% error (see Fig. 7). Several of the other transducers were aged and retested at the same time as the one above. Some of these units did not improve. It was agreed

to by the vendor and ANP personnel that all of the units, except two differential pressure and one absolute pressure transducer, would be returned to
the factory for rework or replacement.

Transducer A, range 0–185 psig was returned to ANP with a range of
0–150 psig. The transducer was then tested as per test II, par. III-1 (see
Fig. 8). The zero shift error was 0.6% for a 151-hour run. This small zero
shift is well within acceptable limits. During this 151-hour test, the transducer was turned off for 6 days at the 79-hour test point. The zero shifted
from -0.027 mv to $+0.062$ mv during this shutoff period. This is a common
occurrence in some transducers.

The transducer was then tested as per test II, par. III-2 (see Fig. 9). The
calculations for span and zero shift are in per cent using the first 250°F
reading as the zero reference for this 50-hour test. This simulates a zero
balance before a 50-hour operational run. The total zero shift error was
0.41% and the total span shift error was 0.58%. This particular transducer
is considered to be satisfactory as the errors are well within the specified
$\pm 2\%$ error band.

2. Transducer B, Range 0–90 psig

This transducer was zero balanced by adjusting wire wound potentiometers as per test I, par. III-1. After balancing, the transducer was then
tested as per test I, par. III-2 at 200°F (see Fig. 10). During the first 54
hours of testing, the zero shifted 3.8%. This transducer was then pressure
cycled for 4000 cycles. Continuation of the test for an additional 52 hours
resulted in a 3.4% zero shift. Again, the transducer was pressure cycled
for 700 cycles. The zero shift continued to increase and as a result the testing was stopped. This is one of the unsatisfactory transducers referred to
in item 1 and it was returned to the factory for repair or replacement.

The transducer with a range 0–90 psig was returned to GE with a range
0–100 psig. The transducer was then tested as per test II, par. III-1 (see
Fig. 11). The zero shift was 0.08% for a 98-hour run.

This transducer was then tested as per test II, par. III-2 (see Fig. 12).
The calculations for span and zero shift are in per cent, using the first
250°F reading as the zero reference for this 54-hour test. The zero shift
error was 1.5% and the span shift error was 0.66%. The large zero shift is
due to the 100°F temperature change. With these errors, it is still within the
$\pm 2\%$ error band.

3. Transducer C, Range 0–35 psig

Owing to the large zero shift in the transducer under item 2, all of this
vendor's transducers were pressure cycled for approximately 3900 cycles
before testing.

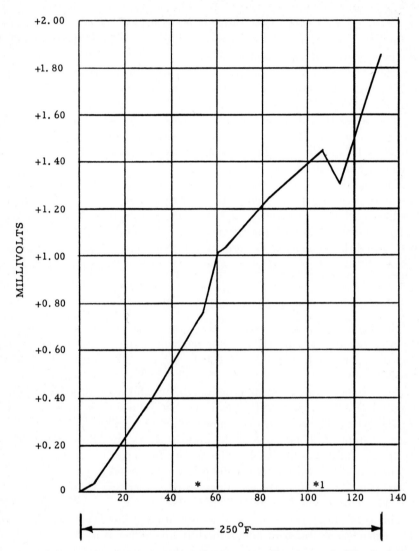

Fig. 10. Transducer B, 0–90 psig. Zero shift vs. time vibration, 4 g's. Wire-wound pot for balance. *—off for weekend. *1—pressure cycled, 700 cycles.

This transducer was tested as per test I, par. III-1 minus the balancing resistors at a temperature of 250°F. The zero shifted 0.27% in 24 hours. This transducer appeared to be satisfactory but in line with the earlier decision, it was returned to the factory.

This transducer, with a range 0–35 psig, was returned to GE with a range 0–185 psig.

The transducer was then tested as per test II, par. III-1 at 250°F (see Fig. 13). This transducer zero appeared to be steadily creeping so it was decided to continue the test for 240 hours. In this test period, the zero shift

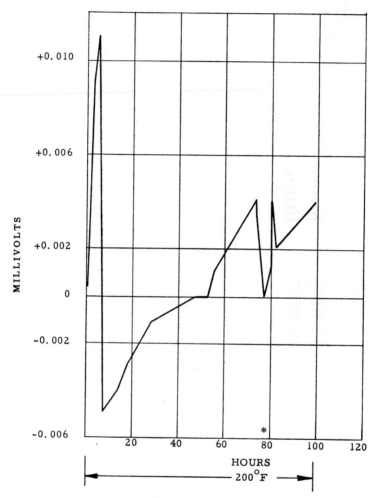

FIG. 11. Transducer B, 0–100 psig. Zero shift vs. time. *—off for weekend.

was 2.0%. This is not excessive since the normal period of operation is 50 hours.

The next test was as per test II, par. III-2 (see Fig. 14). The calculations for span and zero shift are in per cent using the first 250°F reading as a zero reference for this 53-hour test. The zero shift error was 0.44% and the span shift error was 0.38%. This is a satisfactory transducer.

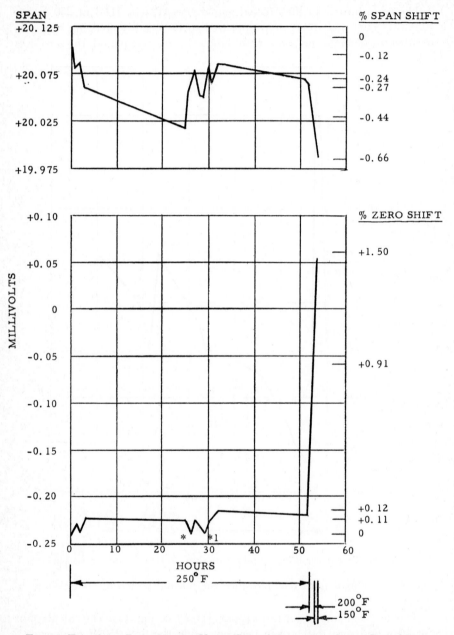

FIG. 12. Transducer B, 0–100 psig. *Upper:* Span shift vs. time. *Lower:* Zero shift vs. time. *—off overnight (power). *1—off for weekend.

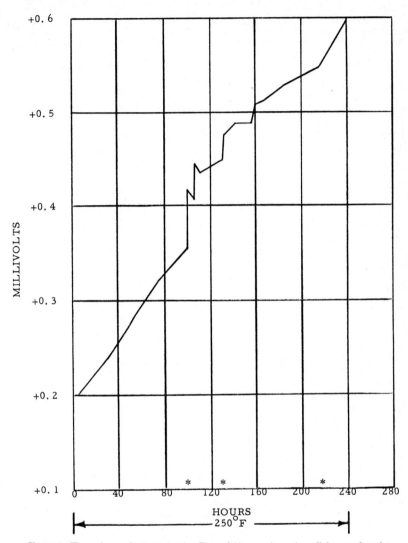

FIG. 13. Transducer C, 0–185 psig. Zero shift vs. time. *—off for weekend.

4. *Transducer D, Range 0–35 psig*

This transducer was pressure cycled for approximately 3900 cycles, then tested as per test I, par. III-1 minus the balancing resistors at a temperature of 250°F. The zero shifted 1.23% in 4 hours. This transducer was then pressure cycled for an additional 700 cycles. The test was then continued for 18 hours with an additional zero shift of 4.29%. This error was excessive and this transducer was returned to the vendor.

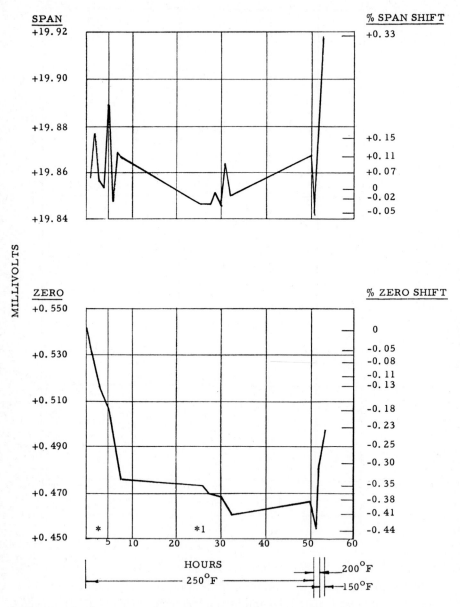

FIG. 14. Transducer C, 0–185 psig. *Upper:* Span shift vs. time. *Lower:* Zero shift vs. time. *—off for weekend. *1—vibration off overnight.

Upon return from the vendor, this transducer had a range 0–100 psig. The transducer was then tested as per test II, par. III-1 (see Fig. 15). In 72 hours of testing, the zero shift error was 0.24%.

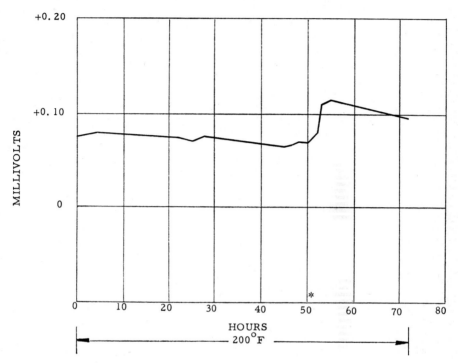

Fig. 15. Transducer D, 0–100 psig. Zero shift vs. time. *—off for weekend.

The next test was test II, par. III-2 (see Fig. 16). The calculations for span and zero shift are in per cent using the first 250°F reading as a zero reference for this 54-hour test. The zero shift error was 0.13% and the span shift error was 0.48%. This transducer is satisfactory.

5. *Transducer E, Range 0–185 psig*

This transducer was pressure cycled for approximately 4200 cycles. The transducer was then tested as per test I, par. III-1 minus the balancing resistors at a temperature of 250°F (see Fig. 17). The zero shifted 0.32% in 51 hours. This transducer was satisfactory, but it was returned to the vendor to be checked along with the others.

Upon return from the vendor this transducer had a range 0–150 psig. The transducer was then tested as per test II, par. III-1 (see Fig. 18).

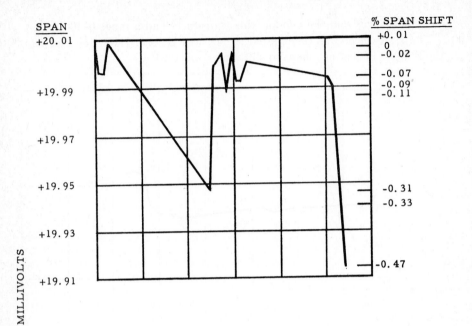

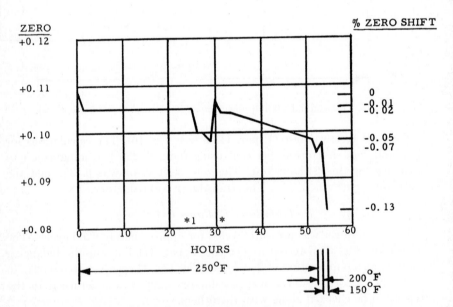

Fig. 16. Transducer D, 0–100 psig. *Upper:* Span shift vs. time. *Lower:* Zero shift vs. time. *—off for weekend. *1—off overnight (power).

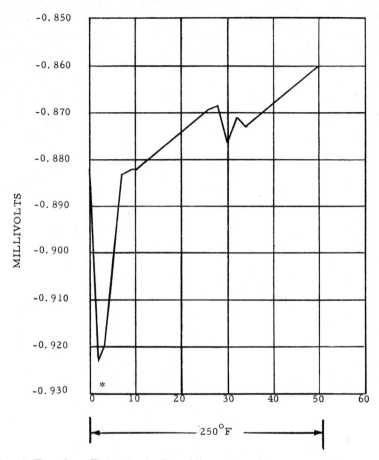

FIG. 17. Transducer E, 0–185 psig. Zero shift vs. time after 4200 cycles (aging). *—off for weekend.

In 151 hours of testing the zero shift error was 0.45%. The majority of this error occurred because of a 6-day shutdown.

The next test was test II, par. III-2 (see Fig. 19). The calculations for span and zero shift are in per cent using the first 250°F reading as a zero reference for this 53-hour test. The zero shift error was 0.77% and the span shift was 0.55%. This transducer is satisfactory.

6. *Transducer F, Range 0–100 psig*

This transducer was pressure cycled for approximately 3500 cycles. The transducer was then tested as per test I, par. III-1 minus the balancing resistors at a temperature of 250°F. After 43 hours of testing, the zero shift was 0.42%. This transducer was returned to the vendor for inspection.

Later this transducer was then tested as per test II, par. III-1 (see Fig. 20). After 72 hours of testing, the zero shift error was 0.31%. Most of this zero shift error occurred because of a weekend shutdown period.

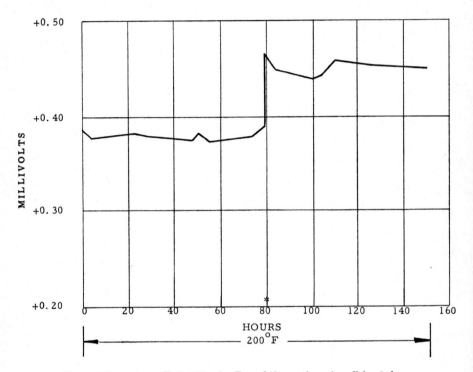

Fig. 18. Transducer E, 0–150 psig. Zero shift vs. time. *—off for 6 days.

The next test was test II, par. III-2 (see Fig. 21). The calculations for span and zero shift are in per cent using the first 250°F reading as a zero reference for this 54-hour test. The zero shift error was 0.25% and the span shift error was 0.36%. The errors are well within the ±2% error band.

7. Transducer G, Range 0–25 psig

This transducer was cycled for approximately 3500 cycles with the transducer under item 6. The first test was test I, par. III-1 minus the balancing resistors at a temperature of 250°F. At the end of 43 hours, the zero shift was 0.15%.

The second test was as per test II, par. III-1 (see Fig. 22). After 72 hours of testing, the zero shift error was 0.32%. Some of the zero shift occurred from a weekend shutdown period.

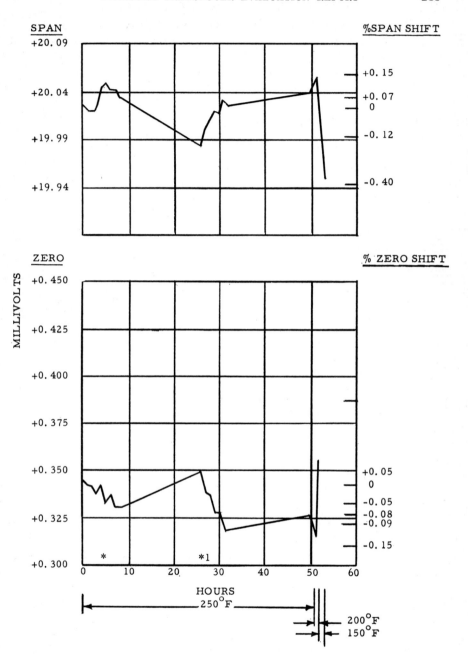

Fig. 19. Transducer E, 0–150 psig. *Upper:* Span shift vs. time. *Lower:* Zero shift vs. time. *—off for weekend. *1—vibration off overnight.

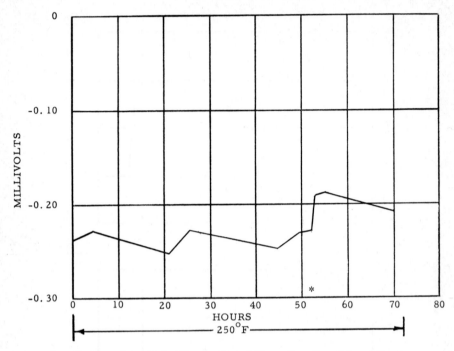

FIG. 20. Transducer F, 0–100 psig. Zero shift vs. time. *—off for weekend.

The third test was test II, par. III-2 (see Fig. 23). The calculations for the span and zero shift are calculated the same as the ones in item 6. The zero shift error was 0.96% and the span shift error was 0.75%. These errors are greater than some of the earlier ones, but they are still within the ±2% error band.

8. *Transducer H, Range 0–125 psia*

This transducer was purchased for off the power plant operation. Normally, it would not be subjected to temperature changes and vibration. The original intent was to order a transducer with a ±1% error band. The specification with the transducer indicated a ±0.7% error band when used at 150°F ± 5°F.

The first test was as per test I, par. II-2 minus balancing resistors with temperatures of 80° and 100°F for a total of 90 hours. Only zero readings were recorded (see Fig. 24). The zero shift error was 0.25%.

The second test was as per test I, par. II-2 minus balancing resistors (see Fig. 25). The calculations for span and zero shift are in per cent using the first 150°F reading as a zero reference for this 82-hour test. The zero shift error was 1.82% and the span shift was 0.33%. The majority of the zero

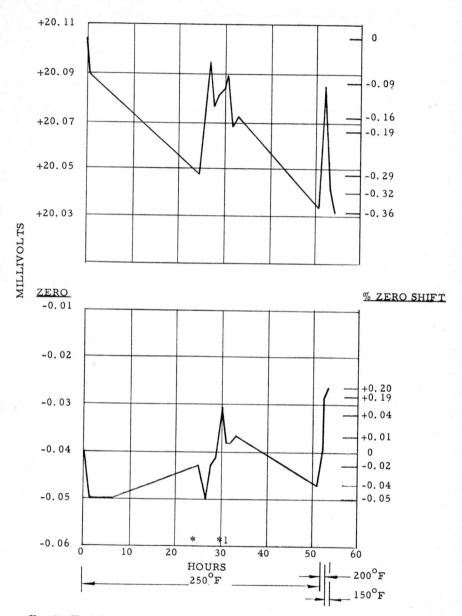

Fig. 21. Transducer F, 0–100 psig. *Upper:* Span shift vs. time. *Lower:* Zero shift vs. time. *—off overnight (power). *1—off for weekend.

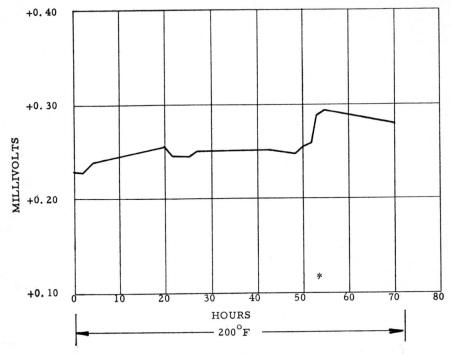

FIG. 22. Transducer G, 0–25 psig. Zero shift vs. time. *—off for weekend.

shift occurred because of a shutdown period. Twenty-two hours after this shutdown, the zero shifted back to a 0.4% error. The 1.82% error shift or drift is greater than ±0.7% specified by the vendor.

It should be noted that all transducers were purchased with the understanding that they would run 50 continuous hours without excitation voltage and temperature being shut off.

9. *Transducer J, Range 0–4 psid*

After approximately 4000 pressure cycles the next series of tests were as per test I, pars. III-2 to III-6a-5 for a total of 636 hours. The various test steps and results are indicated on Figs. 26*A* and 26*B*. After 31 hours of testing, the mercury manometer was replaced by a manometer using a fluid with a specific gravity of 2.95. The readings before the manometer change have not been used in the span calculations. The zero shift error for the complete test run was 1.49%. The span error for 606 hours was 1.3%.

The next test as per test I, pars. III-6b-2 to 6b-5, minus the balancing resistors lasted for a total of 306 hours. In this test, the transducer was mounted with its sensitive axis parallel to the axis of vibration. The sensi-

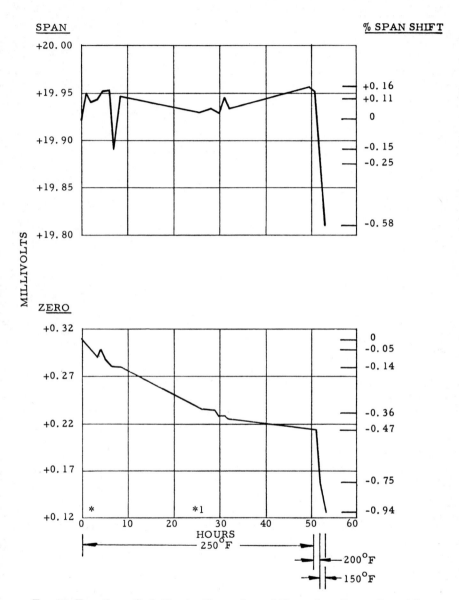

Fig. 23. Transducer G, 0–25 psig. *Upper:* Span shift vs. time. *Lower:* Zero shift vs. time. *—off for weekend. *1—vibration off overnight.

Fig. 24. Transducer H, 0–125 psia. Zero shift vs. time. *—off for 5 weeks.

tive axis of a transducer is defined as the axis perpendicular to the plane of the diaphragm.

During the test time of 943 hours for test I, pars. III-2 to III-6b-5, the zero shift error was 3.05% and the span shift for 912 hours of the same test was 1.6%.

This transducer operated very well over the entire test period which included the sensitive axis. Testing on the sensitive axis introduced some additional zero shift errors. Normally, transducers would not be mounted so that the axis of vibration is perpendicular to the plane of the diaphragm.

10. *Transducer K, Range ±1 psid*

This transducer was cycled for approximately 4000 cycles along with the transducer under item 9.

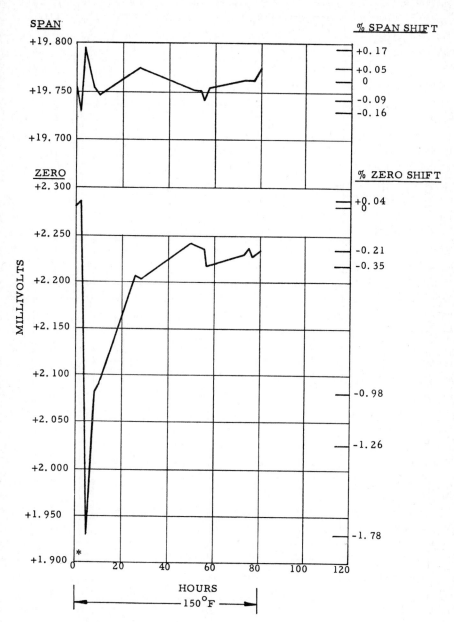

Fig. 25. Transducer H, 0–125 psia. *Upper:* Span shift vs. time. *Lower:* Zero shift vs. time. *—off for weekend.

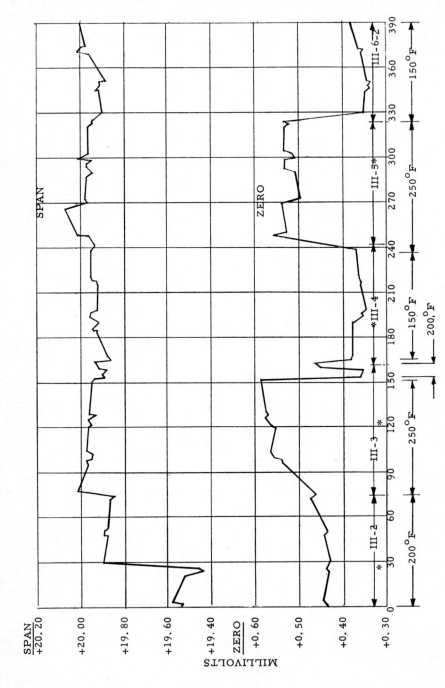

FIG. 26A. Transducer J, 0–4 psid. Zero and span shifts vs. time, test I. *—off for weekend.

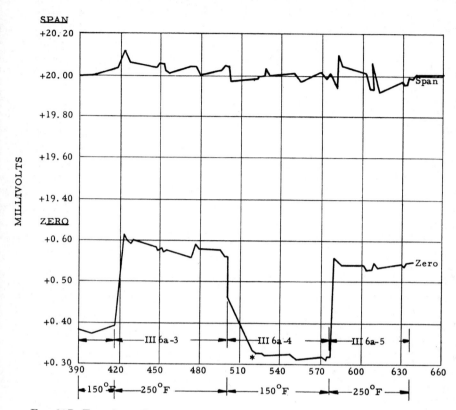

Fɪɢ. 26B. Transducer J, 0–4 psid. Zero and span shifts vs. time, test I. *—off for weekend.

The next series of tests were as per test I, pars. III-2 to 5. The various test steps and results for 312 hours of testing are indicated on Fig. 27. During this test, the zero shift error was 1.3%. The upper portion of the above figure shows the negative and positive span excursions. Total span would be an addition of the negative and positive span excursions (see Fig. 28). Since the positive span excursion remains constant in comparison with the negative span excursion, an addition of these curves would result in an inverted curve similar to the negative excursion. This condition occurs on the negative side when the temperature of the applied air is different than the transducer temperature since the strain gage is located on that side.

Test I, par. III-6a was eliminated since earlier tests on this axis showed no appreciable change. The next test was test I, par. III-6b (sensitive axis). The total test time was 303 hours, but since the continuous duty cycle is 50 hours, only 50 representative hours are shown in Table II and

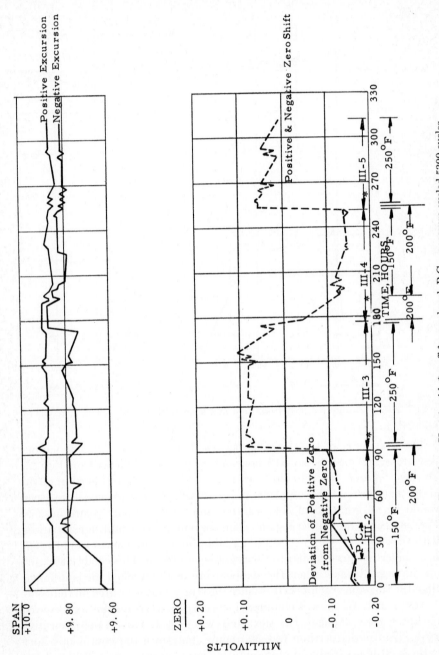

FIG. 27. Transducer K, ±1 psid. *—off for weekend. P.C.—pressure cycled 5300 cycles.

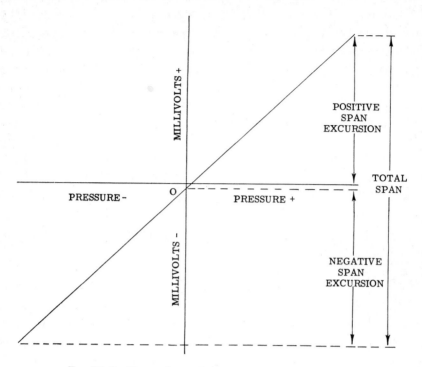

FIG. 28. Positive and negative differential type transducer.

Fig. 29. The zero shift error was 0.11% and the span shift error was 1.99%. Note that the shutoff period considerably affected the span. These errors fall within our ±2% error band.

The following transducers were tested as per test II in order to expedite the transducer test data.

11. *Transducer L, Range 0–25 psig*

After 2900 pressure cycles, the transducer was tested by using test II, par. III-1 for 176 hours (see Fig. 30). The zero shift error was 2.6% which was higher than normal.

The transducer test continued as per test II, par. III-2 for 53 hours (see Fig. 31). The calculations for the zero and span errors used the first 250°F temperature reading as a zero reference. The zero shift error was 8.67% and the span shift was 0.35%. As noted before, there is no relationship between zero shift and span shift. Since the above error is excessive, the transducer was returned to the vendor for repair.

TABLE II
Transducer K ±1 psid Test I Par. III-6b-3 Test Data

Temp. °F	Time (hours)	Span (mv)	Positive excursion (mv)	Negative excursion (mv)	% Span shift	% F.S. pos. excursion shift	% F.S. neg. excursion shift	Average zero (mv)	% F.S. zero shift
243	0	19.171	9.861	9.310	0.0	0.0	0.0	-0.214	0.00
241	2	19.199	9.864	9.335	+0.15	+0.02	-0.13	-0.215	0.00
247	4	19.390	9.853	9.537	+1.14	-0.04	-1.12	-0.204	+0.05
244	6	19.410	9.843	9.567	+1.25	-0.09	-1.43	-0.204	+0.05
244	8	19.438	9.855	9.583	+1.39	-0.03	-1.42	-0.206	+0.04
—a									
246	11	19.552	9.861	9.691	+1.99	0.00	-1.99	-0.219	-0.03
246	13	19.532	9.863	9.669	+1.88	+0.01	-1.87	-0.220	-0.03
245	15	19.353	9.857	9.496	+0.95	-0.02	-0.97	-0.216	-0.01
243	32	19.388	9.873	9.515	+1.13	+0.06	-1.07	-0.224	-0.05
241	34	19.357	9.856	9.501	+0.97	-0.03	-1.00	-0.225	-0.06
242	57	19.408	9.918	9.490	+1.24	+0.30	-0.94	-0.225	-0.06
245	59	19.423	9.925	9.498	+1.31	+0.33	-0.98	-0.225	-0.06

a Weekend pause in data taking.

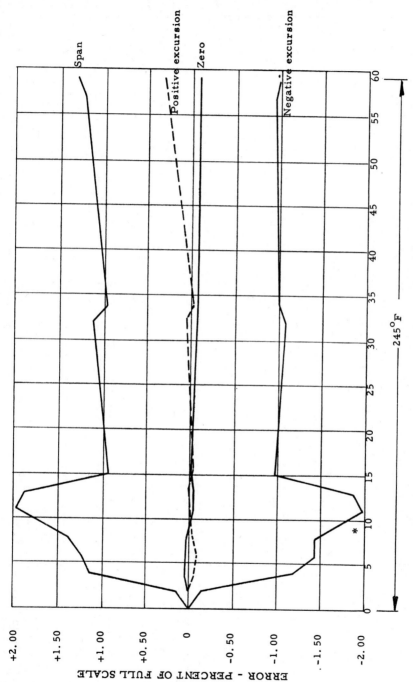

FIG. 29. Transducer K, ±1 psid. Error in per cent vs. time. *—off for weekend.

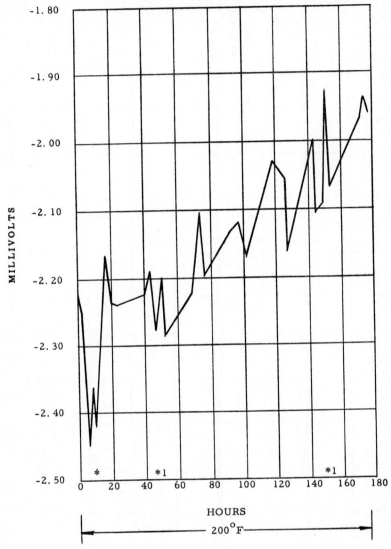

FIG. 30. Transducer L, 0–25 psig. Zero shift vs. time. *—cycle. *1—off for weekend.

12. *Transducer M, Range 0–125 psig*

The first test was test II, par. III-1 (see Fig. 32). During the 138-hour test, the zero shifted 1.53%.

The second test was test II, par. III-2 which lasted for 54 hours (see Fig. 33). The span and zero calculations used the first 250°F reading as a zero

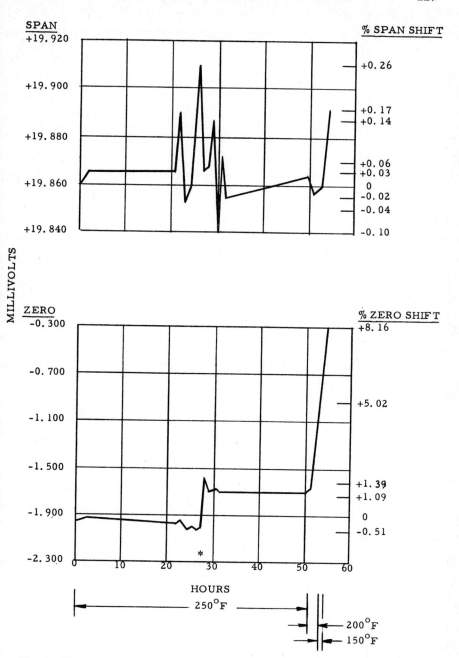

Fɪɢ. 31. Transducer L, 0–25 psig. *Upper:* Span shift vs. time. *Lower:* Zero shift vs. time. *—off for weekend.

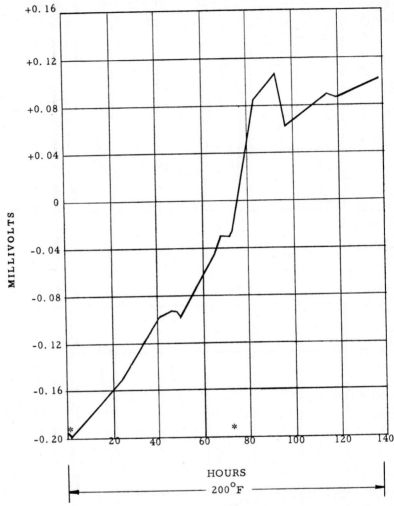

FIG. 32. Transducer M, 0–125 psig. Zero shift vs. time. *—off for weekend.

reference. The zero shift error was 1.71% and the span shift error was 0.93%. These errors are within the ±2% error band as originally specified.

13. *Transducer N, Range 0–90 psig*

The first test was test II, par. III-1 for a total of 41 hours (see Fig. 34). The zero shift error was 0.31%.

The second test was test II, par. III-2 which was for a total of 54 hours (see Fig. 35). The span and zero calculations used the first 250°F reading

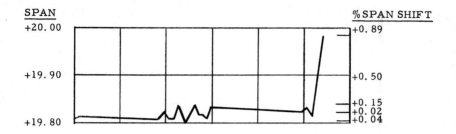

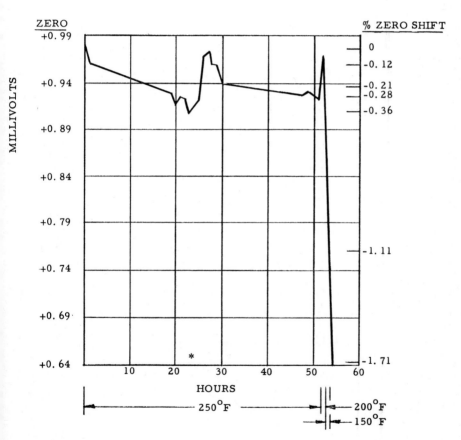

FIG. 33. Transducer M, 0–125 psig. *Upper:* Span shift vs. time. *Lower:* Zero shift vs. time. *—off for weekend.

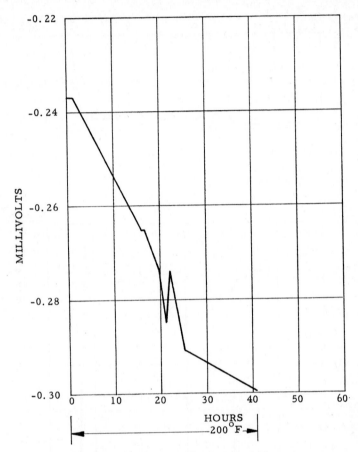

FIG. 34. Transducer N, 0–90 psig. Zero shift vs. time.

as a zero reference. During this test, the zero shift error was 1.02% and the span shift error was 0.57%. This transducer is satisfactory.

14. *Transducer P, Range 0–185 psig*

The next test was test II, par. III-2 (see Fig. 36). The span and zero calculations used the first 250°F reading as a zero reference. This test lasted for 53 hours during which the zero shift error was 1.06% and the span shift error was 0.42%. These errors are within the ±2% error band as originally specified.

15. *Transducer Q, Range 0–185 psig*

The first test was test II, par. III-1, which was for a total of 41 hours (see Fig. 37). During this test, the zero shift was 0.26%.

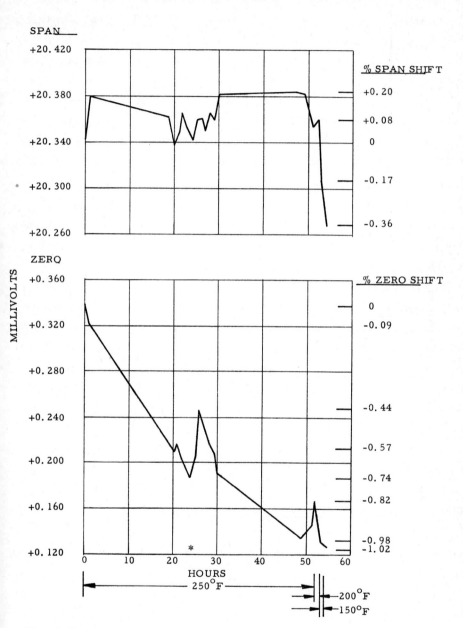

Fig. 35. Transducer N, 0–90 psig. *Upper:* Span shift vs. time. *Lower:* Zero shift vs. time. *—off for weekend.

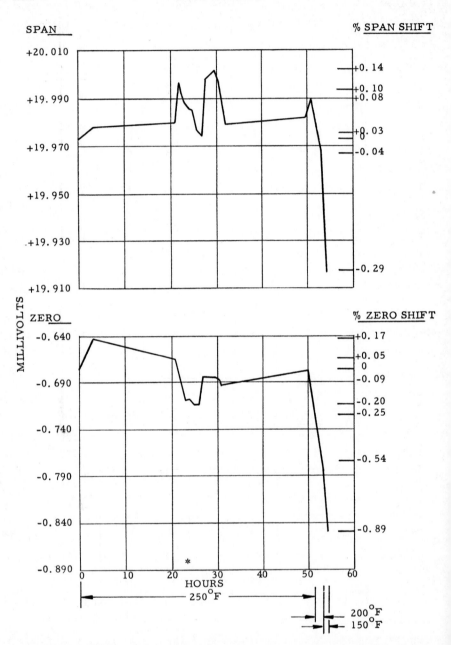

Fig. 36. Transducer P, 0–185 psig. *Upper:* Span shift vs. time. *Lower:* Zero shift vs. time. *—off for weekend.

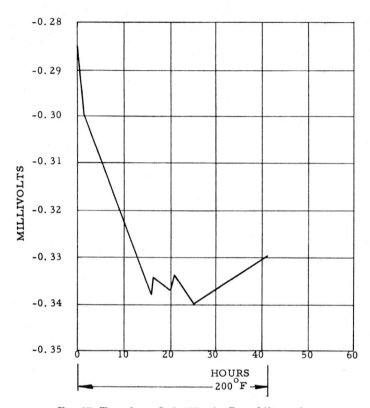

Fig. 37. Transducer Q, 0–185 psig. Zero shift vs. time.

The second test was test II, par. III-2 for a total of 54 hours (see Fig. 38). The span and zero shift calculations for this test were made using the first 250°F reading as a zero reference. The zero shift error was 1.09% and the span shift error was 0.25%.

16. *Transducer R, Range 0–35 psig*

The first test was test II, par. III-1, which lasted for 329 hours (see Fig. 39). In the first 151 hours, the zero shift was 1.04%. Since many of the transducers have less zero shift, it was decided to pressure cycle this transducer for 2900 cycles. After pressure cycling, the same test continued for an additional 178 hours with a resultant zero shift of 0.49%.

As noted previously, pressure cycling made a definite improvement on this particular transducer.

The second test was test II, par. III-2, which continued for 53 hours (see Fig. 40). The calculations for span and zero shift are based on using

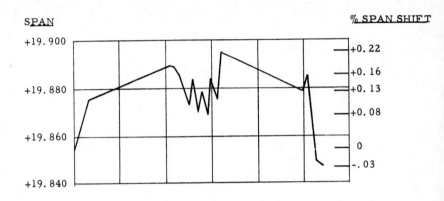

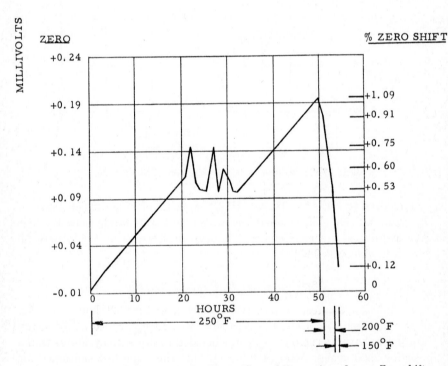

FIG. 38. Transducer Q, 0–185 psig. *Upper:* Span shift vs. time. *Lower:* Zero shift vs. time. *—off for weekend.

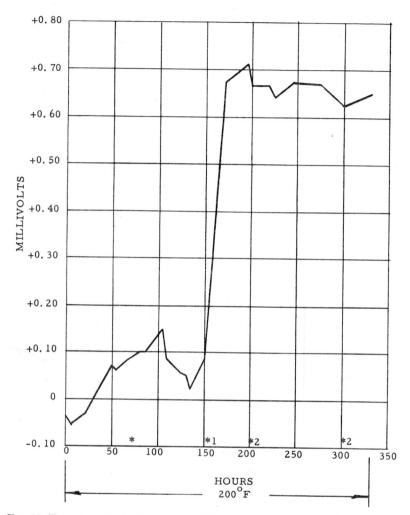

FIG. 39. Transducer R, 0–35 psig. Zero shift vs. time. *—off for 6 days. *1—pressure cycled. *2—off for weekend.

the first 250°F temperature as a zero reference. The zero shift error was 2.5% and the span shift error was 0.27%.

17. *Transducer S, Range 0–35 psig*

The first test was test II, par. III-1, which lasted for 361 hours (see Fig. 41). The first phase of this test lasted for 151 hours with a zero shift error of 1.05%. In hopes of improving this error, the transducer was pressure

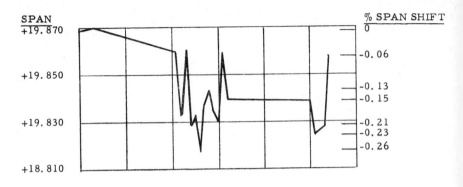

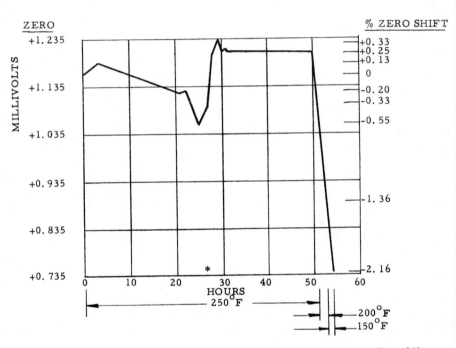

FIG. 40. Transducer R, 0–35 psig. *Upper:* Span shift vs. time. *Lower:* Zero shift vs. time. *—off for weekend.

cycled for 2900 cycles. In the next 213 hours of test, the zero shift was 19.78%.

In discussions with the vendor, it was agreed that they would rework this transducer.

The vendor found a small hole in the diaphragm.

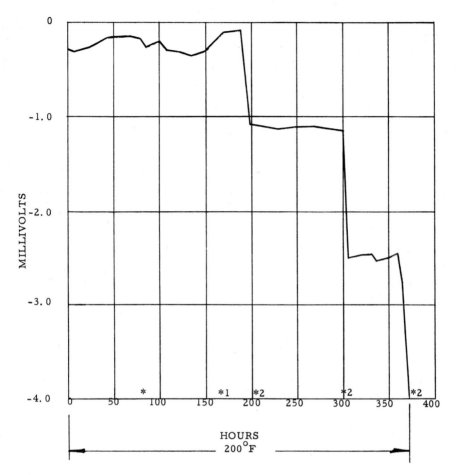

FIG. 41. Transducer S, 0–35 psig. Zero shift vs. time. *—off for 6 days. *1—pressure cycled. *2—off for weekend.

After the return of this repaired transducer, it was immediately tested for 53 hours as per test II, par. III-2 (see Fig. 42). Again, the calculations for zero and span shift were made using the first 250°F reading as a zero reference. The zero shift error was 16.3% and the span shift error was 0.61%. As observed from the above, the zero shift error is excessive.

An additional test was performed on this transducer under the following conditions:

1. Temperatures of 75°, 150°, 200°, and 250°F
2. No vibration
3. Test cycle–126 hours

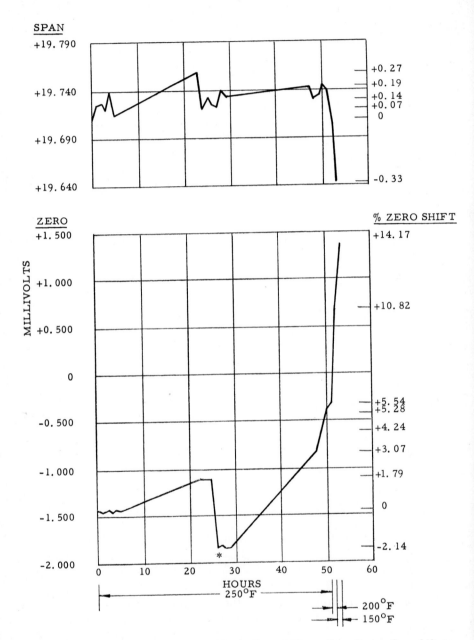

FIG. 42. Transducer S, 0–35 psig. *Upper:* Span shift vs. time. *Lower:* Zero shift vs. time. *—off for weekend.

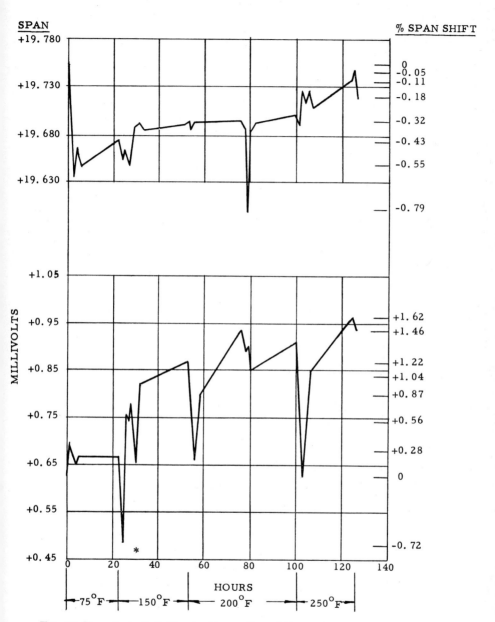

FIG. 43. Transducer S, 0–35 psig. *Upper:* Span shift vs. time. *Lower:* Zero shift vs. time. *—off for weekend.

4. Zero, 50, and 100% of full scale readings were recorded.

See Fig. 43. The calculations for the zero and span shift were made using the first 250°F reading as a zero reference. The zero shift error was 2.34% and the span shift error was 0.79%.

This transducer was again returned to the vendor and it was found that the sealed chamber was leaking. The main difference between the last two tests was vibration. It is believed that the vibration changing the rate of leakage was the cause of the large zero shift error.

OBSERVATIONS AND SUMMARY

General

See Table III for a summary of the span and zero shift errors for the various tests. In addition, average linearity and hysteresis errors for each

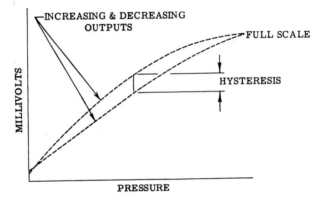

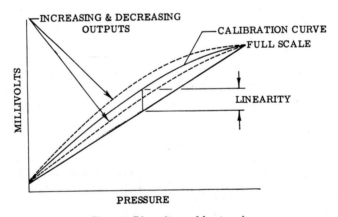

FIG. 44. Linearity and hysteresis.

SUMMARY OF THE SPAN AND ZERO SHIFT ERRORS IN PER CENT OF FULL SCALE[a]

Transducer identification	Range as purchased	Lin.	Hyst.	Test I Par. II-2		Test I Par. III-1	Test I Pars. III-2 thru 5		Test I Pars. III-6-a2 thru 5		Test I Pars. III-6-b2 thru 5		Test II Par. III-1	Test II Par. III-2	
				Z	S	Z	Z	S	Z	S	Z	S	Z	Z	S
A	0–185 psig	0.14	0.13	—		2.40 0.60							0.60	0.41	0.58
B	0–90 psig	0.21	0.06	—		3.80 3.40							0.08	1.50	0.66
C	0–35 psig	0.15	0.18	—		0.27							2.00	0.44	0.38
D	0–35 psig	0.11	0.10	—		1.23 4.20							0.24	0.13	0.48
E	0–185 psig	0.25	0.04	—		0.32							0.45	0.77	0.55
F	0–100 psig	0.12	0.15	—		0.42							0.31	0.25	0.36
G	0–25 psig	0.15	0.08	—		0.15							0.32	0.96	0.75
H	0–125 psia	0.30	0.15	0.24 1.82	0.33	—							—	—	—
J	0–4 psid	0.03	0.10	—		0.54	1.18	1.15	1.49	1.15			—	—	—
K	±1 psid	H 0.11 L 0.58	0.08 0.10	—		0.31	1.30				0.11	1.99	—	—	—
L	0–25 psig	0.20	0.11	—		—							1.10 2.60	8.67	0.35
M	0–125 psig	0.10	0.16	—		—							1.53	1.71	0.93
N	0–90 psig	0.07	0.15	—		—							0.31	1.02	0.57
P	0–185 psig	0.04	0.16	—		—							0.17	1.06	0.42
Q	0–185 psig	0.13	0.14	—		—							0.26	1.09	0.25
R	0–35 psig	0.07	0.15	—		—							1.04 0.49	2.50	0.27
S	0–35 psig	0.05	0.07	—		—							1.05 19.78	16.30	0.61

[a] The above percentages should not be used without referring to the case history of each transducer.

transducer are shown on Table III. See Fig. 44 for a graphical explanation
of hysteresis and linearity.

Temperature

The vendor's transducer specifications indicated a thermal coefficient
of sensitivity of not more than 0.01% of full scale per °F and a thermal
zero shift of not more than 0.02% of full scale per °F. Both vendors will
supply premium sensitivity and zero shift transducers at an added cost.

Test results of span shift errors were 0.87% or less and the zero shift
errors were 8.63% or less for a 100°F temperature change. Transducers
with excessive zero shift errors were returned to the vendor. Figures 26A,
26B, and 27 are good examples of zero shifts with temperature changes.
From the graphs, it can be observed that a change in temperature can either
increase or *decrease* the millivolt output. The direction of this output is
different for each individual transducer and it cannot be predicted before
testing.

The ± differential transducer will show large variations in the negative
span excursion when there is a temperature differential between the transducer and the air pressure applied to the low side of the transducer (see
Fig. 29). This condition is caused by the temperature of the applied air
affecting the temperature of the strain gage, which is located on the low
side of the transducer.

It has been found from these tests, that acceptance testing of transducers
at a constant temperature without vibration for a period of 50 hours
should result in a zero shift of 0.5% or less.

Vibration

Vibration had a negligible effect on the operation of the transducer on all
axes. However, it is recommended that the transducer not be mounted on
its sensitive axis during any operation.

Shutdown Periods

Any shutdown period where the excitation voltage or temperature is
turned off, can result in a permanent or temporary change in the zero
pressure millivolt output (see Figs. 25, 33, 35, 36, 41, and 42). The ± differential transducer had a negative span excursion shift due to a shutdown
period (see Fig. 29).

Once an operational test has been started and the zero has been balanced,
it is recommended that excitation voltage and temperature be maintained
throughout the entire operation.

Aging

Aging is a process of relaxing the metal of a transducer which is normally performed at the vendor's plant.

As can be noted from the case histories of the transducers, additional aging may help to reduce the zero shift. This aging may be accomplished by pressure cycling the transducer at its maximum rated temperature.

An important part of every transducer specification should require as part of the vendor aging process, a minimum of 3000 full scale pressure excursions at the transducers maximum rated temperature. These pressure excursions should be applied *only* to a fully assembled transducer.

Mechanical Considerations

It has been found that this type of transducer can operate for one duty cycle (50 continuous hours) and still be within the $\pm 2\%$ error band for the following conditions:

1. The zero is balanced at the beginning of each duty cycle when the transducer is at a stabilized temperature in its temperature operating range.

2. The excitation voltage remains at rated voltage and is applied several hours before zero balancing.

3. The temperature is maintained between 150° and 250°F.

4. The vibration does not exceed 5 g's at a frequency of 80 cps.

Calibration air will not be required if the average span is known and the zero is balanced before operation.

A part of any transducer program should include transducer acceptance testing. This testing should include zero shift and span checks over its entire operating temperature range. Also, a check should be made for circuit grounds.

All of this testing has been conducted on a somewhat limited number of transducers. Many important facts and considerations have been revealed during this testing. These test results are by no means conclusive, but they do indicate trends.

DEVELOPMENT OF THE SEMICONDUCTOR STRAIN GAGE AND SOME OF ITS APPLICATIONS*

R. O'REGAN

Bell Telephone Laboratories, Incorporated, Murray Hill, New Jersey

I. INTRODUCTION

Semiconductor strain transducers have caused considerable interest among experimenters and transducer manufacturers in the last few years because of their high sensitivity. These piezoresistive devices can be used instead of the conventional wire resistance gages where the obvious advantage is their higher sensitivity and they may also be used for strain transducers where wire resistance gages are not directly applicable.

The solid state theory of piezoresistive semiconductors has been discussed in the literature[1,2] and this paper will be concerned with theory only to the extent that it becomes necessary in the explanation of a particular transducer. The main body of the paper covers applications of these transducers and their fabrication.

II. PIEZORESISTIVE PROPERTIES OF SEMICONDUCTORS

The gage factor of a resistance wire gage is defined as $G.F. = \Delta R/RS$. The change of resistance with strain is caused by dimensional changes of the wire and by its piezoresistance. For small strains this gage factor is

$$G.F. = \Delta R/RS = 1 + 2\nu + \pi_l Y \tag{1}$$

where S represents the strain, ν is Poisson's ratio, Y is Young's modulus, and π_l is a measure of the piezoresistance along the axis of the gage. For wire resistance gages, the greater part of the gage factor is caused by the dimensional changes of the wire. The term 2ν is the effect of the lateral contraction of the cross-sectional area due to a longitudinal stress and the "one" is the effect of the increase in length of the gage. For semiconductor strain gages, the piezoresistance is large and the term $\pi_l Y$ predominates. Equation (1) can be written as

$$G.F. = \Delta R/RS = \pi_l Y \text{ or in terms of stress}$$

$$\Delta R/R_0 = \pi_l T \tag{2}$$

* Presented at the Winter Meeting of the Instrument Society of America, St. Louis, Missouri, January, 1961.

where R_0 represents the resistivity of the material and T represents a simple tension along the axis of the gage. The longitudinal resistivity under a tension T is $R_0 + \Delta R$ and

$$E/i = R_0 + \Delta R. \qquad (3)$$

If we divide (3) by R_0 and substitute the value of $\Delta R/R_0$ from (2), we have

$$E/R_0 = i(1 + \pi_l T). \qquad (4)$$

The above represents the behavior of a semiconductor strain gage as it is most generally used, i.e., a long, thin rod in which the electric field component E, the current i, and the stress T are along the axis of the rod. To understand the more complex behavior of semiconductors, it is necessary to consider a three-dimensional model as shown in Fig. 1. Here the axes

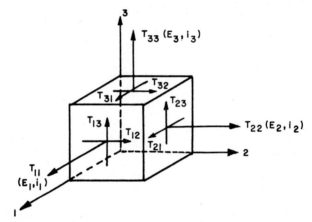

FIG. 1. Element of semiconductor crystal.

1, 2, and 3 are the crystallographic axes of the semiconductor. It has been shown by Mason and Thurston[1] that for a material which exhibits the symmetry of germanium and silicon the electric field components E are represented by the following equations:

$$E_1/R_0 = i_1[1 + \pi_{11}T_{11} + \pi_{12}(T_{22} + T_{33})] + \pi_{44}(i_2 T_{12} + i_3 T_{13}) \qquad (5a)$$

$$E_2/R_0 = i_2[1 + \pi_{11}T_{22} + \pi_{12}(T_{11} + T_{33})] + \pi_{44}(i_1 T_{12} + i_3 T_{23}) \qquad (5b)$$

$$E_3/R_0 = i_3[1 + \pi_{11}T_{33} + \pi_{12}(T_{11} + T_{22})] + \pi_{44}(i_1 T_{13} + i_2 T_{23}). \qquad (5c)$$

It is to be noted that (4) is really a special case of (5); for if we consider (5a) and apply a stress along the 1 axis only, we have $E_1 = i_1(1 + \pi_{11}T)$ which is precisely the same as (4). The additional terms of (5a) are seen to represent the effects of shear stress and the normal stress which are perpendicular to the one axis. An interesting application of these effects will be seen later.

III. Piezoresistive Properties of Silicon and Germanium

Silicon and germanium are the most useful of the semiconductor materials because of their high piezoresistive coefficients. These coefficients are shown in Table I.

TABLE I[a]

ADIABATIC PIEZORESISTANCE COEFFICIENTS AT ROOM TEMPERATURE

Material	ρ ohm-cm	π_{11}	π_{12}	π_{44}	$(\pi_l)_{111}$	Y_{111} 10^{12} dynes/cm²	$Y_{111}(\pi_l)_{111}$
				10^{-12} cm²/dyne			
Germanium	1.5	−2.3	−3.2	−138.1	−94.9	1.55	−147
(n-type)	5.7	−2.7	−3.9	−136.8	−94.7		−147
	9.9	−4.7	−5.0	−137.9	−96.9		−150
	16.6	−5.2	−5.5	−138.7	−101.2		−157
(p-type)	1.1	−3.7	+3.2	+96.7	+65.4		+101.5
	15.0	−10.6	+5.0	+46.5	+31.4		+48.7
Silicon						1.87	
(n-type)	7.8	+6.6	−1.1	+138.1	+93.6		+175
(p-type)	11.7	−102.2	+53.4	−13.6	−81.3		−142

[a] See reference 1.

It has been shown by Mason and Thurston[1] that the piezoresistive coefficient along an axis other than the crystallographic axis is

$$\pi_l = \pi_{11} + 2(\pi_{44} + \pi_{12} - \pi_{11})(l^2m^2 + l^2n^2 + m^2n^2) \qquad (6)$$

where l,m,n are the direction cosines of the direction associated with π_l referred to the crystallographic axes. It can be shown that the quantity $(l^2m^2 + l^2n^2 + m^2n^2)$ has a maximum value for $l = m = n = 1/\sqrt{3}$ which is the 111 axis of the crystal and has a minimum value of zero along a crystallographic axis. It follows from (6) that π_l is a maximum along the 111 axis for $(\pi_{44} + \pi_{12} - \pi_{11} > 0)$. If $(\pi_{44} + \pi_{12} - \pi_{11} < 0)$ the maximum piezoresistance coefficient occurs along a crystallographic axis. The maximum value of π_l for both types of germanium and for p-type silicon occurs along the 111 axis and for n-type silicon it occurs along a crystal axis.

IV. Applications

A. A Torque Transducer

A device for measuring torque is shown in Fig. 2. For the applied torque T_{23}, (5c) becomes simply

$$E_3 = \pi_{44}i_2T_{23}. \qquad (7)$$

If the terminals 3 and 6 are made of one polarity and terminals 4 and 5 are of opposite polarity, the current i_2 changes sign at the 12 plane. Also, the shear stress T_{23} changes sign at the 12 plane. Consequently, the sign of

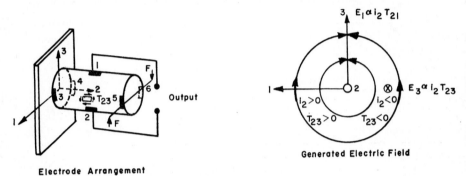

FIG. 2. Torsional transducer.

$i_2 T_{23}$ does not change anywhere in the transducer—this is illustrated in Fig. 2—since i_2 and T_{23} are positive in the left half-plane and are both negative for the right half-plane.

An experimental single crystal germanium transducer like that described above has been made and calibrated. The cylindrical portion had a diameter

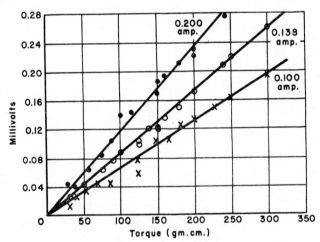

FIG. 3. Voltage-torque relations for torsional transducer.

of 0.130 inch and a length of 0.5 inch. The electrical output for different values of torque and current flow are shown in Fig. 3. A particular advantage of a torque transducer of this type is the negligible angular displacement of the transducer.

B. *Semiconductor Strain Gages*

One of the first applications of semiconductors was the measurement of the elongation of a photoelastic resin at 150°C for tensile calibrations. The use of SR-4 gages as a sensing element was ruled out because they were not sensitive enough. Mechanical devices such as a Huggenberger extensometer and optical devices seemed inappropriate due to the difficulties inherent in obtaining reading in the interior of an oven at 150°C. The scheme illus-

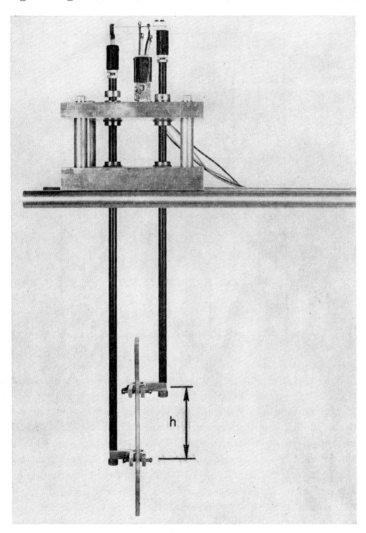

Fig. 4. Piezoresistive extensometer.

trated in Fig. 4 was used successfully. The variation of gage length h determines the positions of the rods which are attached, respectively, to the fixed and free ends of the cantilever beam. The deflection of this cantilever beam is equal to the elongation of h. Germanium rods were attached to the top and bottom faces of this beam and were connected in conjugate arms of a Wheatstone bridge. These arms were connected to an SR-4 indicator and the output was calibrated as a linear function of elongation as shown in Fig. 5. For this experiment the signal from the semiconductor

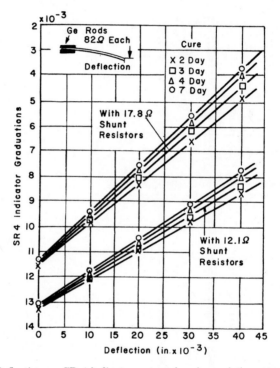

FIG. 5. Deflection vs. SR-4 indicator output for piezoresistive extensometer.

elements was attenuated by using shunt resistors across the gage elements. The purpose of this was to decrease the noise which was transmitted from the vibration of the oven. However, the sensitivity was still 10 times that of an equivalent SR-4 device and was adequate for this experiment.

The semiconductor strain gage can also be used to measure a simple tension or pressure, as illustrated in Fig. 6. Here a semiconductor element "a" is embedded in an epoxy resin base, the element "b" is used as a temperature compensating gage in the same manner as one is used for resistance wire gages. An advantage of an arrangement such as this is that the higher

FIG. 6. Semiconductor dynamometer.

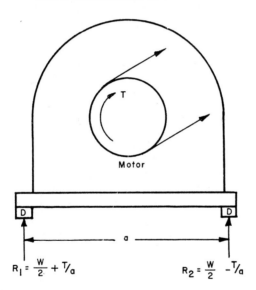

FIG. 7. Torque dynamometer. R_1 and R_2 are functions of torque T; W is the reaction from the weight of the motor; D are the cast dynamometers containing semiconductors.

sensitivity of the semiconductor element over the resistance wire gage (40–90 times greater) may make the use of expensive amplifying equipment superfluous.

An example of the use of such dynamometers is their use as a torque measuring device for a motor. As illustrated in Fig. 7, the inserts D contain the pressure cells, and the Wheatstone bridge in the circuit is balanced for zero torque. The reactions R_1 and R_2 and consequently the output from a Wheatstone bridge are known functions of the applied torque. These inserts can be made quite rigid and the possibility of self excited oscillations minimized.

Another interesting application of semiconductor strain transducers is as a catheter to measure variations in blood pressure. An instrument such as this must be small so that it can fit into the blood vessels or heart without appreciably disturbing the flow. Such a device has been previously attempted using wire resistance gages but their relative lack of sensitivity rendered them of doubtful value. Such a device has been constructed* and has been shown to be successful. This is illustrated in Fig. 8. The pres-

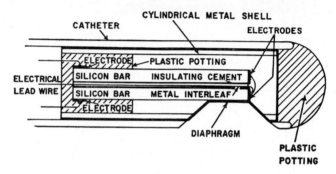

FIG. 8. Construction of the piezoresistive pressure gage in an intracardiac catheter.

sure is applied to the cantilever beam through a diaphragm and semiconductor gages were mounted in the same manner as in Fig. 6.

V. Effect of Impurity Concentration on Piezoresistive Coefficients

In a paper by Mason et al.[3] the variation of the gage factor and the resistance of semiconductors has been determined as a function of the temperature. It has been known that for lightly doped materials, the gage factor varies inversely as the absolute temperature and that the initial resistance varies a considerable amount. These undesirable features have been eliminated to a large degree by using heavily doped material (10^{20} boron atoms per cubic centimeter of silicon). The results of these experiments are shown in Figs. 9 and 10. The gage factor at room temperature for the heavily doped sample is approximately $\frac{1}{3}$ that of the lightly doped sample; however, it remains more than 30 times as sensitive as a wire resistance gage. This heavily doped sample consequently is the most practical gage where the temperature cannot be precisely controlled.

* Gulton Industries, Metuchen, New Jersey.

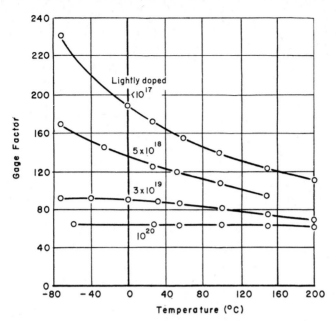

FIG. 9. Variation of gage factor with temperature and impurity level for p-type silicon.

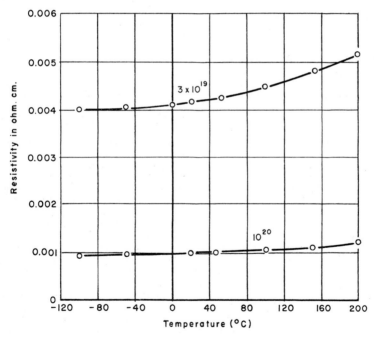

FIG. 10. Variation of unstrained resistances with temperature and impurity level for p-type silicon.

253

VI. Fabrication of Semiconductor Strain Transducers

The process of fabricating a semiconductor strain gage from a silicon ingot involves many operations most of which have been developed by a trial and error basis. The handling of the semiconductor material (silicon or germanium) must be carefully done, since they are quite brittle. A series of steps which have been used with success is described below.

The silicon ingot is obtained from a commercial source* and is doped and oriented to specifications. The first operation is to cut sections perpendicular to the longitudinal axis of the crystal (the 111 axis for p-type material).

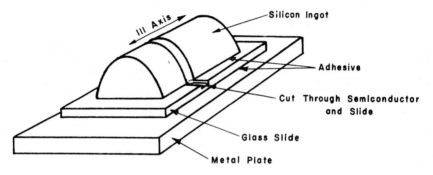

Fig. 11. Initial cut through semiconductor ingot.

The distance between cut sections corresponds to the desired gage length (Fig. 11). A Model SG Sanford surface grinder with a Norton No. D180N 100M DIAR diamond saw was used for this operation. It is important in this and in subsequent operations that the wheel be kept clean. If the wheel becomes loaded or if too large a diamond grit is used, the silicon will certainly chip and may fracture. The ingot is held on a glass slide by Glycol-Phthlate† which can be dissolved by acetone after the cut is made.

The piece of silicon is then removed and oriented as shown in Fig. 12, and another cut is made. The slab is approximately 0.020 inch thick and this is again cemented to a glass slide as shown in Fig. 13. The diamond wheel used for the previous operations is replaced by the finer one (D800S-N75M DIAIR). This fine grit is required to prevent chipping and fracture of the silicon rods. The slab is cut as shown in Fig. 13, and a 0.003-inch web is retained.

The next operation is illustrated in Fig. 14. The assembly is cemented to a lapping fixture and the edge which had been previously cut with a rela-

* Merck, du Pont.

† Supplied by J. H. Young Company, 112 St. Joseph Street, Pittsburgh 10, Pennsylvania.

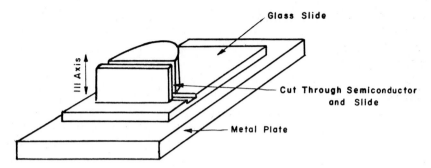

FIG. 12. Cut of oriented semiconductor slab.

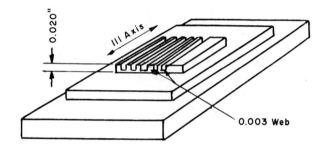

FIG. 13. Cutting of semiconductor rods.

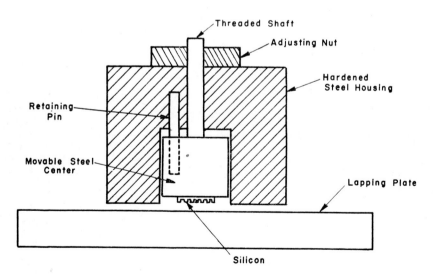

FIG. 14. Diagram of lapping fixture.

tively rough diamond wheel is lapped smooth by progressively finer grits (No. 400 to No. 800). The silicon assembly is now removed from the fixture, inverted and the web is lapped off. The surfaces are now relatively chip-free and nearly smooth.

The cross section of these rods is now approximately 10 mils square and these could be used for strain gages. However, an etching process is highly desirable for two reasons. Pearson *et al.*[4] have shown that the ultimate strain of silicon crystals increases as the diameter becomes small. A reduction from 10 mils to 2 mils in the cross section increases the ultimate strain sevenfold. Secondly, the surface area is damaged somewhat by the cutting operation. Etching removes this damaged surface and also eliminates any surface scratches which tend to reduce the ultimate strain.

An etching solution of 70% nitric acid (95 parts by volume) and 48% hydrofluoric acid (5 parts by volume) has proved satisfactory. The container holding the rods is continuously agitated to ensure an even rate of etch.

The leads which have been used are gold, doped with 0.5% antimony. The doping of the leads is necessary to eliminate the possibility of a rectifying contact between lead wire and silicon rod. The device for attaching these leads is illustrated in Fig. 15. The silicon rod is placed on a flat carbon plate

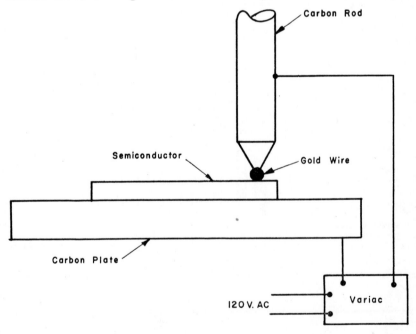

FIG. 15. Attachment of leads to semiconductor strain gage.

and a pencil-shaped carbon electrode is brought down from above compressing the gold wire onto the silicon rod. The compressive force of the carbon electrode is not more than that required to hold the gold wire in position. The current is gradually increased by a Variac in the AC line while the junction is observed through a microscope. As soon as the silicon or gold begins to flow the current is shut off. The resulting bonds are generally mechanically strong and give an ohmic contact. The finished product is a semiconductor strain gage which has a maximum strain of greater than 5000 microinches/inch.

REFERENCES

1. Mason, W. P., and Thurston, R. N., Use of piezoresistive materials in the measurement of displacement, force, and torque, *J. Acoust. Soc. Am.* **29,** 1096 (1957).
2. Geyling, F. T., and Forst, J. J., Semiconductor strain transducers, *Bell System Tech. J.* **39,** 7 (1959).
3. Mason, W. P., Forst, J. J., and Tornillo, L. M., Recent developments in semiconductor strain transducers, see p. 21, this volume.
4. Pearson, G. L., Read, W. T., Jr., and Feldmann, W. L., Deformation and fracture of small silicon crystals, *Acta Met.* **5,** 181 (1957).

ADJUSTING CRYSTAL CHARACTERISTICS TO MINIMIZE TEMPERATURE DEPENDENCY*

ANTHONY D. KURTZ

*Kulite-Bytrex Corporation, Newton, Massachusetts, and
Kulite Semiconductor Products, Inc., Ridgefield, New Jersey*

ABSTRACT

The use of piezoresistive semiconductors in the fabrication of strain gages and strain gage type transducers depends on the control of the mechanical and electrical properties of the ensuing devices. After the discovery of the large piezoresistive effects[1] in semiconductors and the subsequent application of this effect in the form of fabricated strain gages,[2] it was quite evident that two principal problem areas might prevent their widespread use. These were the fragility and low strength of the elements and the fairly large rate of change of the electrical properties with temperature.

This paper discusses how these properties can be controlled and modified and outlines the progress that has been made to date.

MECHANICAL PROPERTIES

Silicon and germanium, as well as most semiconductors, are hard brittle materials which undergo no plastic deformation at room temperature. Extensive studies on the deformation and fracture of silicon by Pearson *et al.*[3] have established the following:

(1) At room temperature silicon crystals exhibit no region of plastic deformation. That is, under load they will deform elastically until the fracture stress is reached.

(2) The fracture strength is dependent on cross-sectional area. For areas greater than 2×10^{-4} cm², the fracture stress is independent of size and is given by 3.5×10^9 dynes/cm² (about 50,000 lb/inch²). For areas less than 2×10^{-5} cm² the fracture stress is also independent of size and is given by 2.2×10^{10} dynes/cm² (about 350,000 lb/inch²). Between these two sizes the strength decreases logarthmically with increasing area.

(3) From room temperature to 600°F silicon will deform elastically up to fracture. At higher temperatures, silicon will exhibit plastic deformation.

Most of the above results have been verified and, in particular, the quality

* Presented at the Winter Meeting of the Instrument Society of America, St. Louis, Missouri, January, 1961.

of surface finish has been shown to effect the fracture strength significantly. In general, the same trend of higher strength with smaller cross sections has been noted. Table I illustrates the effect of size on strength for silicon

TABLE I

EFFECT OF CROSS SECTION ON MAXIMUM STRAIN

Cross-sectional area, cm²	Maximum strain, microinch/inch	Maximum stress, dynes/cm²
6×10^{-4}	2000	4.1×10^9
3.2×10^{-4}	2000	4.1×10^9
1.6×10^{-4}	4000	8.2×10^9
8×10^{-5}	6000	12.4×10^9
3×10^{-5}	10,000	21.0×10^9

which has been etched in a mixture of nitric and hydrofluoric acid. These results are also plotted in Fig. 1 where the data of Pearson, Read, and

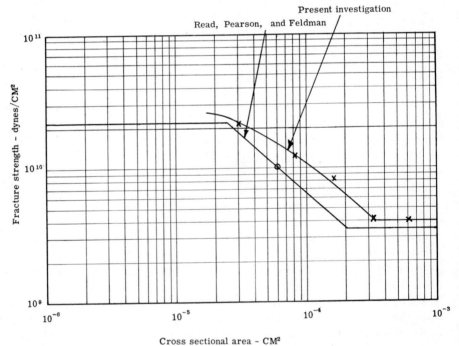

FIG. 1. Fracture stress as a function of cross-sectional area.

Feldman are given for comparison. It will be noted that careful surface preparation which removes surface imperfections and stress raisers left on the silicon bars after cutting is effective in increasing the measured fracture stress, particularly at the larger cross sections. Thus, silicon bars can be fabricated with considerable strength. Moreover, the use of thin bars with these concurrent high strengths gives great flexibility. For instance, bars with cross sections less than about 0.001 × 0.005 inch have been successfully bent in radii less than 0.060 inch.

From these results, it is apparent that careful processing can largely mitigate the fragility problem and can lead to high strength, flexible semiconductor piezoresistive devices.

The useful electrical properties of a semiconductor depend to a large degree on small concentrations of impurities in the lattice. In designing piezoresistive devices the primary properties that are affected by the impurity concentration are:

(1) the resistivity ρ

$$\rho = [eN_i\mu]^{-1}, \tag{1}$$

(2) the temperature dependence of the resistivity

$$\partial\rho/\partial T,$$

(3) the piezoresistive coefficient π,
(4) the temperature dependence of the piezoresistance coefficient

$$\partial\pi/\partial T,$$

(5) the linearity of the piezoresistance coefficient with strain

$$\partial\pi/\partial\epsilon.$$

Qualitatively, one may note the following trends with increasing impurity concentration:

(1) $\rho \downarrow$

(2) $\dfrac{\partial\rho}{\partial T} \downarrow$

(3) $\pi \downarrow$

(4) $\dfrac{\partial\pi}{\partial T} \downarrow$

(5) $\dfrac{\partial\pi}{\partial\epsilon} \downarrow$.

Since the resistivity is inversely proportional to the impurity concentration it is quite clear that the increase in impurity level will decrease ρ. The dependence of the other parameters is not quite as obvious. To consider the temperature dependence of the resistivity one must refer to Eq. (1). At very low impurity levels the number of carriers increases with increasing temperature because of the creation of hole-electron pairs across the energy gap. At somewhat higher impurity levels the carrier concentration increases in the low temperature range as the impurities are ionized. At very high impurity levels (the so-called degenerate range) the number of carriers is essentially independent of temperature.

The temperature dependence of mobility is also markedly influenced by the impurity density. To gain some insight into the nature of this dependence it is necessary to consider the concept of mobility in somewhat more detail.

In the absence of an electric field, electrons and holes move in the crystal with random thermal energy. Acceleration of current carriers by a field results in the development of a net drift velocity in the direction of the force. The drift velocity developed per unit of electric field intensity is called the mobility. Thus $v_D = \mu E$.

Since every time a hole or electron undergoes a collision its acceleration by the field is interrupted, the mobility depends on the nature and frequency of the collisions. The types of collisions most important in semiconductors are those with ionized impurities.

It is useful to speak of the lattice mobility μ_L and the impurity mobility μ_I as the respective mobilities a carrier would have if one scattering process alone were acting.

The amount of lattice scattering increases with increasing temperature because the thermal velocity of the carrier increases and the lattice vibrations are enhanced. The lattice mobility has been shown to vary as $-\mu_L = KT^{-3/2}$. Scattering by ionized impurities is caused by electrostatic forces, and is less effective as the average speed of the carriers increases and thus, as the temperature increases. The impurity scattering mobility is given by

$$\mu_I = \frac{A\,T^{3/2}}{N_I \ln\left[1 + (BT^2/N_I^{2/3})\right]}. \tag{2}$$

Thus, the impurity mobility increases as the temperature increases.

To obtain the actual mobility from μ_L and μ_I the approximation of taking the sum of the separate reciprocals can be used to see in what region each term is important. In fairly heavily doped semiconductors μ_I is very much less than μ_L and there is a region at low temperatures where the mobility (and hence the conductivity) increases with increasing temperature. When the temperature is sufficiently high the lattice mobility is then comparable to the impurity mobility and the mobility decreases with temperature. Thus, in the impurity range 10^{16}–10^{19} there is a minimum in the temperature resistance curve, the position of the resistance minimum occurring at higher temperatures as the impurity concentration increases.

The above theory breaks down for degenerate semiconductors where the impurity concentration is greater than 5×10^{19}. For highly degenerate semiconductors, a large number of the charge carriers form an electron gas which is similar to that in a metal. Thus, once again the mobility goes down with increasing temperature without any minimum in the temperature resistance curve:

$$[\mu \propto v^2 \approx \kappa(1 + \lambda T) \qquad \lambda \ll 1]. \tag{3}$$

Thus, by choosing the proper impurity level the device designer can vary the ρ vs. T curve to obtain within certain limits almost any temperature dependence of resistivity desired (from 2%/100°F to 100%/100°F).

The magnitudes of the piezoresistance coefficients are also determined by the impurity concentration. For the low concentration range the piezoresistance coefficient has the form

$$\pi \approx \frac{\varphi}{kT}\left(\frac{\mu_{\parallel} - \mu_{\perp}}{\mu}\right). \tag{4}$$

This expression is modified in the high concentration range by the replacement of $1/kT$ by $d \ln n^i/d\epsilon_F$ where n^i is the density of carriers in the ith valley and ϵ_F is the Fermi Level. Since n^i is proportional to

$$\left\{\frac{1}{1 + \exp\dfrac{\epsilon^i - \epsilon_F}{kT}}\right\}$$

and $\epsilon_F \approx \epsilon^i$, the dependence varies less strongly than $1/kT$. Moreover, the effect of replacing $1/kT$ by $d \ln n^i/d\epsilon_F$ is to lower the value of the piezoresistance coefficient, particularly when $\epsilon^i \leqslant \epsilon_F$, i.e., when the material is highly degenerate. While these equations form a means for accurately computing both the piezoresistive coefficient and its temperature constant, the calculations are quite laborious, and have only been performed for the case of n-type germanium where there is good agreement between theory and experiment.[4] However, they do enable the device designer to predict to some degree of accuracy the relative magnitude of the piezoresistive coefficients and their temperature variation from low concentration measurements and to select that concentration required for a particular value of either or both of these parameters. In view of the dependence of the important electrical parameters on the impurity concentration, several different methods of attack can be chosen so as to minimize undesirable temperature effects. These are:

(1) Use degenerate material $N_I \approx 10^{20}$; $\rho \approx 0.001$ ohm-cm. This will minimize the variation of $\partial \pi / \partial T$ and still give a fairly low value of $\partial \rho / \partial T$.

(2) Pick a value of N_I such that near, or somewhat below, room temperature $\partial \rho / \partial T \rightarrow 0$: $N_I \approx 5 \times 10^{18}$; $\rho \approx 0.02$ ohm-cm. This gives a fairly small value of $\partial \rho / \partial T \approx 5\%/100°F$ but $\partial \pi / \partial T$ is still of the order of $15\%/100°F$.

(3) Pick a still somewhat lower value of N_I such that the rate of change of $\partial \rho / \partial T$ can be used to compensate for $\partial \pi / \partial T$.

Although the first method has many advantages, the extremely low resistivity makes it quite difficult to fabricate a gage with resistance in excess of 100 ohms. With dimensions of $0.005 \times 0.0004 \times 0.500$ and a resistivity of 0.001, the gage resistance will be about 100 ohms and it is quite difficult to exceed this value. Another approach making use of solid state diffusion and oxide masking techniques allows the fabrication of units with resistances at least a factor of 10 higher. At this point it is appropriate to discuss some applications of these techniques to fabrication of piezoresistive devices.

Solid state diffusion is a fairly well-known technique for the production of highly doped layers on or just below the surface of a semiconductor. Because it is a very slow process, it can be controlled very exactly and diffused layers as shallow as 1μ can be made with ease. Thus, a very degenerate layer can be produced whose dimensions may be independent of the geometry of the bulk crystal, and whose resistance is higher than possible by any other technique in material of comparable doping.

To form an appropriately doped layer by solid state diffusion, a single crystal material is heated in the presence of vapor of the desired impurity. Both the temperature of the semiconductor and the diffusant vapor pressure determine the resulting impurity distribution. For the case of a constant concentration of diffusing impurities at the surface of the semiconductor wafer, a solution of the differential equation for diffusion yields the result

$$C(x) = C_s \operatorname{erfc}\left(\frac{x}{2\sqrt{Dt}}\right)$$

where C_s = the concentration of impurity atoms at the surface of the wafer
$C(x)$ = the concentration of impurity atoms at some distance from the surface
erfc = the complimentary error function
t = the duration of the diffusion process
D = the diffusion constant, which is determined by the diffusing species and the medium through which it diffuses.

The diffusion coefficients are experimentally determined and generally have a temperature dependence of the form

$$D = D_0 \exp - \left(\frac{\Delta H}{RT}\right)$$

where ΔH = the activation energy for diffusion
T = the temperature of diffusion.

For the fabrication of devices, it is important to control the depth of the diffused region and the distribution of impurities within it. Because of the inherently slow nature of diffusion (times of the order of hours are required to produce junction depths of the order of mils), it is comparatively easy to control the depth. Moreover, by varying the diffusion times, temperatures, and surface concentrations, the device designer may obtain the best possible impurity distribution for a given device. If a p-type impurity is allowed to diffuse into an n-type semiconductor material, a $p - n$ junction will result where the net impurity concentration goes to zero. The depth of the diffused junction is dependent on (1) the temperature of the silicon through the diffusion coefficient, D, (2) the total time of diffusion, t, (3) on the impurity concentration at the surface, C_s, and (4) on the initial doping level, C_b, of the bulk semiconductor material. The surface concentration in turn is dependent on the diffusant source temperature which controls the vapor pressure of the diffusant. If the impurity vapor is carried to the semiconductor wafer by a flow of gas, the surface concentration will also be dependent on the rate of flow of the carrier gas. To a first approximation the depth of the $p - n$ junction below the surface is given by

$$x_j = 2 \sqrt{Dt} \left(\ln \frac{C_s}{C_b}\right)^{1/2}.$$

Prediction of the piezoresistive properties is not as simple in the case of diffused layers as in that of bulk crystals because of the inherent nonuniform distribution resulting from diffusion. If one imagines the diffused region subdivided into thin regions of essentially uniform concentration, then the entire sensor could be thought of as composed of a series all in parallel with the various impurity-dependent electrical properties varying according to the concentration. Thus, knowledge of what happens in the homogeneous case still serves as a good guide for deducing what will happen in a diffused structure. Moreover, the high degree of control and repeatability inherent in diffusion makes it a valuable technique for the fabrication of piezoresistive devices. Some results of our studies on diffused units are shown in Fig. 2 where $\partial\rho/\partial T$, π is plotted as a function of surface concentration for a diffusion depth of about 0.0001 inch. It will be noted that $\partial\rho/\partial T$ goes through a minimum and π decreases as the surface concentration increases. Smaller diffusion depths serve to reduce the temperature dependence. The variation of gage factor with temperature was also determined.

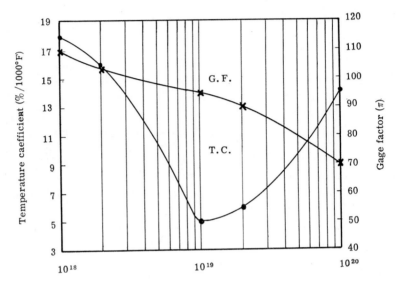

FIG. 2. Temperature coefficient and gage factor vs. impurity concentration for diffused gages.

This variation decreases from about 10%/100°F at surface concentrations of $10^{18}/cm^3$ to about 3%/100°F at surface concentrations of $10^{20}/cm^3$.

The second approach, that of minimizing $\partial\rho/\partial T$ has been used by most manufacturers of semiconductor gages to date and little more need be said about it.

The third approach, that of using the temperature variation of gage resistance to compensate for temperature variation in gage factor is fairly straightforward and has led to significant improvements in temperature stabilization.

If one considers a constant current supply, then the voltage through an active gage is given by

$$V = I_oR(\epsilon, T)$$

at zero strain, the voltage measured at T_1

$$V_0 = I_oR(\epsilon = 0, T_1)$$

and the change in voltage for a strain ϵ is given by

$$\Delta V_1 = I_o R(\epsilon = 0, T_1)(G.F.)_{T_1}.$$

Similarly at a temperature T_2 and the same strain ϵ

$$\Delta V_2 = I_o R(\epsilon = 0, T_2)(G.F.)_{T_2}.$$

Thus, for the same output $\Delta V_1 = \Delta V_2$ or

$$\frac{R(T_1, \epsilon = 0)}{R(T_2, \epsilon = 0)} = \frac{(G.F.)_{T_2}}{(G.F.)_{T_1}}.$$

Thus, if the gage resistance can be made to vary at an inverse rate to the variation of gage factor, output compensation may be obtained. In particular, for variation of gage factor of $1/T$ a T dependence of resistance is required. For a four active arm bridge these considerations lead to the following equation:

$$E_o = \frac{K_1}{T} E_A \epsilon$$

where E_o = bridge output voltage
E_A = applied voltage
K_1/T = total bridge gage factor
ϵ = applied strain with constant current supply $E_o = I_o R_B$.

Thus, for compensation with a constant current source R_B must vary as T. For a constant voltage in series with a compensating resistance as in the circuit shown in Fig. 3,

$$E_A = \frac{R_B E_s}{R_B + R_c}.$$

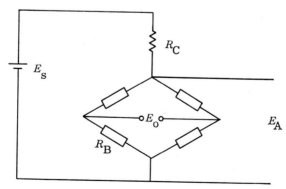

Fig. 3. Compensating resistance circuit.

Assuming $R_B = K_2T$, then

$$E_A = \frac{K_2T}{K_2T + R_c} E_s$$

and

$$E_o = \frac{K_1}{T} E_A \epsilon$$

$$= \frac{K_1K_2}{K_2T + R_c} E_s.$$

Simplifying,

$$E_o = \frac{K_3}{K_4T + R_c}.$$

It can be seen that when K_4T is small with respect to R_c, the output voltage is fairly constant. When K_4T is significant the output voltage will drop with increasing temperature.

In order to illustrate experimentally this type of output compensation with commercially available semiconductor strain gages, tests were made with Kulite DA105 gages.

Figure 4 shows the test setup that was used. To determine the effects of temperature on bridge input resistance, the strain gage bridge and a precision decade box were connected to the strain indicator. The entire bridge was considered a single resistance and connected to the strain indicator as an active gage would be and the decade box was connected in the position normally occupied by the compensating gage. Thus, this setup is similar to a half-bridge strain gage circuit. The decade box was varied to bring the strain indicator to balance at room temperature and the reading recorded. At various higher temperatures up to a maximum of approximately 160°F the decade box was again adjusted to bring the strain indicator to balance and the new reading recorded. In this setup the reading of the decade box is exactly equal to the unknown bridge resistance.

The results of this test are shown on the graph in Fig. 5 and are represented by the curve entitled "bridge input resistance." It is seen that, within the accuracy with which we were able to measure temperature and resistance, the resistance change versus temperature is linear and increases approximately 40%/100°F.

Because of this large change in resistance it is not possible to provide perfect compensation over the entire temperature range since the value of compensating resistance required at 160°F is somewhat different than that required at 60°. As shown in the mathematics the compensation with this type of circuit cannot be perfect since the compensating resistor causes a nonlinearity in the bridge voltage versus temperature.

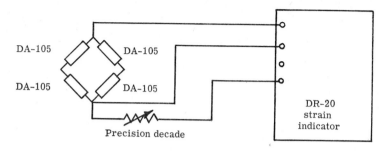

Gage factor at 10
half bridge circuit

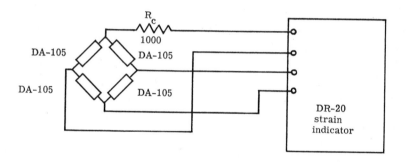

Gage factor at 10
full bridge circuit

FIG. 4. *Upper:* Circuit for measuring bridge input resistance vs. temperature. *Lower:* Circuit for calibration vs. temperature tests. R_c is shorted out for uncompensated tests.

To determine the effects of temperature on the bridge output for a given load we connected the bridge to a DR-20 strain indicator as shown in Fig. 4 and applied a fixed load at the various temperatures. The results are shown in the graph of Fig. 5 by the curve labeled "change in bridge output, uncompensated." It is seen that the sensitivity decreases 17%/100°F as is expected.

A compensating resistor R_c shown in Fig. 4 was selected experimentally to compensate for the temperature effects on sensitivity. The final results are shown in Fig. 5 by the graph labeled "change in bridge output, compensated." When a 1000-ohm resistor is chosen, however, it is seen that the bridge is still slightly undercompensated over the entire temperature range. However, for small temperature variations around room temperature it is pretty closely compensated.

Thus, with the nonlinear characteristics of this compensating circuit it

ANTHONY D. KURTZ

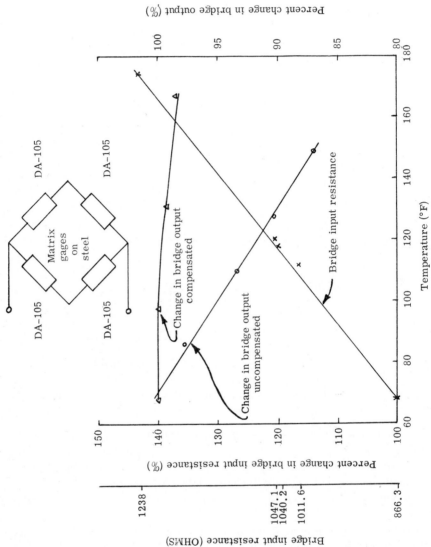

Fig. 5. Temperature compensation of bridge output.

would be desirable to temperature compensate for the specific range of temperature over which the device will operate to obtain optimum compensation. If a semiconductor material with a lower temperature coefficient were used, the compensating resistor would necessarily be larger and thus the nonlinear effects seen above reduced. Future experiments will be performed with materials having a temperature coefficient in the range above 17% but below 30%/100°F.

TEMPERATURE COMPENSATION OF APPARENT STRAIN

One can make use of the variation of temperature coefficient of resistance with impurity concentration to obtain compensation of apparent strain. The coefficient of linear thermal expansion of Kulite gages is low. Therefore, the differential thermal expansion caused by most of the materials to which the gages are cemented causes a tension to be exerted on the gage. This tension added to the resistance change of the gage with temperature results in an "apparent strain" output of the gage. Most of this "apparent strain" can be canceled by the use of a dummy gage (an identical gage held at the same temperature which does not undergo strain) by the same method currently employed with metal gages.

Another method is to select two gages of the same temperature coefficient of resistance but with opposite gage factors (plus and minus). This will similarly compensate for the resistance change with temperature while in addition providing two active adjacent arms of the bridge. If the temperature coefficients of the negative and positive gage factor gages are different, the difference can compensate completely for apparent strain when this composite gage is mounted on a material of a specific expansion coefficient.

Kulite MP series gages are dual element gages so corrected for "apparent strain" on specific materials. One positive and one negative gage-factor crystal are matched in a single gage to provide two active temperature-compensated arms with a composite gage factor in excess of 200.

Mathematically, these considerations may be expressed as follows: For an n-type gage, the change in resistance/°F is given by

$$\frac{\Delta R_n}{R_n} = (T.C.)_n - (\alpha_M - \alpha_{Si})|G.F.|_n.$$

Similarly, for a p-type gage

$$\frac{\Delta R_p}{R_p} = (T.C.)_p + (\alpha_M - \alpha_{Si})|G.F.|_p$$

where R_n, R_p = unstressed resistance at a fixed temperature
$(T.C.)_n, (T.C.)_p$ = temperature coefficients of resistance

α_M, α_{Si} = linear thermal expansion coefficients of the particular metal and silicon

$|G.F.|_n$ and $|G.F.|_p$ = magnitudes of gage factors.

For compensation in two adjacent arms, ΔR_p must equal ΔR_n:

$$(T.C.)_n - (T.C.)_p = (\alpha_M - \alpha_{Si})\{|G.F.|_p + |G.F.|_n\}.$$

Since both the temperature coefficients and the gage factors are a function of impurity density, it is possible to choose such a density that the equation holds. Table II gives the required temperature coefficients for the Kulite MP series compensated gages. These gages are compensated for materials

TABLE II

KULITE MP SERIES COMPENSATED GAGES

Expansion coeff. of material	Temp. coeff. of positive gage	Temp. coeff. of negative gage
$4 \times 10^{-6}/°F$	$0.06\%/°F$	$0.12\%/°F$
$6 \times 10^{-6}/°F$	$0.05\%/°F$	$0.14\%/°F$
$9 \times 10^{-6}/°F$	$0.06\%/°F$	$0.25\%/°F$

whose linear expansion coefficients are $4 \times 10^{-6}/°F$, $6 \times 10^{-6}/°F$, and $9 \times 10^{-6}/°F$, respectively. Using these techniques it is possible to reduce the apparent strain to 1 microinch/inch/°F.

CONCLUSIONS

We have discussed how the mechanical and electrical properties of gages are controlled by imperfections and impurities. The effects of careful surface treatment and small cross section was studied and marked increases in strength and flexibility were observed.

The control of temperature variation by impurity density was studied, and three approaches to temperature compensation were discussed. For impurity concentrations in excess of $10^{20}/cm^3$ the gage factor is essentially temperature independent. For impurity concentrations $5 \times 10^{18}/cm^3$ the resistivity versus temperature curve has a minimum near or somewhat below room temperature. For impurity concentrations of about $10^{18}/cm^3$ the variation of gage resistance with temperature can be used to compensate for gage factor variation with temperature, or apparent strain.

REFERENCES

1. Smith, C. S., *Phys. Rev.* **94,** 42 (1954).
2. Mason, W. P., *Bell. Labs. Record* **37,** 7 (1959).
3. Pearson, G. L., Read, W. T., and Feldmann, W. L., *Acta Met.* **5,** 181 (1957).

STRAIN GAGE CIRCUITS FOR SEMICONDUCTOR GAGES*

Peter K. Stein

Arizona State University, Tempe, Arizona

Abstract

The constant current circuit is the only one which will work with semi-conductor strain gages; and it is also the one which gives twice the output for conventional gages, than does the constant-voltage Wheatstone bridge configuration. It is the only perfectly linear system which makes it ideal for semiconductor gages.

Introduction

The resistance strain gage is a non-self-generating transducer in that it requires two energy inputs in order to produce one energy output:

(a) mechanical input energy from the mechanical system on which strain is to be measured;

(b) electrical input energy from an auxiliary or biasing electrical energy supply.

The entire performance of the strain gage system (which must be considered to include the auxiliary electrical supply as well as the strain gage itself) is dictated not only by the basic properties of the strain gage, but also by those of the auxiliary electrical supply.

An electrical supply is usually described by its internal impedance. If this impedance is low, the supply is described as a *voltage* supply; if the internal impedance is zero, it becomes a *pure voltage* supply. When the internal impedance is high, the supply is known as a *current* supply, and when the impedance becomes infinite, a *pure current* or *constant current* supply.

Maximum power transfer occurs when the internal impedance of the electrical supply is equal to the internal impedance of its load (the strain gage); maximum power is also transferred from the strain gage circuit to the read-out meter when the internal impedance of the strain gage circuit equals that of the meter.

It must be emphasized, however, that in numerous applications it is not output *power* which is demanded but output *voltage*, and the criteria for maximum output voltage are *different* from those describing maximum power or maximum current output.

* Presented at the Winter Meeting of the Instrument Society of America, St. Louis, Missouri, January, 1961.

The conditions under which the output observations on passive strain gage circuits are made usually are divided into two classes.

1. *Voltage Measurement*

When the instrument with which the strain gage circuit output is measured is a high-impedance voltage sensing device, the circuit sensitivity may be expressed as

$$S_{\mathrm{v}} = e/\epsilon = I \cdot R \cdot K \cdot n_{\mathrm{c}} \cdot n_{\mathrm{m}}(1 - \delta). \tag{1}$$

S_{v} = system voltage sensitivity in units of microvolts circuit output per microstrain in the specimen beneath the gage: $\mu v/\mu\epsilon$.

e = strain induced output voltage from the circuit.

ϵ = strain in the specimen beneath the gage.

I = current in the gage in amperes.

R = gage resistance in ohms.

n_{c} = efficiency with which the circuit of which the gage forms a part approaches constant current conditions.

n_{m} = efficiency of signal transfer from the *circuit* to the *voltage measuring instrument*. This efficiency is unity when the measurement is made under open circuit conditions, i.e., when the measuring instrument does not load the circuit.

K = gage factor of the strain gage.

δ = nonlinearity between input strain ϵ and output voltage e. δ is a function of the circuit efficiency n_{c} and of the strain level ϵ.

It may be seen that under ideal efficiency and linearity conditions the *maximum system sensitivity* is determined exclusively by three characteristics of the gage:

$$S_{\mathrm{v_{max}}} = I \cdot R \cdot K. \tag{2}$$

2. *Current Measurement*

When the instrument with which the strain gage circuit output is measured is a current-sensing device, the circuit sensitivity may be expressed as

$$S_{\mathrm{a}} = i/\epsilon = I \cdot K \cdot n_{\mathrm{c}} \cdot n_{\mathrm{m}}(1 - \delta). \tag{3}$$

i = strain-induced output current from the circuit.

   The other symbols have the same significance as in Eq. (1) although their numerical values, especially for n_{c} and n_{m}, may be different.

S_{a} = system current sensitivity in units of microamperes circuit output per microstrain in the specimen beneath the gage: $\mu a/\mu\epsilon$.

It may be seen that under ideal efficiency and linearity conditions the maximum system sensitivity (now under short-circuit conditions) is a function of only two basic strain gage characteristics:

$$S_{a_{max}} = I \cdot K. \tag{4}$$

Purpose of the Paper

Other papers have been published on methods for increasing system sensitivity by raising the current carrying capacity I of the gage, its gage factor K, the instrument matching efficiency n_m, and the circuit efficiency n_c. For metallic strain gages the values normally achieved for circuit nonlinearity δ are so small as to be negligible in all but the finest transducer work. For semiconductor strain gages, however, for which the gage factor K has been made extremely large, the values for nonlinearity δ assume large proportions.

It is the purpose of this paper to investigate (1) the circuit conditions for which linearity exists between strain-induced resistance change input and voltage or current output, and (2) methods for controlling the degree of nonlinearity between resistance change and electrical output so that certain linearizing operations can be carried out.

Analysis

It can be shown that for both the voltage and current sensing cases

$$\delta = \frac{(r/R)(1 - n_c)}{1 + (r/R)(1 - n_c)} \tag{5}$$

where r is the strain-induced resistance change in the gage such that

$$r/R = \epsilon \cdot K \tag{6}$$

when transverse sensitivity effects are not considered.

Corollary: It may be seen from Eq. (5) that the nonlinearity factor becomes zero when $n_c = 1$ or under constant current conditions. For constant voltage circuits used for current measurement, $n_c = 0$ and a finite nonlinearity continues to exist. It therefore becomes necessary to investigate methods of achieving constant current conditions of arbitrary efficiencies for controllable nonlinearity.

Methods of Achieving Constant-Current Conditions

1. *"Brute Force"*

Figure 1 illustrates the common manner of achieving a constant current source, i.e., by placing a high-voltage source in series with a high resistance.

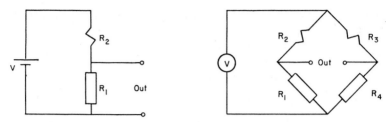

Fig. 1. Constant current conditions by "brute force" techniques.

This method is extremely wasteful in terms of power consumed because all the power dissipated in this high resistance is essentially wasted. The combination of the voltage source V and the resistance R_2 then provides a constant current source of sorts. The efficiency of this system in generating constant current is

$$n_c = \frac{R_2}{R_2 + R_1} = \frac{a}{1 + a} \tag{7}$$

$$a = R_2/R_1. \tag{8}$$

Figure 1 illustrates the general circuit both for dynamic strain measurement where it is not required that the circuit output for zero strain input be zero, as well as the common bridge circuit used for static strain measurement when it is required that the initial circuit output be zero. In the special case for which all four bridge arms are of equal resistance, the common equal-arm-bridge is obtained for which the circuit efficiency is 50%, providing only one-half the maximum output.

As shown in Fig. 1, the bridge circuit is electrically temperature compensated provided that R_1 and R_2 represent strain gages of the same type and of the same heat transfer characteristics exposed to the same thermal environment at the same time. Thus, controlling linearity or circuit efficiency can be accomplished without affecting any computing characteristics of the bridge circuit, such as electrical temperature compensation.

Example: Figure 2 shows a four-equal-arm four-gage transducer on the

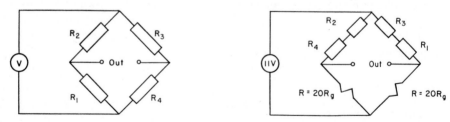

Fig. 2. Almost doubling four-active-arm transducer by "brute force" constant current method.

left-hand side. With the circuit rearranged as indicated on the right-hand side, no computing functions of the circuit have been affected but its output is now 80% higher than before because the circuit efficiency has been raised from 50 to 91%.

Note that it is necessary to maintain *constant gage current* to take advantage of this method and that 11 times the supply voltage is needed for the modified circuit.

Linearity Relationships

Figure 3 shows a plot of strain-induced resistance-change input vs. circuit voltage output for either of the circuits shown in Fig. 1, assuming a single active strain gage R_1. The input-output curves are shown for various values of the resistance ratio a [Eq. (8)] or for various degrees of constant-current-conditions expressed as per cent of true constant-current conditions. Note the marked degree of nonlinearity for the equal-arm bridge condition of $a = 1$.

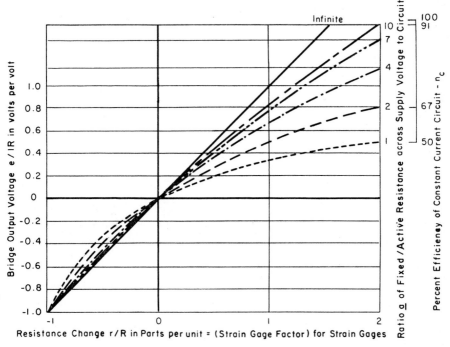

FIG. 3. Resistance change in a bridge arm vs. bridge output voltage for various values of ratio a at constant current:

$$\frac{e}{IR} = \frac{a \cdot r/R}{1 + a + r/R} = \frac{n_c(r/R)}{1 - (1 - n)(r/R)}.$$

Sensitivity Relationships

It can be shown from Eqs. (1), (5), and (6) that

$$S_v = e/\epsilon = I \cdot R \cdot K \cdot \frac{n_c}{1 - (1 - n_c)\epsilon \cdot K} \tag{9}$$

$$= I \cdot R \cdot K \cdot n_c \cdot (1 - \delta)$$

or

$$e/IR = \frac{n_c(r/R)}{1 - (1 - n_c)(r/R)}. \tag{10}$$

It may be seen that with increased linearity there also ensues increased sensitivity, an extremely happy circumstance which is also borne out by Fig. 3.

2. *"Wastefulness"*

In certain cases it is possible to achieve constant current conditions by having two transducers in the circuit change resistance in equal amounts but opposite in sign. Thus, in Fig. 4, gages 1 and 2 on the cantilever beam

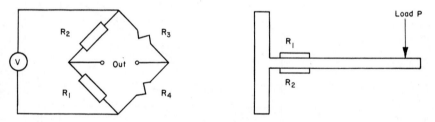

Fig. 4. Constant current conditions by "wasteful" method.

will be subjected to strains of the same magnitude but of opposite sign. With identical gage characteristics, this will lead to the condition of equal resistance changes in R_1 and R_2 but of opposite sign. In this case, the current through gages 1 and 2 remains constant even though only a finite voltage V is applied to the circuit.

This condition achieves perfect linearity between strain in the gages and circuit output voltage, but note that it has taken *two* transducers to achieve this aim. The circuit output is no more than could be ideally achieved by the "brute force" method with a single gage.

3. *"Sheer Elegance"*

What is the simplest way of achieving a constant-current circuit? By designing a constant-current source on purpose to begin with! Until now

(January 1961), current sources capable of fulfilling the stringent conditions of this application have not been commercially available. It is required, for example, that the ripple of such a current source for conventional metallic gages be in the order of 1 to 10 ppm, something unheard of in line-operated devices and more in the region of battery-operated transistor circuits.

Figure 5 illustrates the basic simplicity of this system for both dynamic

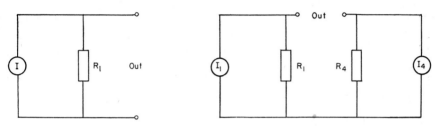

FIG. 5. Constant current conditions by "sheer elegance" techniques.

and static strain measurements. Connect the two terminals of the gage to the current supply and to a high-impedance voltage sensing device such as a CRO and that is it! If the gage is supplied with four terminals, two go to the supply and two to the read-out; then the entire system is also completely independent of lead-wire resistance, switch-contact resistance, or slip-ring resistances in any of the four paths! The circuit shown for static strain measurement is temperature compensated if R_1 and R_4 are two gages of identical thermal properties exposed to the same thermal environment at the same time. This circuit can also be used to form the standard computing systems such as torquemeters independent of thrust, bending, tension, temperature, etc., thrust meters independent of torque, bending, temperature, etc.

Suitable variable resistors can be incorporated into the circuit for initial zero balance. It is even possible to feed both current sources from the same batteries initially so that any battery run-down will affect both sources in the same manner thus not affecting circuit output.

Static vs. Dynamic Strain Gage Circuits

In Figs. 1 and 5 circuits are shown for static and dynamic strain measurement. The only real difference between them is that the circuit shown for dynamic measurement does not exhibit zero output voltage for zero strain such that a frequency-selective filter must be used at the circuit output to eliminate the initial DC level. Thus, one need use the static circuits only when static strain measurements are to be made. It is important to note that certain dynamic signals can contain DC components when a frequency-based Fourier-type analysis is made.

Advantages of the Dynamic Strain Circuits

(1) Output for a constant current system is almost twice that for a normal equal-arm bridge.

(2) Noise levels are lower because the supply voltage (or current), strain gage, and read-out instrument are connected to the same ground line.

(3) No auxiliary circuitry such as balancing network is required.

(4) Linearity between input strain and output voltage is controllable and can be made as close to ideal as desired by approaching constant current conditions.

(5) The circuit is simpler than a static strain circuit and therefore less likely to go wrong.

Sample Calculations for Typical Strain Gage Outputs and Current Source Performance

Metallic Gages

Resistances range from 60 to 5000 ohms commonly, current level ratings up to 50 ma, gage factors from 2 to 4 roughly. Assuming common values we obtain the following values.

Static strain measurement:

$$I = 0.010 \text{ amp}$$
$$R = 120 \text{ ohms}$$
$$K = 2.0 \ \mu\text{ohm/ohm/}\mu\epsilon$$
$$S_{v_{max}} = 2.4 \ \mu\text{v/}\mu\epsilon.$$

Dynamic strain measurement:

$$I = 0.035 \text{ amp}$$
$$R = 1000 \text{ ohms}$$
$$K = 3.6 \ \mu\text{ohm/ohm/}\mu\epsilon.$$
$$S_{v_{max}} = 126 \ \mu\text{v/}\mu\epsilon.$$

Assuming a permissible noise level of 10 $\mu\epsilon$ in terms of ripple, drift, etc., the requirements of a constant-current source would be to maintain, for static strain:

$$10 \ \mu\epsilon = 24 \ \mu\text{v}$$
$$V = I \cdot R = 1.2 \text{ volts}$$
$$\text{ripple or noise factor} = 24/1.2 \text{ ppm or 20 ppm;}$$

for dynamic strain:

$$10 \ \mu\epsilon = 1260 \ \mu v$$
$$V = I \cdot R = 35 \text{ volts}$$
$$\text{ripple or noise factor} = 1260/35 \text{ ppm or 36 ppm.}$$

Semiconductor Gages

$$I = 0.020 \text{ amp}$$
$$R = 120 \text{ ohms}$$
$$K = 120 \ \mu\text{ohm/ohm}/\mu\epsilon$$
$$S_{v_{max}} = 288 \ \mu v/\mu\epsilon$$
$$10 \ \mu\epsilon = 2880 \ \mu v$$
$$V = I \cdot R = 2.4 \text{ volts}$$
$$\text{ripple or noise factor} = 2880/2.4 \text{ ppm or 1200 ppm.}$$

Resistance Change Comparison

Metallic static:	0.24 ohm/1000 $\mu\epsilon$
Metallic dynamic:	3.6 ohms/1000 $\mu\epsilon$
Semiconductor:	14.4 ohms/1000 $\mu\epsilon$.
From Eq. (6),	$r = \epsilon \cdot K \cdot R.$

Summary

Constant current circuits for use with metallic gages require little regulation in terms of load resistance changes, but specifications on noise level due to ripple or drift are quite severe. Note that even though the maximum sensitivity of the semiconductor gage shown is only about twice that for the dynamic metallic gage illustrated, that the permissible current source noise level is so much greater for the semiconductor gage that a feasible system could be designed easily. Note, however, that resistance changes in semiconductor gages are relatively large and that current source regulation requirements become correspondingly more stringent. Controllable linearity characteristics can be achieved by controlling the internal resistance of the current source.

CONCLUSIONS

The only truly linear circuit for strain gages, i.e., where output open circuit voltage is linearly related to strain gage resistance change, is the constant current form of auxiliary strain gage electrical supply.

The degree of linearity between strain gage resistance change and open circuit output voltage can be controlled between certain limits by controlling the effective internal impedance of the auxiliary supply. This feature can be used to offset certain nonlinearities in the transducer (strain gage, resistance thermometer, etc.).

The use of a constant current auxiliary strain gage energy supply is accompanied by the following advantages:

(1) up to twice the output sensitivity available from constant voltage sources;

(2) elimination of parasitic resistance effects as in switching or sliprings through the use of the double-corner circuit;

(3) absolute linearity between resistance change and output voltage.

There are no commercially manufactured constant current sources available at this time (January 1961) which are satisfactory for use with metallic strain gages since the required ripple factor is 20 ppm maximum. Such a supply would have to be battery operated and could be, and should be made available without too much difficulty.

For semiconductor gages the permissible ripple is 1.2 parts per thousand, which can be achieved with line-operated supplies.

It is to be hoped that appropriate supplies will be available soon for both metallic and semiconductor strain gage use.

REFERENCE

1. See also Parasitic resistances in Strain Gage Circuits, *Strain Gage Readings* **2**, No. 2, 3 (1959).

STRAIN INDICATOR FOR SEMICONDUCTOR GAGES*

Eugene Frank

B & F Instruments, Inc., Philadelphia, Pennsylvania

Abstract

The increasing influence of the semiconductor strain gage for experimental stress analysis has brought to light its incompatability with conventional strain gage instrumentation. This paper presents a brief summary of the presently known characteristics of semiconductor gages and discusses the parameters and design of an instrument for indicating the output of the semiconductor strain gage.

Introduction

The semiconductor strain gage differs from the well-known wire and foil strain gages in three main respects:

(1) The change in resistance with strain is approximately 60 times higher than that of a conventional gage.

(2) The gage factor varies with the strain level.

(3) The gage factor varies with temperature.

There are several other differences which must be considered before one can utilize the semiconductor gage with confidence. The characteristics of semiconductor gages are very ably presented by Sanchez and Wright.[1] Several papers presented at this session also describe many of the features of semiconductor gages which must be considered if they are to be effectively used as a working tool to measure strain, or as a transducer element. The characteristics of semiconductor gages pertaining to the proper design of a strain indicator for use with these gages are repeated here for emphasis.

The only reason for the existence of the semiconductor gage is its great sensitivity. It is very necessary, therefore, to learn how to deal with the corresponding large resistance change and to design circuits that utilize this resistance change without decreasing the sensitivity and losing the only advantage of a semiconductor gage.

The conventional Wheatstone bridge employed with low gage factor strain gages is essentially a nonlinear circuit when a single active strain gage is used. The formula for the output is

$$E_o/E_I = \Delta R/(4R + 2\Delta R)$$

* Presented at 16th Annual Instrument-Automation Conference and Exhibit, September 1961, Los Angeles, California.

283

where E_o = output voltage
  E_I = input voltage
  R = gage resistance
  ΔR = change in gage resistance.

When ΔR is small compared to R, this reduces to $\Delta R/4R$ and for practical purposes, with conventional gages, we assume a linear circuit.

With high sensitivity gages such as semiconductor gages or temperature elements, ΔR cannot be ignored. Figure 1 presents output curves of a

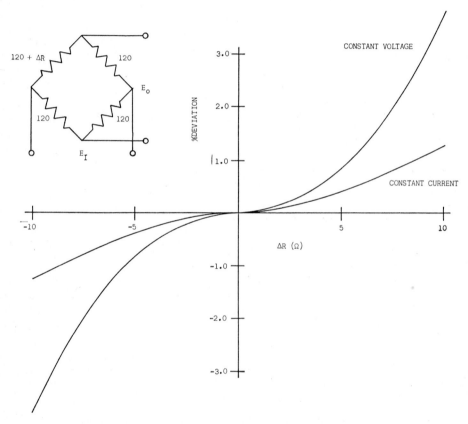

Fɪɢ. 1. Output voltage vs. resistance change for constant input voltage and current.

Wheatstone bridge employing a single active 120Ω element with ΔR varying $\pm 10\Omega$. The per cent deviation from a straight line is plotted to emphasize the nonlinearity. Two curves are shown: one for constant voltage, and one for constant current. The advantage of a constant current supply is easily discerned.

A further improvement of linearity can be obtained with the asymmetric bridge shown in Fig. 2. By increasing the resistance of two arms of the bridge approximately 20 times, excellent linearity can be achieved. Figure 2 is plotted for a very large ΔR, as this circuit is usually employed with resistance temperature gages. Mack[2] describes this in detail. To employ this circuit with a semiconductor gage, without losing the advantage of increased sensitivity, a very high excitation voltage must be employed.

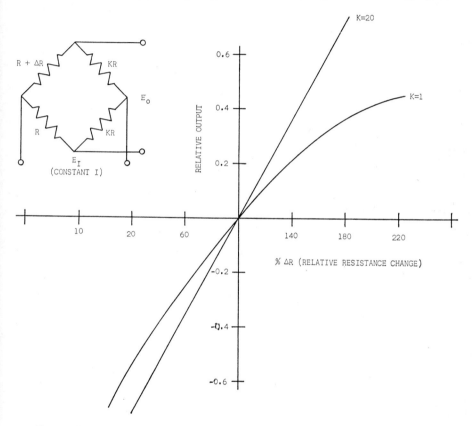

FIG. 2. Output voltage vs. resistance change for asymmetric bridge—a method to improve linearity.

For practical purposes this is undesirable. It is difficult to design a high voltage solid state power supply, and the high voltages required would physically shock operating personnel.

The preceding discussion describes the nonlinearity of a Wheatstone bridge employing resistance elements, where these elements are either semiconductor gages, temperature elements, or any large variable resist-

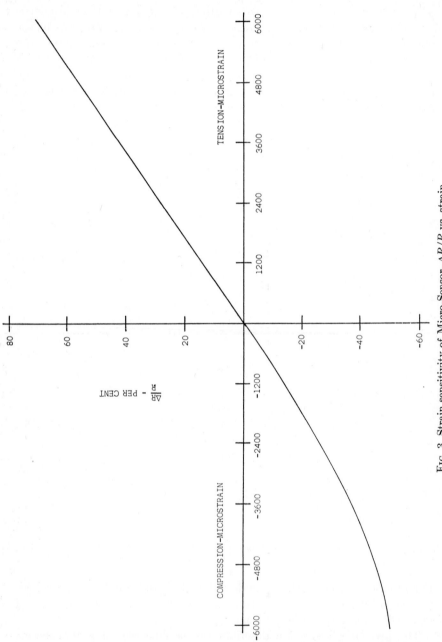

FIG. 3. Strain sensitivity of Micro-Sensor. $\Delta R/R$ vs. strain.

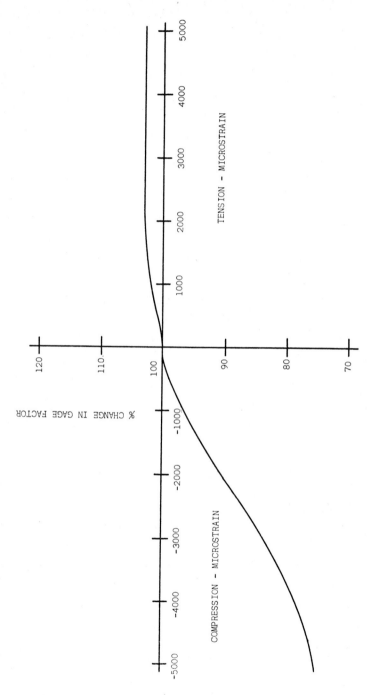

FIG. 4. Gage factor vs. strain for Micro-Sensor MS105-350. Per cent deviation from gage factor at 100 microstrain tension.

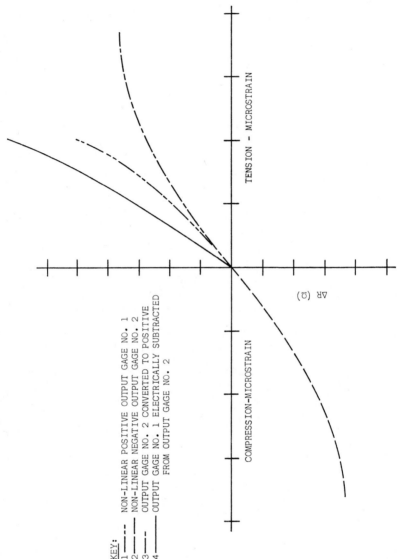

TENSION - MICROSTRAIN

ΔR (Ω)

COMPRESSION - MICROSTRAIN

KEY:
1 —··—·· NON-LINEAR POSITIVE OUTPUT GAGE NO. 1
2 ———   NON-LINEAR NEGATIVE OUTPUT GAGE NO. 2
3 —·—   OUTPUT GAGE NO. 2 CONVERTED TO POSITIVE
4 ————   OUTPUT GAGE NO. 1 ELECTRICALLY SUBTRACTED
         FROM OUTPUT GAGE NO. 2

FIG. 5. Resistance change vs. strain—linearity compensation using one gage in tension and one gage in compression.

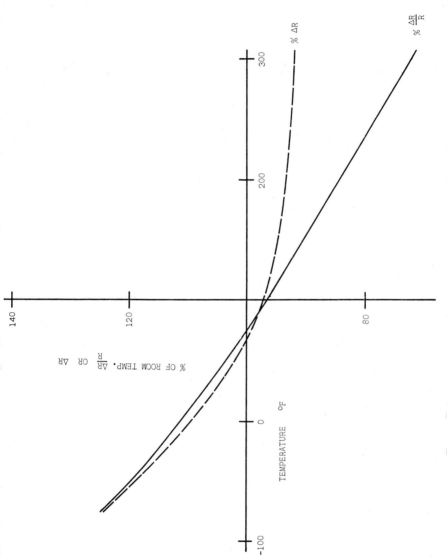

FIG. 6. Relative resistance change vs. temperature for Micro-Sensor.

ance. Next it will be shown how a circuit, other than a Wheatstone bridge, is employed to provide a linear signal for these elements by producing an output directly proportional to ΔR. The following discusses adverse characteristics peculiar to semiconductor gages, some of which can be compensated for with a specially designed strain indicator, but practical and economic limitations prevent the design of an indicator that can compensate for all adverse characteristics.

The output of a semiconductor strain gage is not linear with strain. Figure 3 presents $\%\Delta R/R$ vs. strain. Figure 4 shows this nonlinearity as per cent change in gage factor vs. strain. Though the output is essentially linear when the gage is subjected to tension, it is extremely nonlinear when the gage is subjected to compression. The linearity is between $\pm\frac{3}{4}\%$ between -500 and $+500$ microinches. Methods of linearizing are discussed by Sanchez and Wright.[1] It should be noted that some of these methods decrease the sensitivity of the gage. Another method would be to utilize two active arms wherever possible. Figure 5 shows the improvement in linearity when two active gages are utilized: one in tension, and one in compression. This technique essentially doubles the gage output and now some of the methods suggested by Sanchez and Wright,[1] to improve linearity at the expense of sensitivity, can be employed.

The third adverse characteristic is perhaps the most critical. Figure 6 shows the change in output of a semiconductor gage vs. temperature. The solid line shows the per cent change of $\Delta R/R$ which is obtained with a constant voltage supply; and the dashed curve shows the per cent change of ΔR as obtained with a constant current supply. The improvement is noticeable.

It is now evident that a device employing a constant-current supply, whose output is proportional to ΔR, will provide linear readings for a high sensitivity resistive element and will decrease the effect of temperature on the output of a semiconductor gage.

Design Considerations

From the foregoing, it is seen that a strain indicator employing a constant-current supply will correct or at least improve two of these three conditions: (1) an output directly proportional to ΔR will be a decided improvement over a Wheatstone bridge, and (2) it will reduce the effect of temperature on the sensitivity of semiconductor gages. However, this constant current device will not improve the linearity with strain level and this is a limitation which must be considered whenever a semiconductor gage is employed.

If it is decided that the output of a strain indicator for semiconductor gages must be proportional to ΔR and not $\Delta R/R$, a re-examination of the definition of gage factor may be in order. Gage factor is defined as $\Delta R/R$ per unit strain. This is a very convenient formula when using conventional gages in Wheatstone bridges. The output of a Wheatstone bridge is proportional to $\Delta R/R$ and, therefore, it is proportional to gage factor times strain. Regardless of the resistance of the gage, the gage factor is a true measure of the sensitivity of the gage.

This, however, is no longer true when a constant current device is used and the output is proportional to ΔR. Since ΔR = gage factor $\times \epsilon \times R$, the output is very much affected by the value of R. In fact, a 240Ω gage with a gage factor of 100 will provide twice the output of a 120Ω gage with the same gage factor. Gage factor is no longer a true indication of the sensitivity of a gage used in a true constant current instrument. It is suggested that a new term, "gage sensitivity," may be more useful for semiconductor gages where gage sensitivity is defined as $\Delta R/\epsilon$.

The strain indicator described in this paper utilizes constant-current circuitry and has an output directly proportional to gage sensitivity and not gage factor. Naturally, since gages are identified as to gage factor and resistance, controls had to be provided and labeled for the entry of these parameters. One control for gage sensitivity would have been more appropriate. As described further on, it will be shown that the gage factor must be corrected for the actual resistance of the gage because this affects the true sensitivity. It will also be shown that the gage manufacturer's correction factor for mounted gages can be ignored since the true sensitivity of the gage does not change.

Design Parameters

The basic design parameters set up for the strain indicator discussed here are as follows:

(1) It will be capable of measuring the output of 1, 2, or 4 active gages.

(2) The gage resistance will be 120Ω ± 10% or 350Ω ± 10%.

(3) The gage factor (or gage sensitivity) will be between 80 and 150.

(4) The maximum allowable wattage is approximately 0.12 watts per gage.

(5) The total range will be ±1000 microinches/inch.

(6) The resolution will be 1 microinch/inch static strain on a meter.

(7) The output shall also be displayable on an external dynamic indicator.

(8) The accuracy of the indicator shall be better than the accuracy of the semiconductor strain gage. (The actual accuracy achieved will be discussed further on.)

EUGENE FRANK

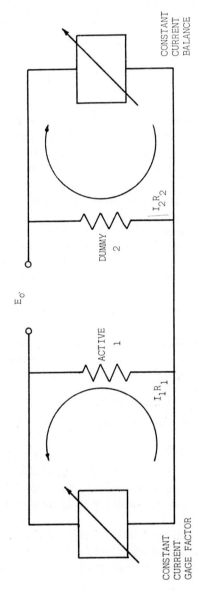

FIG. 7. Basic circuit diagram for single active gage.

Basic Circuitry

Figure 7 is the basic circuit for a single active gage which will provide constant current through the gage and a bucking voltage across a dummy

$$E_o = I_1R_1 - I_2R_2 = 0; \text{ therefore, } I_1R_1 = I_2R_2;$$
$$E_o = I_1(R_1 + \Delta R_1) - I_2R_2 = I_1(R_1 + \Delta R_1) - I_1R_1 = I_1\Delta R_1.$$

gage so that we can obtain a zero output at the initial strain level of the gage and an output which is proportional to ΔR as the gage resistance varies. It will be apparent that the constant current supply across the active gage will be the gage factor or sensitivity control. The constant current supply across the dummy gage will be the balance control. For any setting of current through the active gage, the output can be adjusted to zero by varying the current through the dummy. As the active gage is stressed, the output will be directly proportional to ΔRI and, since I is a constant, the output will be in proportion to ΔR. In the case of two active arms, the dummy can be replaced with another active gage subjected to opposite strain. (The constant current supplies are described in the Appendix.)

To accommodate four active arms, the circuit of Fig. 8 is used. It will be noted that, unlike conventional four-arm transducers in a Wheatstone bridge, like strains must be in adjacent arms. It must be also noted that the bridge must be open. Since four-arm transducers can be used with constant voltage circuitry, it is anticipated that the strain indicator will be used primarily with one or two active gages; however, complete facilities are included for 1, 2 or 4-active gages.

A circuit has now been devised that will accommodate any number of active arms with constant current, the output is proportional to ΔR and zero and span controls have been provided.

Calibration or Standardization

It is now necessary to devise a means of setting the current in the active gage so that the output will be proportional to strain regardless of different gage factors and different gage resistances. The true sensitivity of the semiconductor gages is proportional to the gage factor and the resistance of the gage; therefore, the maximum current was chosen for a 120Ω gage with a gage factor of 80. (This neglects the fact that the resistance tolerance is $\pm 10\%$, but the adjustments were designed to provide this much leeway.) The maximum current in the gage is limited by the allowable dissipation; 30 ma through a 120Ω gage will dissipate 0.108 watt. This was chosen as the maximum current. Once this value was chosen, the current required in 120Ω gages of different gage factors was calculated:

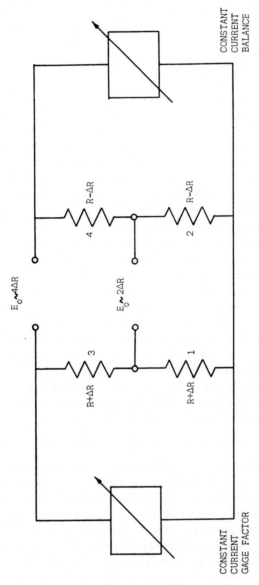

FIG. 8. Basic circuit for two or four active gages.

120Ω Gage:

Gage factor:	80	100	120	140
Current (ma):	30	24	20	17.14

Likewise, if the amplification of the indicator is maintained constant, the current in a 350Ω gage is proportionally lower for the same gage factors:

350Ω Gage:

Gage factor:	80	100	120	140
Current (ma):	10.28	8.23	6.86	5.88

The wattage dissipated in a 350Ω gage for the critical case of 10.28 ma is 0.036 watt which is well below the maximum allowable. It will be noted that

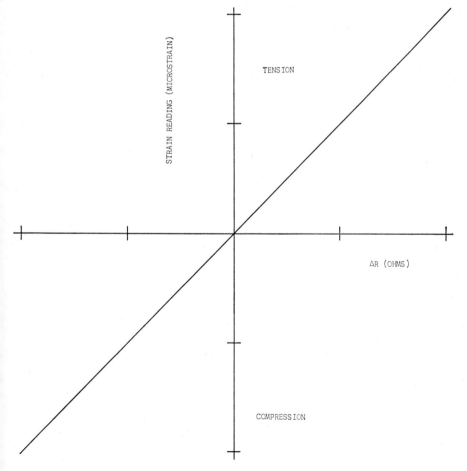

Fig. 9. Output of strain indicator vs. resistance change—to prove linearity of indicator.

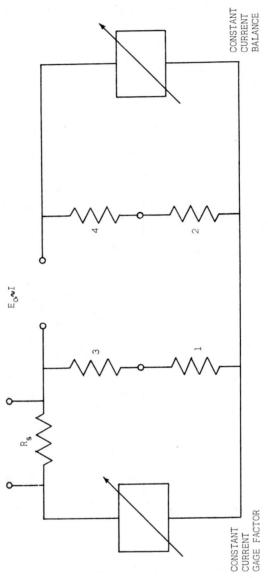

Fig. 10. Basic circuit; four active gages; R_s for gage factor adjustment.

had the amplifier gain been reduced for the 350Ω gage by the ratio of 120/350 to maintain the same current for a corresponding gage factor, the maximum allowable wattage would have been exceeded.

If controls are provided so that the above currents can be maintained, the output of the indicator will be directly proportional to ΔR regardless of the gage factor and of the resistance of the gage. Since the strain is proportional to ΔR (see Fig. 9), the output of this indicator will, therefore, be proportional to strain. The method of setting the current is shown in Fig. 10. By measuring the voltage drop across a fixed series resistor, the current of the gage can be measured. Even when two active gages are used, one in each circuit, only the current in gage "1" is measured. The current in the other gage is automatically set to the correct value when the circuit is nulled. It will be shown further on how the same amplifier and meter, used to measure strain, will be switched over to measure the current. This is done not only for convenience but to increase the accuracy of the instrument. Using the same amplifier and meter to set up the current in the gage, the gain of the indicator is automatically calibrated out and the accuracy is independent of the exact gain of the amplifier and meter. This is very much superior to a calibrated "gage factor" control.

It is worth noting here that this method of calibration must be used with semiconductor gages. The well-known method of shunt calibration, employed with standard low gage factor strain gages, is not workable with large gage factor gages. This is true because the strain duplicated by a shunt calibration resistor is directly proportional to the resistance of the gage across which it is placed. As stated before, one of the prime factors which must be remembered is that the resistance of a semiconductor gage varies greatly with strain and is not a constant.

Amplifier and Output Circuitry

The circuit has now been designed so that the output is proportional to strain regardless of the resistance of the gage and the gage factor of the gage. The output can, therefore, be calculated for the minimum strain, $\Delta R = K\epsilon R$ where K is the gage factor, ϵ is the strain, and R is the resistance of the gage. For a 120Ω gage with a gage factor of 80 and a strain of 1 microinch, $\Delta R = 9.6 \times 10^{-3}\Omega$. The output voltage for a single active gage $= \Delta RI = 9.6 \times 10^{-3} \times 30 \times 10^{-3} = 288~\mu v$. Under all conditions of gage resistance and gage factor, this is the output produced by 1 microinch of strain. Using a 200-division zero-center meter, an amplifier was designed to produce a reading of one division for an input voltage of 288 μv. Thus 28.8 mv will produce full scale and will be equivalent to 100 microinches of strain.

A solid state chopper stabilized amplifier was designed with a fixed gain to provide full scale on the meter for a 28.8-mv signal. A ±100-μa meter was employed so that a relatively low gain amplifier could be used. This permitted the design of a very stable amplifier. (The amplifier is described in the Appendix.) It can now further be seen why it was initially decided to compensate for different gage factors and different gage resistances by varying the current. This permitted the use of one fixed gain amplifier for all conditions.

If two active gages are employed, twice the output will be produced; and, if four active gages are employed, four times the output will be produced. A 3-position switch is used to attenuate the output accordingly so that the same fixed gain is required for all cases. This switch is labeled 1, 2, and 4 and it also switches the output from terminals AB to terminals CD (see Fig. 11).

Since full scale meter reading will be obtained for 100 microinches, a bucking voltage must be applied for strains above this value. This is a DC voltage applied in series with the meter. A 10-position Range switch is used to choose the range and to apply the proper bucking voltage. Ten ranges are available from 0 to 100 microinches through 900 to 1000 micro-inches so that a constant resolution of 1 microinch is obtained throughout the entire range. (This bucking voltage supply is described in the Appendix.)

To use this same amplifier and meter to read gage current, one position on the Range switch is used to switch the amplifier from the output of the gages to the series resistor across which the current drop is measured. Actually, two resistors are used, one for 120Ω and one for 350Ω, so that the amplifier would read the same gage factor regardless of the resistance of the gage. It will be noted from the tabulations of gage current vs. gage factor that the current is inversely proportional to gage factor; therefore, the circuit was designed to reverse the direction of the meter during this operation so that the gage factors would be read in a more conventional manner. A different bucking voltage was also incorporated so that a larger portion of the scale could be utilized. Using the tabulations of gage factor vs. current, the meter was hand-calibrated to read gage factor directly. By making the series resistor for the 350Ω gage, 350/120 times the series resistor for the 120Ω gage, the gage factor setting is made independent of the basic resistance of the gage.

The above arrangement provides for direct setting of gage factor only for gages that are either exactly 120Ω or exactly 350Ω. Semiconductor gages are currently being produced with a tolerance of approximately ±10%. Therefore, the gages may have a resistance quite different from the basic 120 or 350Ω values. A method of varying the series resistors to compensate for this tolerance was devised, but it was deemed too impractical to use. Instead, it was decided to first correct the actual gage factor by referencing it to an equivalent gage factor for a 120 or 350Ω gage. As an example, if the gages are marked 125Ω, gage factor 100, the corrected gage factor is 100 × 120/125. This is the gage factor that must be set when the switch is in the 120Ω position. This again points out the fact that with semiconductor gages, the true sensitivity of the gage is not the gage factor alone but the gage factor times the resistance of the gage. If gage manufacturers would label their gages with this true sensitivity factor, exact resistance of the gage is unimportant when used in a circuit of this type.

Users of semiconductor gages will note that the manufacturer suggests a gage factor correction based on the change in the resistance of the gage after it is mounted on the structure. This correction is as follows: $K_m = K_o \times R_o/R_m$, where K_o is the gage factor noted on the package, R_o is the resistance noted on the package, K_m is the gage factor after mounting, and R_m is the resistance after mounting. Since this instrument is sensitive to the sensitivity of the gage and not to the gage factor of the gage, this correction does not have to be made; therefore, it is not necessary to know the mounted resistance of the gage. All semiconductor gages may change their resistance when mounted. This feature, therefore, saves considerable time.

To summarize, the gage factor must be corrected for the difference in the actual resistance of the gage from a standard 120 or 350Ω gage, but it is not necessary to correct the gage factor to compensate for the resistance change that occurs when mounting the gage on a structure.

Over-All Configuration

Figure 11 is the over-all circuit diagram of the instrument and photographs of the strain indicator are shown in Figs. 12–14. Figure 15 shows one of the test setups used to check the strain indicator. Semiconductor gages were mounted side by side with conventional foil gages on a constant strain beam. An SR-4* Indicator was used to measure the output of the foil gages.

The instrument is housed in a small portable chassis and is powered from 110 volts, 60 cycles. It absorbs approximately 20 watts. All controls are in the front and the terminals for mounting the strain gages or the bridge completion resistors are mounted in the rear. The basic components are as follows:

(1) Two constant current supplies capable of producing 15 to 35 ma through a 240Ω load and 5 to 12 ma through a 700Ω load. Each supply has a 10-turn potentiometer as the current control. One potentiometer is labeled Gage Factor and the other potentiometer is labeled Balance.

(2) A chopper stabilized solid state amplifier producing a full scale

* Registered Trade Mark, Baldwin-Lima-Hamilton Corporation.

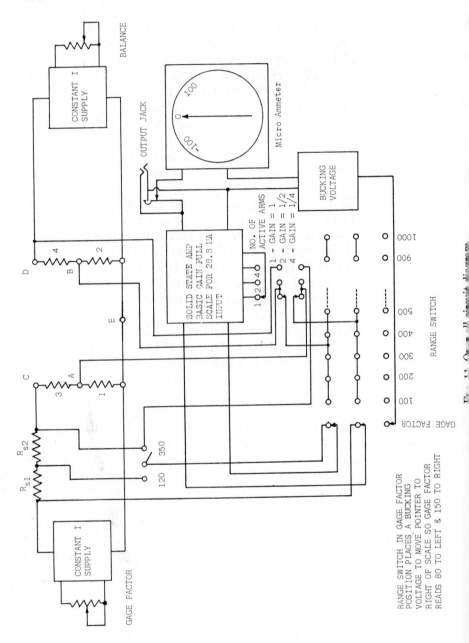

Fig. 11. Over-all circuit diagram.

FIG. 12. Front view of strain indicator Model No. 1-110 SC.

output for 28.8 mv input. It must be capable of handling input signals as high as 288 mv.

(3) A bucking voltage supply capable of producing from 10 through 90 mv in nine equal steps.

(4) A 100-0-100 microammeter.

(5) An 11-position Range switch.

(6) A 3-position Active Arm switch.

(7) A 2-position Gage Resistance switch.

(8) An output jack by-passing the bucking voltage to enable the recording of transients.

(9) A power switch and an indicator lamp.

(10) Five input terminals to accommodate active or dummy gages.

OPERATION

(1) *Gage connections:* A single gage is always placed across terminals AE. Dummy arms of equal resistances should be placed across the other three arms. Two active gages of opposite polarity must be placed across terminals

AE and BE with dummy arms across AC and BD. Four active arms must be placed across all terminals with like strains across arms AE and AC and like strains of opposite polarity across arms BE and BD. *Note:* In each case, the polarity of the indicator will be determined by the polarity of the gage placed across arm AE. If this gage is in tension, the meter will read tension; if this gage is in compression, the meter will read compression.

FIG. 13. Rear view of strain indicator Model No. 1-110 SC.

(2) The Gage Resistance switch should be placed in either the 120 or 350Ω position, depending upon the basic resistance of the gage as noted on the gage.

(3) The Range switch must be placed on the Gage Factor position. The arm switch must be placed in position No. 1.

(4) If the resistance of the gage differs from 120 or 350Ω, the gage factor must be corrected, as follows: $K = K_o \times 120/R_o$ where K_o and R_o are the manufacturer's values noted on the gage and K is the value which will be set on the indicator scale. Adjust the Gage Factor control until the meter indicates the correct gage factor on the gage factor scale.

(5) Place the Range switch in position No. 1; place the Arm switch in the position corresponding to the number of active arms. *Note:* If total strain is required rather than the average strain, the Arm switch should be left in position No. 1.

(6) The indicator is now set to read ±100 microinches directly. When full scale has been exceeded, rotate the Range switch to position No. 2.

FIG. 14. Internal view of strain indicator Model No. 1-110 SC.

The exact strain will be the reading of the meter plus 100 microinches. Likewise, in position No. 10, the exact strain will be the meter reading plus 900 microinches.

(7) When the output Jack is used for external recording, the output voltage will be proportional to strain, from 0 to 1000 microinches, as long as the Range switch is in any position from No. 1 to No. 10. The exact position is unimportant as the bucking voltage has been by-passed. *Note:* The Range switch must not be in the Gage Factor position.

Fig. 15. Evaluation test setup for strain indicator.

Appendix

1. *Constant Current Power Supplies*

The circuit system in this equipment has a voltage regulated power supply which operates as a preregulator common to both current regulated outputs. The preregulator removes the changes due to line fluctuations to the degree of its regulating ability and, in addition, provides one fixed voltage reference common to the two current regulators. Differential drifts thus tend to cancel and the current regulating circuitry may be less complex.

The currents in the two strain gage arms are adjusted with separate 10-turn potentiometers.

All regulating and adjusting resistances are of low temperature coefficient materials. The basic regulator temperature coefficient is less than $0.01\%/°C$, and the net differential temperature coefficient, as seen by the indicator section of the system, is even less due to the cancellation action referred to above.

The preregulator section has four transistors in its circuitry, and the two current regulating sections use three transistors each, for a total of ten.

The entire indicator operates from one power transformer; with this power supply section operating from one winding.

The output currents are adjustable from below 5 ma to 35 ma in each arm with a maximum voltage drop across the current terminals of 15 volts. This range more than covers the various gage resistances and power operating levels encountered in normal operation.

The regulating action is such that for input power line variations of from 90 to 135 volts AC, the output currents will vary less than 0.1%; with the differential between output currents being even less.

The change in current with load resistance variations is regulated to less than 0.1% for resistance changes from zero to the maximum.

Noise and hum in the current outputs is a form of regulation shortcoming, and, in this equipment, is less than 0.02%. Ripple components in the currents through the gage arm cancel at balance but do appear when the strain gage is giving an output. The ripple is proportional to the output, but will be considerably less than the percentage in the individual current outputs.

The power transformer and equipment construction provides shielding isolation from noise and power frequency strays, such that less than 10 mv peak-to-peak will appear across a grounded readout equipment for each 350Ω of load impedance to ground.

2. Amplifier

The output of semiconductor gages is high compared to other gages and, therefore, the indicating meter requirements are less complicated. However, sensitive indicating meters have loading effects and if a low impedance readout device is used with a single active gage, linearity is affected. The voltages available are appropriate, but an impedance changing circuit must be used to provide a practical system.

This equipment has a low level power amplifier which changes the meter impedance, as seen by the gage circuits, to a high value to prevent loadings. This amplifier has a low voltage gain but, since it operates in the low millivolt region part of the time, its zero stability requirement can only be met with chopper type circuitry. A mechanical chopper is used to both modulate and demodulate the input and output of a simple AC amplifier which, combined with suitable filtering components, operates as a DC amplification system. The zero stability is a function of the chopper system action, and the gain stability and linearity are functions of feedback in the AC amplifier.

One transformer winding is used to operate the chopper coil and the solid state AC amplifier power supply. The AC amplifier does not require regulation of its power supply because of the feedback stabilization. A total of three transistors is used. The over-all voltage gain is less than 10.

The metering stability is better than 0.25% for line fluctuations of 90 to 135 volts AC.

3. Meter Bucking Voltage Supply

A stable reverse current must be passed through the meter coil for versatile depressed zero operation of the meter scale ranges. In this strain indicator, nine of the ten ranges have a depressed zero. The maximum bucking current is applied on the 1000 microinch range and is 9 times the center-to-full scale meter current, or approximately 900 μa.

The source of this reverse current is a double zener regulated power supply operated from one winding of the transformer with a nominal output of 4.7 volts at 2 ma. The output current is retained at a constant 2 ma and a stable resistor network is switched, for the various ranges, to divert into the meter the proper reverse current for the range being used.

By having a 4.7 volt source to buck a meter movement drop of less than 10 mv, a coupling network results which gives good isolation of the meter driving circuitry. This makes possible a current ratio network of precision resistors for fixing these bucking currents using a minimum of trimming adjustments.

The stability of this section is better than that of the meter movement with respect to temperature. Power line fluctuations are regulated to less than a 0.1% change of bucking current. Thus, in the 900- to 1000-microinch range, the most critical, an error of less than 1 microinch may result.

ACKNOWLEDGMENTS

The author wishes to thank J. Steimer, A. Leiby, R. Kuehner, and G. Kingan for their help in fin shing the prototype evaluation and gathering the data in time for this report.

REFERENCES

1. Sanchez, J. C., and Wright, W. V., Recent developments in flexible silicon strain gages, see p. 307 in this volume.
2. Mack, D. R., Linearizing the output of resistance temperature gages, *Proc. Soc. Exptl. Stress Anal.* **18**, 122 (1961).

RECENT DEVELOPMENTS IN FLEXIBLE SILICON STRAIN GAGES*

J. C. SANCHEZ

Micro Systems, Inc., San Gabriel, California

AND

W. V. WRIGHT

Electro-Optical Systems, Inc., Pasadena, California

ABSTRACT

The properties of semiconductor silicon strain gages are reviewed noting the high available gage factors (> 100) coupled with reasonable temperature stability. A specific flexible commercially available silicon strain gage, the Micro-Sensor, has been used at temperatures exceeding 500°F. Methods of installation, temperature, compensation techniques, linearity, hysteresis, and fatigue properties of the Micro-Sensor are given. Temperature stability at least equal to conventional strain gages has been observed and negligible hysteresis noted. Example Micro-Sensor applications in aircraft instrumentation and physiological measurements are presented wherein data were obtained under conditions that essentially precluded the use of any other type of strain measuring device.

INTRODUCTION

The use of metallic electrical strain gages has been widespread in the instrumentation and stress analysis field for about 20 years and certain fundamental problems such as low signal level and thermal drift have remained persistently. As a result, costly and complex electronic systems have been developed to calibrate and accurately measure the response of these relatively low gage factor metallic strain gages. Higher gage factor materials were known but they suffered from unacceptable thermal changes of properties. A breakthrough in this important field was heralded by a physicist who reported the piezoresistive properties of two semiconductors, silicon and germanium, in 1954.[1] Curiously, this basic work was little noticed, and in 1957 the application of semiconductor strain measuring elements to transducers was described.[2] The work described in this article began in 1958 and has resulted in a practical semiconductor strain gage

---

* Presented at the Winter Meeting of the Instrument Societ of America. St. Louis, Missouri, January, 1961.

(bonded or unbonded) which can be used exactly as the prior metallic strain gage but with a gage factor approximately 65 times larger. This large gage factor is accompanied by a thermal rate of change of resistance also approximately 65 times higher than conventional gages, hence the semiconductor strain gage is relatively as stable as the metallic strain gage but at a much higher output level. In addition, straightforward temperature compensation methods are applicable to the semiconductor strain gage, which

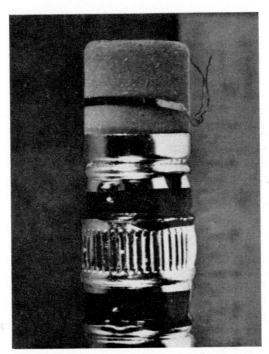

FIG. 1. Micro-Sensor flexibility (curved around pencil).

enhance its usefulness and allow the measurement of "microstrain" formerly beyond the realm of convenient measurement. Temperature compensation methods and other application notes are discussed later.

Since the semiconductor strain gage promises a breakthrough in instrumentation techniques, a brief description of the device should prove useful. The most widely used semiconductor strain gage material is silicon. Semiconductor silicon is chemically inert, exhibits suitable temperature stability coupled with a large gage factor (>100), and can be fabricated in a form which is mechanically strong ($>0.5\%$ maximum strain) and geometrically flexible. The large piezoresistance effects in semiconductors occur along specific crystallographic axes and silicon strain gages must be fabricated

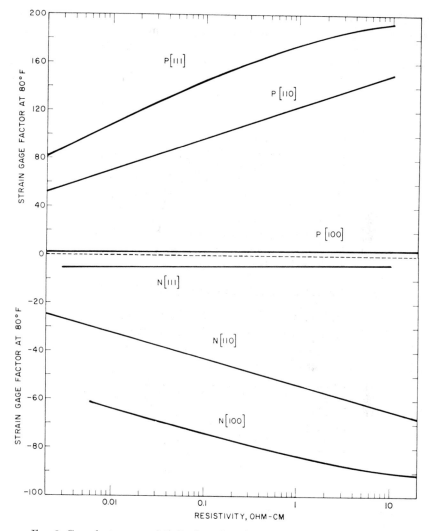

FIG. 2. Gage factor vs. resistivity for selected types and crystal orientations.

from oriented single crystals of silicon in order to obtain the highest gage factor coupled with stability. The mechanical properties of silicon are somewhat like those of quartz; and silicon will not deform plastically below 1000°F. Even though silicon is brittle, it is strong and will bend through a 0.125-inch radius if fabricated with suitable geometry and surface finish as shown in Fig. 1. The elastic nature of single crystal silicon below 1000°F is nearly perfect and essentially free of hysteresis.

Semiconductor silicon can be controlled over a wide range of electrical resistivity (0.0005 to 10,000 ohm-cm) by the addition of suitable impurities (doping materials) to nearly pure silicon. An extensive study of the effects of crystal orientation and various kinds and amounts of impurities in silicon on gage factor and temperature coefficients was conducted at Electro-

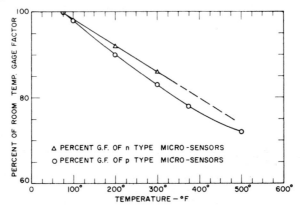

FIG. 3. Gage factor vs. temperature for *n*- and *p*-types (unbonded) tested in tension.

Optical Systems, Inc., with the support of Picatinny Arsenal, U. S. Army Ordnance Corps, and the results of that study were presented earlier.[3] Additional company-sponsored work has resulted in a commercially available flexible silicon strain gage, the Micro-Sensor, which is described in

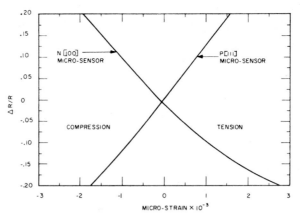

FIG. 4. $\Delta R/R$ vs. strain for *n*- and *p*-types.

detail later. The most recent data on silicon strain gage factor, temperature effects, linearity, and crystal orientation are summarized in Figs. 2–5. We conclude that *p*-type silicon, 0.01 ohm-cm, [111] crystal orientation, is a nearly optimum material for tension strain measurements near room tem-

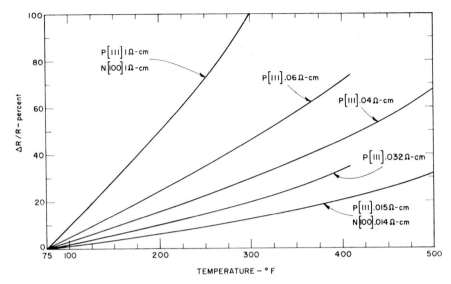

Fig. 5. $\Delta R/R$ vs. temperature for selected resistivities and types of semiconductor elements. *Note:* Gages are unbonded.

perature. Note that suitable gage factor and stability can be obtained to 500°F with low resistivity silicon strain elements. A comparison of the Micro-Sensor to conventional strain gages is given in Table I.

TABLE I

COMPARISON OF MICRO-SENSOR PROPERTIES TO THOSE OF METALLIC FOIL
STRAIN GAGES (TYPICAL VALUES)

| | Strain gage | | |
Property	Micro-sensor	Metal foil gage	Ratio Micro-Sensor metal foil gage
Gage factor	130	2	65
Typical "apparent strain" on steel, Uncompensated gages (microstrain/°F)	6–8	6–10	Approx. $\cong$ 1
Thermal coeff. of expansion (ppm/°F)	1.3	5	0.26
Thermal coeff. gage factor (%/100°F)	10	1	10

Additional work is being conducted on higher temperature semiconductor strain gages and on other forms of silicon strain gage elements. The Micro-Sensor is presently applied similarly to conventional strain gages. The advantages of the high semiconductor gage factor have already been profit-ably employed and demonstrated. Although early indications showed cer-tain undesirable temperature effects, compensation techniques have been developed which can overcome this early problem area. The single crystal nature of the element material results in extremely repeatable results. Preliminary laboratory and commercial usage of the Micro-Sensor has indicated a high degree of reliability for the device.

PHYSICAL DESCRIPTION—STANDARD GAGES

The Micro-Sensor[tm]* Models MS 105–350 and MS 115–350 are the first in a complete line of semiconductor strain gages.

The MS 115-350 (Fig. 6) is a flexible rectangular filament of single crystal silicon, type p, [111], with a resistivity, ρ, of 0.017 ohm-cm and whose di-mensions are 0.0007 thick × 0.020 wide × 0.75 inch long. The active gage length is 0.50 inch and terminal resistance is 350 ohms. Gold lead wires of

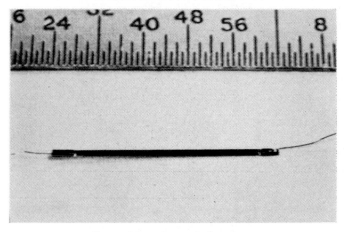

FIG. 6. Micro-Sensor MS 115–350.

0.003-inch diameter are provided. The MS 115 series of gages may be installed around radii of $\frac{1}{8}$ inch or larger without failure of the filament (see Fig. 1). The temperature limit of this gage is approximately 650°F, but the availability of suitable strain gage adhesives generally precludes its use above 550°F. Gages of other resistances than 350 ohms are available on special order.

The MS 105-350 gage (Fig. 7) consists of a standard MS 115-350 strain filament mounted on an epoxy base carrier for ease of handling and installa-tion. Integral tinned terminal tabs are provided. The gage is easily installed around diameters of 1-inch without fracture of the filament (see Fig. 8).

* tm—Trade Mark.

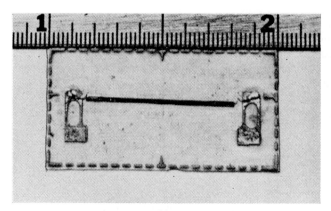

Fig. 7. Micro-Sensor MS 105–350.

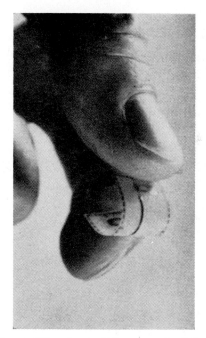

Fig. 8. Micro-Sensor MS 105–350 flexibility.

High Temperature Gages

A weldable high temperature Micro-Sensor for use up to 500°F (Figs. 9 and 10) will be available in the near future. This gage is easily attached to most test surfaces in a matter of minutes. In addition, the linear operating strain range of the gage has been considerably extended by the use of the

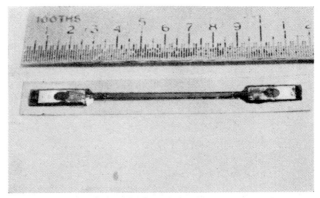

FIG. 9. Weldable type.

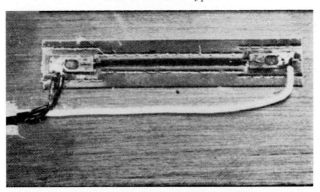

FIG. 10. Weldable type installed.

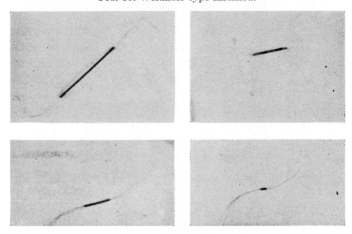

FIG. 11. A. Short gage length types.

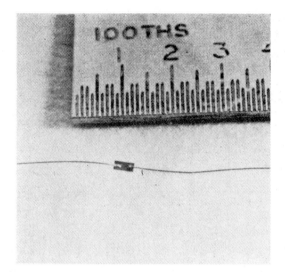

Fig. 11. B. Short gage length type.

prestressing techniques mentioned later. Higher temperature (up to 1500°F) gages are in an advanced stage of development.

Short Gages

Micro-Sensors with active gage lengths of approximately 0.10 and 0.3 inch will soon be available. Figures 11a and 11b shows typical gage sizes currently being produced in prototype quantities. Gages as short as $\frac{1}{64}$ inch have been produced.

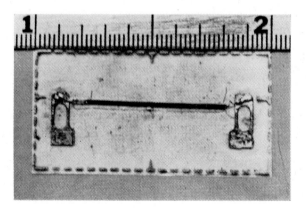

Fig. 12. Temperature-compensated thermistor type.

Temperature-Compensated Gages

Self-temperature-compensated Micro-Sensors are currently being evaluated in the Engineering Laboratory. Two configurations appear promising for many applications.

1. The thermistor-compensated Micro-Sensor shown in Fig. 12 employs a miniature thermistor in shunt with the active strain filament. A typical curve (Fig. 13) for the $\Delta R/R$ versus temperature of an uncompensated Micro-Sensor is compared with that of a compensated unit when mounted on 2024-T6 aluminum.

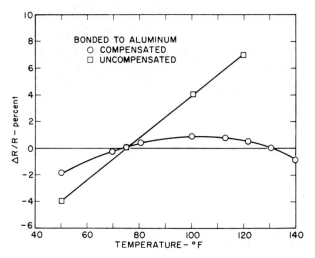

Fig. 13. Relative resistance change vs. temperature for Micro-Sensor with and without thermistor temperature compensation.

2. The half-active bridge Micro-Sensor shown in Fig. 14 utilizes a p-type (positive gage factor) filament in conjugate bridge arms with an n-type (negative gage factor) filament. Since both type filaments have positive temperature coefficients, self-temperature compensation will result if care is exercised in the selection of the proper filaments. The method by which temperature compensation is achieved is discussed elsewhere. An additional advantage of the p-n gage combination is that a fully active 4-arm bridge may be placed on one side of a tension or bending member.

Both methods of self-temperature compensation tend to improve the gage linearity at or about room temperature. This condition can reverse at higher temperatures depending on the thermal expansion coefficient of the test material and the strain filaments used.

An additional method of minimizing temperature effects is to fabricate strain filaments of even more heavily doped (lower resistivity) materials.[3,4] Micro-Sensors of this type will be available in the near future.

Present plans are to market Micro-Sensors which are self-temperature compensated for materials whose expansion coefficients are 6, 9, and 12

FIG. 14. Temperature-compensated semiconductor strain gage, *p-n* type.

ppm/°F. Such gages will not be available commercially, however, until the completion of the exhaustive evaluation and qualification program currently being conducted.

METHOD OF INSTALLATION

The Micro-Sensor is quite flexible and rugged and can be installed, as shown in Fig. 15, on test specimens in the same way as conventional epoxy-backed metal foil gages. Some care must be exercised in handling so as to avoid excessive local pressure or bending in the filament area.

Most of the room temperature curing *rigid* epoxy adhesives as well as Eastman 910 "contact cement" are suitable for use with the Micro-Sensor.

Particularly recommended for room temperature use are Armstrong A-2,* Baldwin† EPY-150, and SGAC‡ No. 121 or 122, which are epoxies, and the Eastman 910 kit supplied by the Instrument Division of the Budd Company.§ The adhesive used should be prepared and mixed in accordance with the manufacturer's instructions.

The test specimen is sanded or sandblasted and cleaned with Acetone. When using the epoxies, a thin layer of adhesive is then spread on the part and the Micro-Sensor placed in the desired position. A mild clamping

---

* Armstrong Products Co., Warsaw, Ind.

† Baldwin-Lima-Hamilton Corporation, Waltham, Massachusetts.

‡ Strain Gage Accessories Company, B. J. Wolfe Enterprises, P. O. Box 281, Northridge, California.

§ Instrument Division of Budd Company, Phoenixville, Pennsylvania.

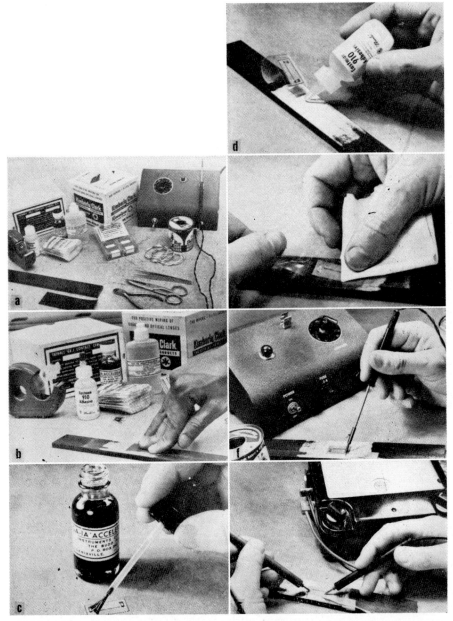

FIG. 15. Installation of semiconductor strain gages. (a) Equipment; (b) surface preparation; (c) apply catalyst; (d) apply cement; (e) apply gage; (f) hook up lead wire; (g) check-out.

pressure (2–5 psi) is recommended to assure uniform contact. In the case of Eastman 910, the normal procedure used to install conventional strain gages is quite satisfactory.

The epoxy adhesives are cured overnight at room temperature (75°–80°F); if temperatures in excess of the cure temperature are expected, the installation should be post cured for 2 to 4 hours at that temperature.

After curing of the adhesive, lead wires, previously tinned, are attached to the pretinned integral terminals with a soldering pencil rated at 40 watts or less.

The resistance to ground should be checked using a vacuum-tube voltmeter. The resistance value should be in excess of 100 megohms.

The resistance of the Micro-Sensor is then checked and noted using a Wheatstone bridge (or a strain gage indicator and decade box) to the nearest 0.1 ohm. The shrinkage of the adhesive and/or differential contraction induced by curing at a slightly elevated temperature may have changed the resistance of the Micro-Sensor from the nominal value which will have a direct effect on the strain sensitivity or gage factor. Gage factor is expressed as follows:

$$G.F._0 = \frac{\Delta R/R_0}{\epsilon} \tag{1}$$

where $G.F._0$ = gage factor noted on package
ΔR = change in resistance due to applied strain, ϵ
R_0 = resistance noted for each gage.

The gage factor of the mounted installation may be computed as follows:

$$G.F._m = G.F._0 \times \frac{R_0}{R_m} \tag{2}$$

where R_m = resistance of mounted installation
$G.F._m$ = corrected gage factor of mounted installation.

Strain Sensitivity

The strain sensitivity (or gage factor) of the Micro-Sensor is defined as the unit resistance change caused by an axial strain. Unfortunately, this resistance change is not entirely linear with strain, especially in compression, as shown in Figs. 16 and 17 where $\Delta R/R$ versus strain is plotted from -6000 to $+6000$ and -500 to $+500$ microstrain. Information about linearity compensation will be presented in a later section. It is important, then, for the gage manufacturer to note the strain level at which gage factor measurements are made.

The room temperature gage factor of the Micro-Sensor is determined at a tensile strain level of 1000 microstrain. The nominal gage factor of

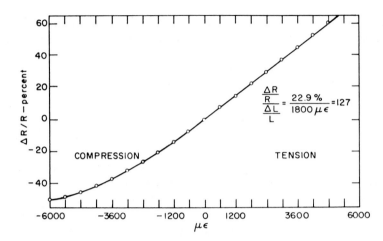

Fig. 16. Strain sensitivity ($\Delta R/R$ vs. strain, ϵ) of type MS 105–350 bonded to aluminum with Eastman 910 cement; tested in constant moment fixture from -6000 to $+6000$ microstrain.

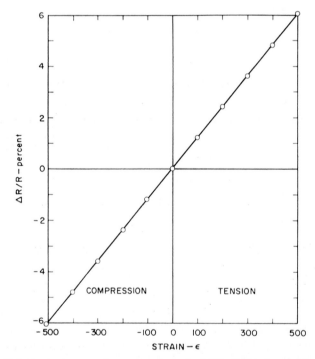

Fig. 17. Relative resistance change vs. strain for MS 105–350 bonded with Eastman 910 cement; tested in constant moment fixture from -500 to $+500$ microstrain.

the MS 105-350, 350-ohm unit, is 130, that of the 120-ohm unit is 120. The sensitivity of the Micro-Sensor to strain transverse to the filament has been found to be less than 1% of the axial sensitivity.

MAXIMUM STRAIN RANGE

The specified operating strain range of current Micro-Sensor models is ±3000 microstrain. The gages are somewhat stronger in compression than in tension. Most units will actually withstand 4000–6000 microstrain in tension. All production units are factory tested to a tensile strain level of 3500 microstrain. The gage factor of each Micro-Sensor is also obtained as a result of these tensile strain tests. Resulting information is used to provide matched sets to specifications.

FATIGUE LIFE

Studies on the room temperature fatigue life of Micro-Sensor Model MS 105-350 are currently being conducted at 500, 1000, 1500, 2000, 2500, and 3000 microstrain in tension. Preliminary data at the 500, 1000, and 1500 microstrain levels indicate fatigue life in excess of 5 million cycles without failure of the Micro-Sensors. Different coupons are used for each strain level data point and S/N curves will be published upon the completion of the test program.

HYSTERESIS AND STABILITY

The Micro-Sensor filaments are stable (re: zero drift and creep) and free from hysteresis up to 500°F due to their single crystalline nonductile nature.

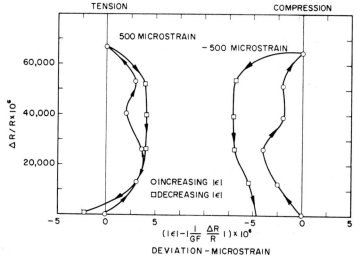

FIG. 18. Strain deviation at room temperature; strain range, ±500 microstrain.

The carrier and bonding adhesives used will introduce hysteresis and instability effects in the same manner and order of magnitude as in conventional strain gage technology. The results from a typical first cycle strain test from zero to $+500$ to -500 and back to zero microstrain are given in Fig. 18. The data are presented as strain deviation versus strain, where strain deviation equals

$$\left| \epsilon \right| - \left| \frac{1}{G.F.} \left(\frac{\Delta R}{R} \right) \right| \times 10^6 \text{ microstrain} \tag{3}$$

and $\quad \left| \epsilon \right|$ = true strain on test part
$\left| \dfrac{1}{G.F.} \left(\dfrac{\Delta R}{R} \right) \right|$ = apparent strain indicated by resistance change of Micro-Sensor.

Note that the observed hysteresis and/or zero offset does not exceed 1% of full scale in the first cycle. After 3 to 4 cycles hysteresis, less than 0.1% has been noted.

Maximum Power Dissipation

The Micro-Sensor, when bonded to a good heat sink, is capable of dissipating in excess of 1 watt of power at room temperature without failure or burn-out; however, the effect of the induced self-heating at this power

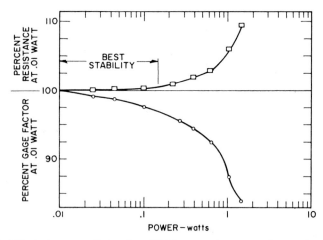

Fig. 19. Effect of power dissipation (E^2/R) on resistance and gage factor of gage bonded to aluminum.

level is rather drastic on stability, resistance change, and sensitivity, as shown in Fig. 19. The data shown in this curve were obtained using several gages (120, 350, and 1000 ohms resistance) bonded to aluminum. Best stability and over-all static performance is obtained with power dissipations per gage of less than 0.10 to 0.15 watt, which is equivalent to gage currents of about 35 and 20 ma, respectively, for 120- and 350-ohm gages. Higher power levels may be used for dynamic tests.

Temperature Effects

The Micro-Sensor is affected by an increase in temperature in several ways.

1. The filament resistance increases.

2. The filament changes in length due to its expansion coefficient ($\alpha = 1.3$ ppm/°F) as well as due to the expansion coefficient (α) of the material to which the gage is attached.

3. The strain sensitivity of the filament decreases.

The result of the above effects causes two undesirable properties of the Micro-Sensor. The first is a relatively high zero shift ($\Delta R/R$) versus temperature for an unloaded specimen commonly called "apparent strain."

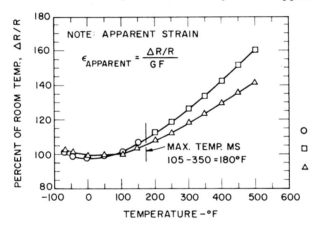

Fig. 20. Relative resistance change, % $\Delta R/R$ vs. temperature. O: MS 105–350 mounted on 17–4 PH steel; □: MS 115–350 mounted on 17–4 PH steel; △: MS 115–350 unmounted.

Figure 20 shows the relative resistance change for a Micro-Sensor filament unbonded as well as bonded to steel between $-70°$ and $+500°F$. The apparent strain,

$$\epsilon_{\text{apparent}} = \frac{\Delta R/R}{G.F.}, \tag{4}$$

is roughly equivalent to conventional uncompensated wire and foil gages.

The second effect of temperature on the Micro-Sensor is a rapid change of relative gage factor (or $\Delta R/\epsilon R$) due to an applied strain. Figure 21 shows this relative change in gage factor as a function of temperature from

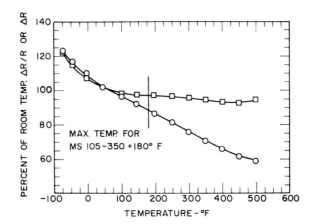

FIG. 21. Relative resistance change $\% \ \Delta R/R$ and $\% \ \Delta R$ vs. temperature for a semi-conductor strain gage bonded to 17–4 PH steel. Strain level $= \pm 500$ microstrain; tested on constant stress beam. $\bigcirc$: $\% \ \Delta R/R$ for MS 115–350 (and MS 105–350 to 180°F) $\square$: $\% \ \Delta R$ for MS 115–350 (and MS 105–350 to 180°F).

$-70°$ to $+500°$F. Included is a curve of ΔR alone versus temperature. It will be shown later that under certain conditions the bridge sensitivity versus temperature can be made nearly proportional to $\Delta R/\epsilon$ instead of $\Delta R/\epsilon R$. The constant stress beam and setup used to determine the variation of $\Delta R/\epsilon$ and $\Delta R/\epsilon R$ versus temperature is shown in Figs. 22 and 23.

CIRCUITRY

The Micro-Sensor is normally used with conventional strain indicating circuits and equipment for the measurement of small strains (0.1–500 microstrain).

If higher strain excursions are expected, the bridge output will be sufficiently large as to allow more direct measurements using galvanometers, millivoltmeters, and perhaps voltmeters, or sensitive ohmeters.

The open circuit output of a bridge circuit (neglecting nonlinearity of the bridge) is normally expressed as follows:

$$E_o = \frac{G.F. \times \epsilon_{\text{tot}} \times E_{\text{in}}}{4} \tag{5}$$

where E_o = output voltage (volts)
$G.F.$ = gage factor (dimensionless)
ϵ_{tot} = total strain in all four arms of the bridge (inches/inch)
E_{in} = bridge supply voltage (volts)

FIG. 22. Constant stress beam installation.

FIG. 23. Gage factor vs. temperature, test setup.

Examples

1. For a 350-ohm Micro-Sensor, we can safely use a bridge supply voltage of 12 volts DC

$$(E^2/4R = 0.1 \text{ watt});\tag{6}$$

and if a single active gage is subjected to a tension strain level of 100 microstrain, an output of

$$E_o = \frac{130 \times 100 \times 10^{-6} \times 12}{4} = 39 \text{ mv}\tag{7}$$

would be realized.

2. If a 4 active (bending) bridge were subjected to a strain level of 2000 microstrain, and if a bridge supply voltage of 20 volts DC were used in conjunction with a 1000-ohm Micro-Sensor, an output of approximately 5.2 *volts* would be expected (see Figs. 24 and 25).

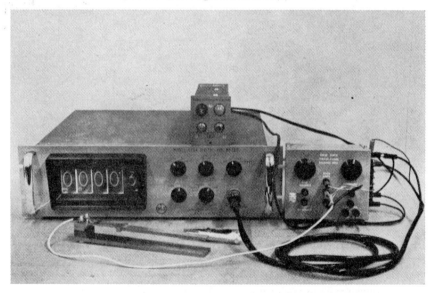

FIG. 24. Bending beam at zero deflection.

It should be emphasized here that if a single active arm bridge circuit is used with 3 dummy gages of the same resistance, considerable nonlinearity will exist in the relationship of $\Delta R/R$ versus bridge output. This nonlinearity in per cent will be approximately equal to one-half of the $\Delta R/R$ excursion in per cent (i.e., for strains of 100 microstrain, $\Delta R/R = 1.3\%$ nonlinearity = 0.6%; for 3000 microstrain, nonlinearity = 18%). This problem is seldom encountered in the use of conventional type strain gages due to the relatively low gage factors and consequently small unit resistance changes.

If a half-bridge (or a full bridge) circuit is used with one leg in tension and the other in compression, the resultant nonlinearity is reduced to second-order effects providing the junction of the active legs is at an output

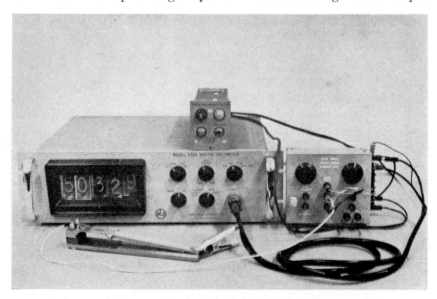

Fig. 25. Bending beam deflected, 5-volt output.

corner of the bridge. The basic requirement which must be fulfilled is that each current carrying half-bridge as seen from the input leads must have a minimum total resistance change, thus keeping the current (I) constant. More information on linearity compensation is presented later.

Temperature-Compensation Techniques

Zero shift or apparent strain compensation in a single active Micro-Sensor may be accomplished in one of four ways:

1. A dummy gage on an unstressed sample of the test material may be wired in conjugate bridge arms with the active gage and if kept at the test temperature the induced temperature effects will cancel; limited only by the matching of the gages and any possible temperature gradient between the two gages.

2. A thermistor network may be used in series or shunt with the active gage such that the equivalent resistance change of the active bridge leg as a function of the temperature is minimized. Figure 13 compares the $\Delta R/R$ versus temperature for an uncompensated and compensated Micro-

Sensor when mounted on 2024-T6 aluminum. A further advantage of this technique is that the $\Delta R/R$ versus strain curve is somewhat linearized by the shunting effect of the thermistor.

3. A self-temperature compensated Micro-Sensor is created by using a p-type [111] strain filament which has a positive gage factor and a positive temperature coefficient ($\Delta R/R$ versus temperature) in conjugate bridge arms with an n-type [100] filament which has a negative gage factor but a positive temperature coefficient. Both filaments may be contained in the same gage geometry complete with integral terminal tabs (see Fig. 14). It can be shown (Fig. 26) that for self-temperature compensation, the following conditions must exist:

$$[\Delta R/R]_{p-\text{gage}} + [(+G.F.)(\Delta T)(\alpha_s - \alpha_g)]_{p-\text{gage}}$$
$$= [\Delta R/R]_{n-\text{gage}} + [(-G.F.)(\Delta T)(\alpha_s - \alpha_g)]_{n-\text{gage}} \quad (8)$$

where $\Delta R/R$ = unit resistance change of the unmounted p- or n-gage due to a temperature change ΔT

$\quad G.F.$ = gage factor, positive for p-gages, negative for n-gages, neglecting nonlinearities

$\quad \alpha_s$ = thermal expansion coefficient of test material

$\quad \alpha_g$ = thermal expansion coefficient for gage material (silicon).

In the above expression, we will assume that ΔT, α_s, and α_g are the same for each gage location; simplifying:

$$[\Delta R/R]_{p-\text{gage}} - [\Delta R/R]_{n-\text{gage}} = [|\ G.F._p\ | - |\ G.F._n\ |][(\Delta T)(\alpha_s - \alpha_g)] \quad (9)$$

or, if we substitute λ_p and λ_n for the slope of the $\Delta R/R$ versus temperature curves, the expression further reduces to

$$\lambda_p - \lambda_n = [|\ G.F._p\ | - |\ G.F._n\ |][\alpha_s - \alpha_g]. \quad (10)$$

Since within certain limits we can select p- or n-gages with any positive value of λ (dependent on the material resistivity), it is apparent how self-temperature compensation may be achieved (see Fig. 26).

4. An additional method of minimizing temperature effects in Micro-Sensors involves the use of low resistivity (highly doped) silicon strain filaments (see references 3 and 4 for a discussion on the effects of doping levels on the temperature sensitivities of silicon strain gages). This benefit is derived only at the expense of a lower initial gage factor.

Zero shift compensation in a half- or full bridge is accomplished by using 2 or 4 active filaments of the same resistivity and gage factor. At best, however, since several quantities with very high slopes are electrically subtracted, the resultant curve as a function of temperature is not quite zero. Furthermore, if the gages are mounted on a curved surface and if all of the active elements are not on the same radius of curvature, some net

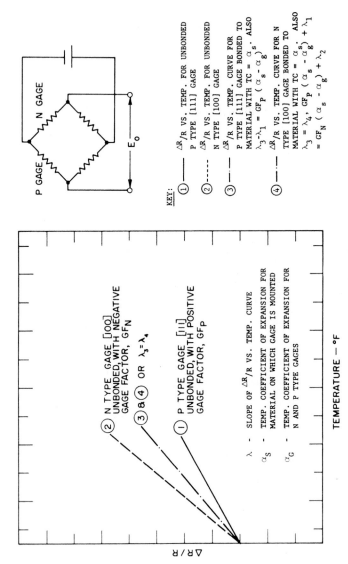

Fig. 26. Temperature compensation using *p*- and *n*-types.

output as a function of temperature will be realized.[5] In a full bridge circuit the installation is first temperature calibrated in an oven to determine the output (voltage) versus temperature. The proper amount of compensator wire which has a high positive temperature coefficient is inserted in the appropriate leg of the bridge to provide temperature compensation. The

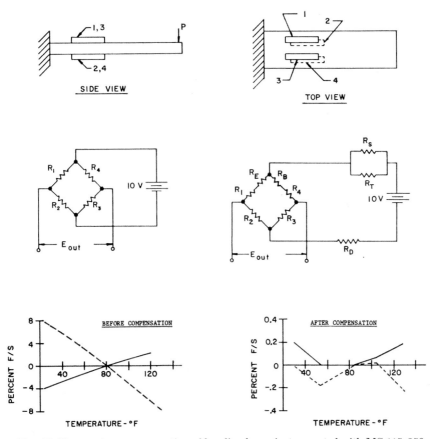

FIG. 27. Temperature compensation of bending beam instrumented with MS 115–350. Span shift: - - - -; zero shift: ———. $F/S = 1.000$ volt; R_B (Balco) $= 58\Omega$; R_E (Evanohm) $= 54\Omega$; R_T (thermistor) $= 198\Omega$; R_S (shunt) $= 174\Omega$; R_D (full span adjust) $= 55\Omega$.

zero load (room temperature) output is then trimmed to zero by placing a resistance wire (with zero temperature coefficient) in the proper bridge leg. A typical example of this technique is illustrated in Fig. 27 where a bending beam was instrumented with 4 active Micro-Sensors of a nominal 500-ohm resistance. The zero shift versus temperature was 6% of F/S

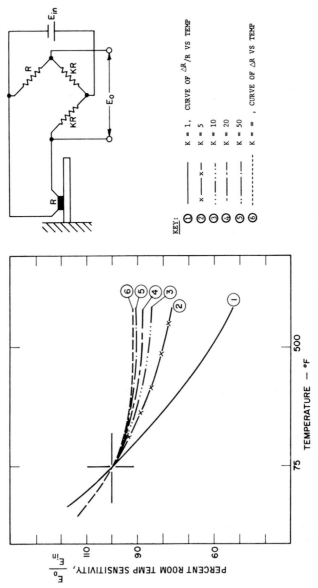

FIG. 28. Strain sensitivity vs. temperature for relative bridge output change vs. temperature for semiconductor gages bonded to 17-4 PH steel. Strain level = ±500µε; tested on constant stress beam.

output per 100°F from 30° to 130°F before compensation. After compensation this was reduced to 0.2% of F/S output per 100°F.

Sensitivity or gage factor compensation, if required, may be accomplished in several ways:

1. A single gage or half-active bridge can be used as an asymmetric bridge, e.g., two bridge arms higher in resistance than the active arm(s) by a factor of K (Figs. 21 and 28). Figure 21 shows the per cent deviation in $\Delta R/\epsilon R$ for a fixed strain level as a function of temperature. This curve is representative of gage factor versus temperature. The slope of this line is quite significant. Plotted on this same graph is a curve of the per cent deviation of $\Delta R/\epsilon$ alone at the same strain level as a function of temperature. Bridge output versus temperature can be made nearly proportional to the $\Delta R/\epsilon$ versus temperature curve by maintaining constant or nearly constant bridge current, consequently the (zero-strain) voltage drop across the active gage(s) is kept proportional to gage resistance. Figure 28 shows how the arrangement of the asymmetric bridge is employed to compensate for bridge output versus temperature. A similar effect may be achieved in full or half-bridges by using a constant current power supply.

2. In full (or half) bridge configurations, a thermistor and resistive shunt network may be placed at the bridge location and wired into the input legs in such a manner that the supply voltage available at the bridge is made to increase at the same rate that the bridge gage factor decreases. Figure 27 shows how a bending beam transducer which had a 14% drop of sensitivity from 30° to 130°F was compensated within 0.2% of full scale (or ±0.1%) over this same range.

3. The use of degenerate materials (heavily doped) will result in gages whose sensitivity change with temperature is greatly reduced.[3,4] Such materials are currently being evaluated in the Engineering Laboratory of Micro-Systems, Inc. The use of such materials, however, will result in lower initial gage factors.

LINEARITY COMPENSATION

As shown in Fig. 16, the $\Delta R/R$ or unit resistance change in strain for a Micro-Sensor is not entirely linear (see reference 6 for basic linearity data). As shown in Fig. 17, the gage is linear to within $\pm\frac{3}{4}\%$ between -500 and $+500$ microstrain. The gage factor increases somewhat in tension and decreases rapidly at strain levels in excess of 500 microstrain in compression. There are many ways to compensate for these nonlinearities (if necessary), some of which are as follows:

1. A single active gage may be shunted with a resistor to linearize the $\Delta R/R$ of the gage as function of strain. Figure 29 displays how this is achieved as well as the resultant loss of sensitivity that occurs.

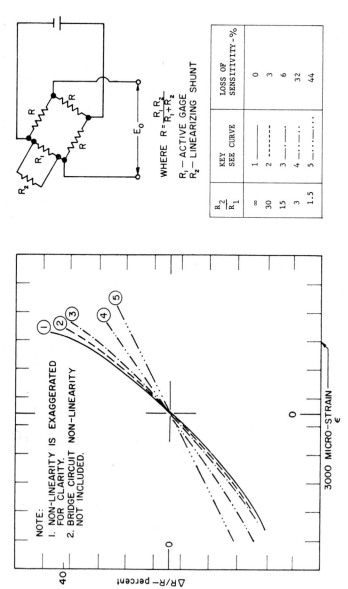

$\dfrac{R_2}{R_1}$	KEY SEE CURVE		LOSS OF SENSITIVITY - %
∞	1	————	0
30	2	-------	3
15	3	—·—·—	6
3	4	—··—··—	32
1.5	5	—···—···—	44

WHERE $R = \dfrac{R_1 R_2}{R_1 + R_2}$

R_1 — ACTIVE GAGE
R_2 — LINEARIZING SHUNT

NOTE:
1. NON-LINEARITY IS EXAGGERATED FOR CLARITY.
2. BRIDGE CIRCUIT NON-LINEARITY NOT INCLUDED.

3000 MICRO-STRAIN — ϵ

FIG. 29. Linearity compensation using a resistive shunt.

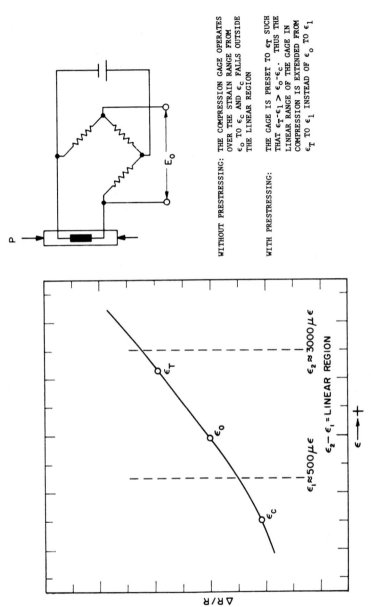

WITHOUT PRESTRESSING: THE COMPRESSION GAGE OPERATES OVER THE STRAIN RANGE FROM ϵ_0 TO ϵ_C AND ϵ_C FALLS OUTSIDE THE LINEAR REGION

WITH PRESTRESSING: THE GAGE IS PRESET TO ϵ_T SUCH THAT $\epsilon_T - \epsilon_1 > \epsilon_0 - \epsilon_C$. THUS THE LINEAR RANGE OF THE GAGE IN COMPRESSION IS EXTENDED FROM ϵ_T TO ϵ_1 INSTEAD OF ϵ_0 TO ϵ_1

$\epsilon_2 \approx 3000 \mu\epsilon$

$\epsilon_1 \approx 500 \mu\epsilon$

$\epsilon_2 - \epsilon_1 = $ LINEAR REGION

FIG. 30. Linearizing by prestressing in tension.

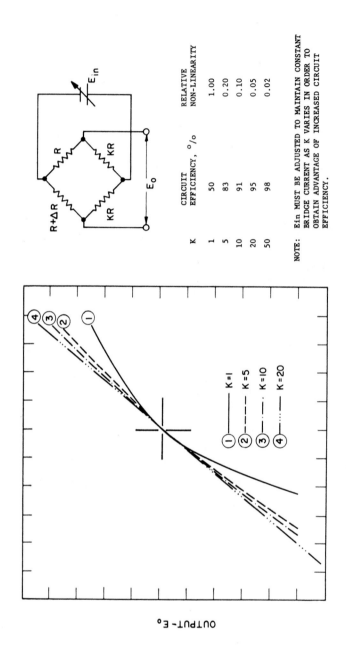

FIG. 31. Nonlinearity of Wheatstone bridge.

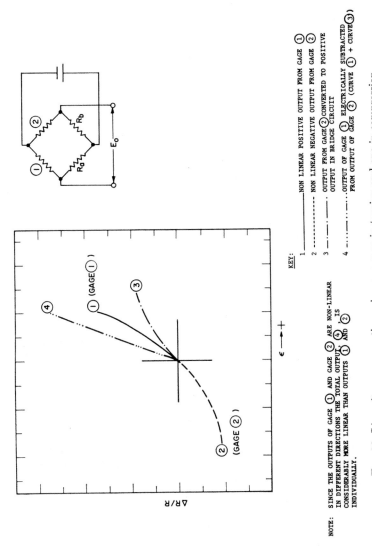

KEY:

1 ———————— NON LINEAR POSITIVE OUTPUT FROM GAGE ①

2 ------------ NON LINEAR NEGATIVE OUTPUT FROM GAGE ②

3 —·——·—— OUTPUT FROM GAGE ② CONVERTED TO POSITIVE OUTPUT IN BRIDGE CIRCUIT

4 ····——····—— OUTPUT OF GAGE ① ELECTRICALLY SUBTRACTED FROM OUTPUT OF GAGE ② (CURVE ① + CURVE ③)

NOTE: SINCE THE OUTPUTS OF GAGE ① AND GAGE ② ARE NON-LINEAR IN DIFFERENT DIRECTIONS THE TOTAL OUTPUT ④ IS CONSIDERABLY MORE LINEAR THAN OUTPUTS ① AND ② INDIVIDUALLY.

FIG. 32. Linearity compensation using one gage in tension and one in compression.

2. Since the most linear operating range of the Micro-Sensor is at higher strain levels in tension, a Micro-Sensor may be preset in tension, then attached to a structure, thus extending the linear operating range in compression. This technique is explained in Fig. 30. In transducer work this is usually accomplished by maintaining a compressive force (strain) on

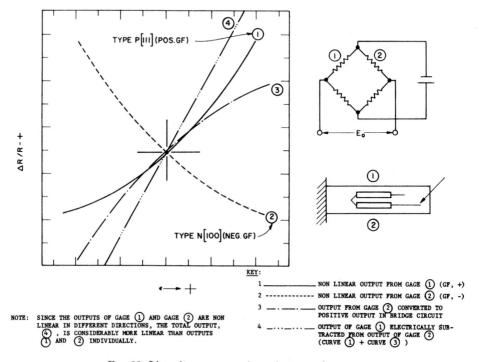

FIG. 33. Linearity compensation using *p*- and *n*-types.

the part during the bonding process. After the cement is cured, the force is released and the gage is driven into tension. The new weldable Micro-Sensor has the strain filament preset in tension by approximately 1000 microstrain so that the linear range is ±1500 microstrain instead of −500 to +2500 microstrain.

3. The basic nonlinearity of the Wheatstone bridge circuit can be used to advantage if an active gage (or half-bridge) is used with dummy legs of higher resistance (asymmetric bridge). Figure 31 displays the bridge output as a function of the unit resistance change of an active gage (assuming linear gage response). It is apparent that the nonlinear curvature is opposite to that of the Micro-Sensor curve shown in Fig. 16. The ratio of dummy gage resistance to active gage resistance (*K*) may be adjusted to nearly compensate for Micro-Sensor nonlinearity.

4. The nonlinearity effect is minimized when a full bridge is used with two gages in tension and two gages in compression. As shown in Fig. 32, the gage factor drop-off of the compression gages is partially offset by the gage factor increase of the tension gages.

5. Positive gage factor Micro-Sensors (*p*-type) may be used in conjugate bridge arms with negative gage factor Micro-Sensors (*n*-type) (Fig. 14). The outputs of both gages when subjected to the strain of the same sign (e.g., tension) will be additive, but since the individual outputs are nonlinear in different directions, the total output is linearized (see Fig. 33 for explanation). Incidentally, this *p/n* gage combination is of the same type for self-temperature compensation.

6. Other methods are being evaluated for linearity compensation. These include internal electrical networks incorporated in the gage configuration, readout circuitry design, and basic strain filament material studies.

Recent Applications

Douglas C-133A Nose Boom

The inboard section of the nose boom of the Douglas C-133A aircraft shown in Fig. 34 was instrumented with Micro-Sensors to measure normal

Fig. 34. C-133A nose boom on aircraft.

and lateral bending forces. Figure 35 shows a close-up of the instrumented boom section and Fig. 36 shows the gage location with the spools of wire and disk thermistors used for temperature compensation. The stress level

FIG. 35. C-133A nose boom instrumented section.

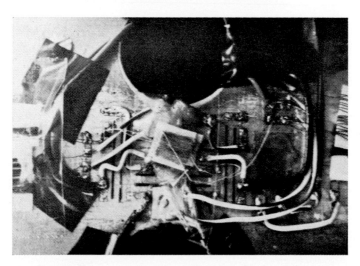

FIG. 36. Temperature-compensation network on nose boom.

at the gage locations for a 2g normal bending condition was 200 psi (only 20 microstrain). The holes (stress raisers) were drilled to raise the stress at the gage locations to 370 psi (37 microstrain). The full-scale output for 2g loading was approximately 2 mv/volt and the transducer was temperature compensated for both gage factor and zero shifts. Figure 37 shows the calibration setup at the Testing Division of Douglas Aircraft Company.

Fig. 37. Calibration setup of nose boom.

Physiological Applications

Spacelabs, Inc., Van Nuys, California, has successfully applied Micro-Sensors to the monitoring of various physiological data.

To date, Spacelabs has incorporated these semiconductor strain elements into systems generically known as Biotels. These are biological telemetering systems.

Single-parameter devices utilize pulse-rate principles, and multiparameter complexes employ FM/FM techniques.

Figure 38 illustrates a six-channel 11-ounce transmitter contained in a specially designed vest. The vest accommodates most of the sensing elements. A transducer in the flexible midriff section makes use of strategically placed Micro-Sensors to sense respiration volume and rate, canceling the usual errors caused by postural changes. Other sensors developed by this company which utilize Micro-Sensors include those for transducing the peripheral pulse pressure wave. In all cases, the Micro-Sensor resistance change causes a deviation in frequency of its FM subcarrier, which is transmitted by the FM master carrier to a remote receiver, with demodulators and recording device.

Figure 39 is a single-channel Biotel for surgical implantation in experimental animals. The transmitter can accept any of a number of physiological input signals, and all animals so instrumented appear unaffected and unaware of their cargo. A nickel-cadmium cell in the transmitter may be recharged an indefinite number of times by a low frequency RF generator placed near the skin of the animal.

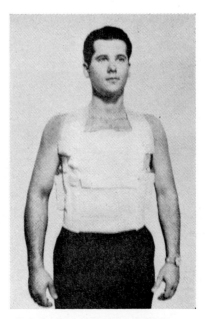

FIG. 38. Spacelabs, Inc., Biotel vest.

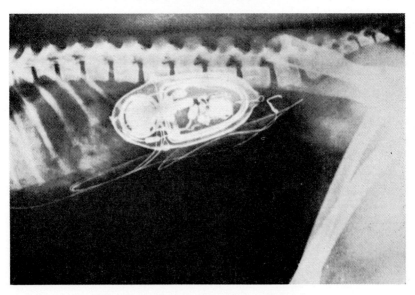

FIG. 39. Single-channel transmitter in monkey.

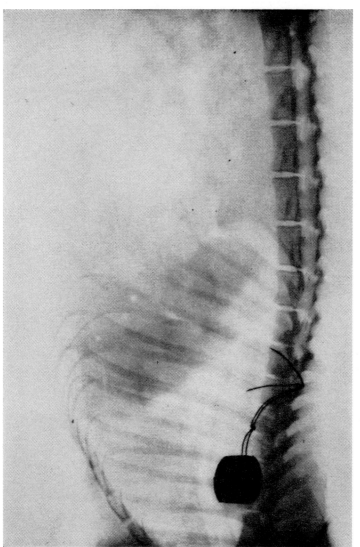

FIG. 40. X-Ray of transducer in monkey.

Figure 40 is an X-ray of a transducer utilizing a Micro-Sensor, which detects changes in intrathoracic pressure, a faithful analog of respiratory ventilation. It compares thoracic pressure with a "captive" 1-atmosphere standard, and conveys the information to the transmitter (Fig. 39). The recorded respiration pressure wave may be seen in Fig. 41. In this case the

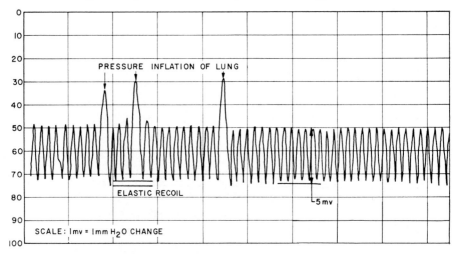

Fig. 41. Intrathoracic pressure measurements of respiration in a Rhesus monkey from an internally implanted transducer.

transducer is sutured to the left of the spine in the chest. The transmitter is in the abdomen near the left kidney. The subject is a 5-pound Rhesus monkey. There were no surgical complications, and the animal was alert and active the following day.

Spacelabs has already devised means for employing the Micro-Sensor in the radio monitoring of blood pressure from the aorta, of cardiac output, of essential kidney function, and of other important physiological parameters. A multichannel FM/FM telemetry package, smaller than the single-channel package of Fig. 39, is now being tested. Correlation of resulting data in healthy, unanesthetized primates should yield extremely valuable information in medical research and in early space probes.

In selecting an element for the transducing of biophysical phenomena, Spacelabs explored various techniques. Results are as follows:

1. Capacitive transducers require additional circuitry, are generally unreliable as to calibration, and are not practical at standard IRIG sub-carrier frequencies.

2. Inductance-type transducers are bulky at IRIG subcarrier frequencies, and in the presence of high-dielectric body electrolytes generally cause intermodulation distortion by random-phase electromagnetic coupling in FM/FM systems.

3. Conventional resistance strain gages have insufficient gage factor, requiring additional preamplification and power drain in an application where volume, power consumption, and baseline drift are prime considerations.

4. Semiconductor strain gages may be used without temperature compensation, since Mother Nature provides one of the best thermostats known. However, other types used were too inflexible because of greater thickness, and were too brittle to withstand the extreme physical activity of small animals. Further, they could not be applied about small diameters such as blood vessels. The Micro-Sensor appears to minimize these limitations of prior semiconductor strain gages, and is regarded by Spacelabs as being the best device in the present state of the art for transducing biophysical phenomena which can be sensed by strain gage techniques.

Summary

Recent developments in semiconductor strain gage technology have been described. These include new strain gage designs and configurations, additional performance data, and recently developed techniques to compensate for temperature and linearity effects. Several applications of the Micro-Sensor are cited.

The staff of Micro Systems, Inc., is conducting an aggressive development and evaluation program in order to offer the strain gage user the latest and most complete technical information regarding its products. Many new types of gages will be offered in the near future and application notes and papers will be published on a continuous basis.

Acknowledgments

The authors wish to express their appreciation for the assistance given by Mr. C. Shearer and Mr. M. Takizawa of Micro Systems, Inc., in the preparation of this paper.

References

1. Smith, C. S., Piezoresistive effect in germanium and silicon, *Phys. Rev.* **94** (1954).
2. Mason, W. P., and Thurston, R. N., Use of piezoresistive materials in the measurement of displacement, force, and torque, *J. Acoust. Soc. Am.* **29** (1957).
3. Padgett, E. D., and Wright, W. V., Silicon piezoresistive devices, see p. 1 in this volume.
4. Mason, W. P., Forst, J. J., and Tornillo, L. M., Recent developments in semiconductor strain transducers, see p. 109 in this volume.
5. Hines, Frank F., Baldwin-Lima-Hamilton Corporation, Waltham, Massachusetts, Effect of mounting surface curvature on the temperature coefficient of bonded resistance strain gages, presented at the Western Regional Strain Gage Committee Meeting, November 3, 1960.
6. Sanchez, J. C., Micro Systems, Inc., The Micro-Sensor, a new tool for the experimental stress analyst, presented at the Society for Experimental Stress Analysis, Meeting of the Southwest Chapter, October 12, 1960.

Bibliography on Semiconductor Strain Gages

Compiled by

MILLS DEAN, III

This compilation has been prepared to provide an up-to-date one-source listing of works pertaining and directly related to semiconductor strain gages at the time of publication.

The quantity of technical papers presently available in this field is quite limited due in large part to the comparatively recent marketing of the semiconductor strain gage.

A portion of the listings was furnished to the compiler by Peter K. Stein from his *Strain Gage Readings*. For a continuing listing of current bibliographic data it is suggested that the researcher refer to this bi-monthly publication, published by Stein Engineering Services, 5602 East Monte Rosa, Phoenix, Arizona.

All semiconductor references cited at the end of each chapter in this book have been repeated here for the convenience of the reader. Press releases, newspaper articles, etc., have not been included for obvious reasons.

The following annual indexes were consulted extensively: Applied Science and Technology Index, The Engineering Index, The Industrial Arts Index, and Science Abstracts.

Dr. William M. Murray kindly furnished a book list of general references, and these are marked with an asterisk (*).

The General Reference section lists a number of sources which discuss Wheatstone bridge nonlinearity due to large resistance changes. Although this problem is discussed in this volume, it was felt that some readers might possibly wish to pursue the subject in greater detail inasmuch as semiconductor gages can generate large resistance changes.

The compiler expresses appreciation for the kind assistance and the many courtesies shown him by the staff of the Technical Library of the David Taylor Model Basin.

BIBLIOGRAPHY

Abrahams, S. C., and Stockbridge, C. D. Whisker growth from quartz. *Nature* **193,** 670–671 (Feb. 17, 1962).

Albers, W. A., Jr., and Thomas, J. E., Jr. Observations of surface transverse magneto-resistance effects on n-type germanium. *J. Phys. & Chem. of Solids* **14,** Pergamon Press (1960).

Allen, C. C., and Runyan, W. R. An A. C. silicon resistivity meter. *Rev. Sci. Instr.* **32** (July 1961).

Allen, F. G., Eisinger, J., Hagstrum, H. D., and Law, J. T. Cleaning of silicon surfaces by heating in high vacuum. *J. Appl. Phys.* **30,** 1563–71 (Oct. 1959), and Bell Tele. Labs. Monograph 3444.

Allen, M. The effect of tension on the electrical resistance of single bismuth crystals. *Phys. Rev.* **42,** 848 (1932).

Allen, M. The effect of tension on the electrical resistance of single antimony crystals. *Phys. Rev.* **43**, 569 (1933).

Allen, M. The effect of tension on the electrical resistance of single tetragonal tin crystals. *Phys. Rev.* **52**, 1246 (1937).

Allen, M. The tension coefficients of resistance of hexagonal crystals zinc and cadmium. *Phys. Rev.* **49**, 248 (1936).

Anderson, O. L., Andreatch, P., Jr., and McSkimin, H. J. Method and apparatus for measuring predetermined pressures. Pat. 2,938,386.

Anon. Coating semiconductors with silicon-carbide skin. *Electronics* **34**, 150 (Nov. 1961).

Anon. Liquid semiconductor. *Mech. Eng.* **77**, 343 (Apr. 1955).

Anon. Monitoring physiological data with strain gages. *Med. Electr. News* **1**(2), 26 (June 1961).

Anon. New electrochemical technique for polishing semiconductor wafers. *Bell Labs. Rec.* **39**(3), 107 (Mar. 1961).

Anon. New strain gages for the space age. *ISA J.* **6**, 50–1 (Feb. 1959).

Anon. Piezoelectric strain gauges. *Automobile Eng.* **51**, 141 (Apr. 1961).

Anon. Pressure sensing with solid state. *Electronic Industries* **19**(10), 85 (Oct. 1960).

Anon. Semiconductor element is major transducer advance. *Military System Design.* (Sept.–Oct. 1960).

Anon. Semiconductor growing process eliminates manual assembly; vapor growth developed by IBM. *Prod. Engr.* **31**, 20 (July 11, 1960).

Anon. Semiconductor strain gauge. *Electronic & Radio Eng.* **36**(3), 90 (Mar. 1959).

Anon. Semiconductors increase strain-gage outputs. *Electronic Design* **10**(13), 45–47 (June 21, 1962).

Anon. Semiconductors for strain gages. *Electronics* **32**, 68–9 (Feb. 6, 1959).

Anon. Semiconductors by vapor growth. *Elec. Ind.* **19**, 89–90 (Aug. 1960).

Anon. Silicon crystals in ribbon form. *Bell Labs. Rec.* **39**(12), 448 (Dec. 1961). Described at Metallurgical Soc. AIEE, Detroit, Nov. 1961.

Anon. Silicon threads grown for strain-gage uses. *Electronics* **34**, 68–69 (Mar. 3, 1961).

Anon. Slicing and dicing operations on crystals of silicon and germanium. *Machy, London* **94**(2409), 92–4 (Jan. 1959).

Anon. Slicing shock-sensitive materials. *Instruments and Control Systems* **32**, 887 (June 1959).

Anon. Slicing thin sections of semiconductors; Gillings-Brownwill thin sectioning machine. *Electronics* **33**, 154–5 (Aug. 12, 1960).

Anon. Soviets irradiate polymers, get semiconductivity. *Chem. Engr.* **38**, 42 (Jan. 18, 1960).

Anon. Sputtered resistors make high component density possible. *Bell Labs. Rec.* **37**(9), 359 (WESCON, San Francisco Aug. 19, 1959).

Anon. Statham claims solid-state transducer using Si wire. *Electronic News* (May 30, 1960).

Anon. Strain gage with high sensitivity made of semiconductor material. *Aviation Week and Space Technology* (Feb. 1, 1960).

Anon. Strainistor temperature correction instructions. Strainistor Application Notes No. 5, Century Electronics & Instruments Inc. (June 28, 1960).

Anon. Stress changes resistance of whisker-sized semiconductor. *Machine Design* **32**, 27 (Mar. 3, 1960).

Anon. Transparent gallium phosphide prepared as aid to semiconductor research. *Bell Labs. Rec.* **38**, 230–1 (June 1960), and *Elec. Manuf.* **65**, 9–10 (June 1960).

Ashton, G., and Marshall, S. Metallographic examination of semiconductor devices. *Instn. Elec. Engrs. Proc.* **106** (Pt. B, Supp. 15) 437–41 (May 1959).

Baker, D. Improved machine for lapping very thin slices of semiconductor material. *J. Sci. Instr.* **36**, 145–7 (Mar. 1959).

Bardeen, J. Pressure change of resistance of tellurium. *Phys. Rev.* **75**, 1777 (1949).

Bardeen, J., and Shockley, W. Deformation potentials and mobilities in monatomic semiconductors. *Phys. Rev.* **77**, 407–8 (Feb. 1, 1950).

Barry, J. F., and Seeley, N. C. Method of shaping semiconductive bodies. Pat. 2,827,427.

Bean, K. E., Medcalf, W. E., and Starks, R. J. Research in physical chemistry and metallurgy of semiconducting materials. PB 161–353 from O.T.S.

Bechmann, R., and Parsons, P. L. General post office engineering report No. 9 in piezoelectricity. Her Majesty's Stationery Office, London, p. 293 (1957).

Bennett, J. A., and Flanagan, T. P. Instrument for recording the resistance during the deposition of a thin film. *J. Sci. Instr.* **37**, 143–4 (Apr. 1960).

Benson, F. A. Voltage stabilisation. *Instrument Practice* (London) Part 1 **16**(4), 433–443 (Apr. 1962), Part 2 **16**(5), 568–575 (May 1962), and Part 3 **16**(6), 742–750 (June 1962).

Bertolotti, M. Effects of nuclear radiation on semiconductor devices. *Alta Frequenza* **30**, 631–642 and 862–872 (Sept. and Dec. 1961).

Birss, R. R., and Horne, R. J. The thermal expansion of a silicon single crystal. *Proc. Phys. Soc.* **LXXV**, 793–5, England (1960).

Bloom, L. Simplified guide aids selection of semiconductor voltage regulators; data file. *Control Eng.* **8**, 83–84 (Jan. 1961).

Blumberg, R. H. Effect of elastic strain on the superconducting critical temperature of evaporated tin films. *J. Appl. Phys.* **33**(1) 163–168 (Jan. 1962).

Boltaks, B. I., and Gutorov, Y. U. A. Some results on diffusion of impurities and their effect on electrical properties of gallium antimonide. *Soviet Phys., Solid State* **1**(7), 930–5 (Jan. 1960). English translation of article indexed in *Engineering Index* p. 1236, 1959, from *Fizika Tverdogo Tela* (July 1959).

Bond, W. L. The depth of diffused layers. *Bell Labs. Rec.* **35**, 1–5 (Jan. 1957).

Bond, W. L., and Kelly, E. M. Vapor deposited metal films. Pat. 2,842,463.

Bowers, R. Magnetic susceptibility of germanium. *Phys. Rev.* **108**, 683 (1957).

Bradley, C. C., Faber, T. E., Wilson, E. G., and Ziman, J. M. A theory of the electrical properties of liquid metals II. Polyvalent metals. *The Philosophical Magazine* **7**(77), 865–887 (May 1962).

Brattain, W. H. Historical development of concepts basic to the understanding of semiconductors. Presented at Int'l. Conf. on Transistors, London, England (1959).

Braun, J. H. Photosensitive etching of silicon. *J. Electrochem. Soc.* (June 1961).

Breidt, P., Jr., Hobstetter, N., and Ellis, W. C. Some effects of environment on fracture stress of germanium. *J. Appl. Phys.* Vol. 79/2 (Feb. 1958).

Brentano, J., and Goldberg, C. Electrical conductance of pressed powders, in particular of zinc oxide. *Phys. Rev.* **94**(1), 56–60 (Apr. 1, 1954).

Brice, J. C., and Moore, P. Contactless resistivity meter for semiconductors. *J. Sci. Instr.* **38**, 307 (July 1961).

Brice, J. C., and Wright, H. C. Apparatus for measurement of thermal e.m.f. in semiconductors. *J. Sci. Instr.* **35**, 146 (1958).

Bridgman, P. W. Certain physical properties of single crystals of tungsten, antimony, bismuth, tellurium, cadmium, zinc, and tin. *Am. Soc. Arts and Sci. Proc.* **60**(6), 305–383 (Oct. 1925).

Bridgman, P. W. The compressibility of thirty metals as a function of pressure and temperature. *Am. Acad. Arts and Sci. Proc.* **58**(5), 165–242 (Jan. 1923).

Bridgman, P. W. The compressibility and pressure coefficient of resistance of ten elements. *Am. Acad. of Arts and Sci. Proc.* **62**(8), 207–226 (Dec. 1927).

Bridgman, P. W. Compressibility and pressure coefficient of resistance, including single crystal magnesium. *Am. Acad. Arts and Sci. Proc.* **66**(7), 255–270 (Mar. 1931) and **67**(2), 29–41 (Jan. 1932).

Bridgman, P. W. The effect of homogeneous mechanical stress on the electrical resistance of crystals. *Phys. Rev.* **42**, 858 (1932).

Bridgman, P. W. Effect of pressure on electrical resistance of single metal crystals at low temperature. *Proc. Am. Acad. Sci.* **68**, 95 (1933).

Bridgman, P. W. Effect of pressure on electrical resistance of certain semiconductors. *Am. Acad. Arts and Sci. Proc.* **79**(3), 125–148 (Apr. 1951).

Bridgman, P. W. Electric resistance to 30,000 Kg/cm² of twenty nine metals and intermetallic compounds. *Am. Acad. Arts & Sci. Proc.* **79**(3), 149–79 (Apr. 1951).

Bridgman, P. W. The electrical resistance of metals. *Phys. Rev.* **17**(2), 161–194 (Feb. 1921).

Bridgman, P. W. The effect of tension on the transverse and longitudinal resistance of metals. *Proc. Am. Acad. of Arts and Sci.* **60**(8), 423–449 (Oct. 1925).

Bridgman, P. W. Effects of high shearing stress combined with high hydrostatic pressure. *Phys. Rev.* **48**, 825–847 (1935).

Bridgman, P. W. The effect of tension on the electrical resistance of certain abnormal metals. *Proc. Am. Acad. of Arts and Sci.* **57**(3), 41–66 (Apr. 1922).

Bridgman, P. W. The electrical resistance of metals under pressure. *Proc. Am. Acad. Arts and Sci.* **52**(9), 573–646 (Feb. 1917).

Bridgman, P. W. The electron theory of metals in the light of new experimental data. *Phys. Rev., N.S.,* **19**(2), 114–134 (Feb. 1921).

Bridgman, P. W. Physics of high pressure. Macmillan Co. (1951).

Bridgman, P. W. Recently discovered complexities in properties of simple substances. *Am. Inst. of Min. and Met. Engrs., Trans.* General Meeting 17–37 (Sept. 1931).

Bridgman, P. W. Resistance of nineteen metals to 30,000 Kg/cm². *Proc. Am. Acad. Sci.* **72**, 159 (1938).

Brooks, H. Radiation effects in materials. *J. Appl. Phys.* **30**(8), 1118–1124 (Aug. 1959).

Brophy, J. J. Organic semiconductors. *Phys. Today* **14**, 40–41 (Aug. 1961).

Brown, M. A. C. S. Deviations from ohm's law in germanium and silicon. *J. Phys. Chem. Solids* **19**, 218–227 (May 1961).

Brown, W. L., Augustyniak, W. M., and Waite, T. R. Annealing of radiation defects in semiconductors. *Bell Tele. Labs. Monograph* 3420.

Buehler, E., and Teal, G. K. Process for producing semiconductive crystals of uniform resistivity. Pat. 2,768,914.

Burns, F. P. Piezoresistive semiconductor microphone. *J. Acoust. Soc. Am.* **29**, 248 (1957).

Burns, F. P. Piezoresistive semiconductor microphone. Pat. 2,905,771.

Burns, F. P., and Fleischer, A. A. Piezoresistive effect in indium antimonide. *Phys. Rev.* **107**(5), 1281–2 (Sept. 1, 1957).

Catz, J. Basic strain gage instrumentation. *ISA J.* **9**(4) (Apr. 1962).

Christensen, H. Electrical contact with thermocompression bonds. *Bell Labs. Rec.* **36**, 127–130 (Apr. 1958).

Chudnovskii, A. F., and Stumbur, V. K. Semiconductor strain gage for agricultural research (with summaries in English, German and French). *Vest. sel'khoz.nauki* **6**(2), 114–117 (Feb. 1961).

Cole, M., Bucklow, I. A., and Grigson, C. W. B. Technique for the rapid, accurate and strain-free machining of metallic single crystals. *British J. Appl. Phys.* **12**, 296–7 (June 1961).

Conference on radiation effects in semiconductors. Gatlinburg, Tenn. May 6–9, 1959. *J. Appl. Phys.* **30**, 1115–1316, Discussion 1317–1322 (Aug. 1959).

Conference on Semiconducting Compounds held at General Electric Research Laboratory 14–16 June 1961. Published as Supplement to *J. of Applied Physics*, **32**, 2063–2304, L. C. No. 61–18498 (Oct. 1961).

Conwell, E. M. Properties of silicon and germanium. *Proc. IRE* **40**, 1327 (1952) and **46**, 1281 (1958).

Conwell, E., and Weisskopf, V. F. Theory of impurity scattering in semiconductors. *Phys. Rev.* **77**, 388–90 (Feb. 1, 1950).

Cookson, J. W. Theory of the piezoresistive effect. *Phys. Rev.* **47**, 194 (1935).

Dash, W. C. Growth of silicon crystals free from dislocations. *J. App. Phys.* **30**, 459 (1959).

Crites, N. A. Which type of stress-analysis method? *Prod. Eng.* **32**, 90–96 (Oct. 16, 1961) ; 63–72 (Nov. 27, 1961) ; **33**, 69–81 (Feb. 19, 1962). To be continued.

Dacey, Geo. C. Esaki diodes. *Bell Labs. Rec.* **39**(4), 122–125 (Apr. 1961).

Dermatis, S. N., and Faust, J. W., Jr. Silicon sheets for the manufacture of semiconductor devices. A.I.E.E. Conference Paper 62–514.

Dodson, G. A., and Howard, B. T. High stress aging to failure of semiconducting devices. Presented at Reliability and Quality Control 7th Nat'l. Symposium, Philadelphia, Pa. (ACF Electronics Div., ACF Industries, Inc., 11 Park Pl., Paramus, N. J.). Jan. 9–11, 1961.

Donovan, P. F. Recipes for detector fabrication paint-on particle detectors (recipe No. 2). Semiconductor Nuclear Particle Detectors, Nat'l. Acad. of Sci. Nat'l. Research Council 871 268–269 (1961).

Dorsey, James, and Reiters, Ludwig O. Bakelite backed semiconductor strain gages. *Instr. Soc. of Am. Conference Preprint* No. 146–LA–61 (Sept. 11–15, 1961).

Doucette, E. I., and Spector, C. J. Semiconductor capacitor. Pat. 2,964,648.

Duga, Jules J. An analysis of electrical properties of the plastically deformed semiconductor indium antimonide. Dissertation to Office of Naval Research for Graduate School Ohio State Univ. and Battelle Inst. (Battelle Nonr. 1870 (00) T. R. 4) (Jan. 12, 1961).

Duga, J. J. Plastic bending of InSb. *J. Appl. Phys.* **33**(1), 169–177 (Jan. 1962).

Eisner, R. L. Tensile tests on silicon whiskers. *Acta Metallurgica,* pp. 1–2 (July 1955).

Ellis, R. C., Jr. Method for preparation of semiconductor grade silicon. *Semiconductor Prod.* **3**(8), 36–8 (Aug. 1960).

Esaki, L. Kink effect in bismuth semiconductors. *Electronics* **35**, 84 (Jan. 12, 1962).

Esaki, L., and Miyahara, Y. A new device using the tunneling process in narrow p-n junctions. Solid-State Electronics, Pergamon Press, **1**(1), 13–21 (1960).

Fischer, G., *et al.* Apparatus for the measurement of galvanomagnetic effects in high resistance semiconductors. *Rev. of Sci. Instr.* **32**, 842–846 (July 1961).

Folberth, O. G. Zur technologie de halbleiter. Technology of semiconductors; preparation of semiconductor elements or compounds; importance and methods of purification; preparation of perfect crystals; doping; mechanical working; contact materials; surface treatment; semiconductor components. *Zeitfuer Metall-Kunde* **49**(11), 570–5 (Nov. 1958).

Forst, J. J., and Geyling, F. T. Applications of semiconductor transducers in strain gages and rigid dynamometers. *Proc. Soc. Exptl. Stress Anal.* **17**, 143 (1960).

Fraichet. Molecular deformation of metals in elongation. *Technique Moderne* **17**(16), 490–495 (Aug. 15, 1925).

Fritzsche, H. Effect of shear on impurity conduction in n-type germanium. *Phys. Rev.* **119**, 1899–1900 (1960).

Fritzsche, H. Piezoresistance of n-type germanium. *Phys. Rev.* **115**, No. 2 (July 15, 1959).

Fuller, C. S. Interactions between solutes in germanium and silicon. *Bell Tele. Labs. Monograph* 3282.

Gaertner, W. W. Temperature dependence of carrier densities, mobilities, diffusion constants and conductivities in germanium and silicon. *Semiconductor Prod.* **3**(7), 29–31 (July 1960).

Gallagher, C. J. Plastic deformation of germanium and silicon. *Phys. Rev.* **88**(4), 721–2 (Nov. 15, 1952).

Galt, J. K., and Herring, C. Elastic and plastic properties of very small metal specimens. *Phys. Rev.* **85**(6), 1060–1061 (Mar. 15, 1952) and **86**(4), 656 (May 15, 1952).

Garrett, C. G. B., and Pfann, W. G. Semiconductor varactors using surface space-charge layers. *I.R.E. Proc.* **47**(11), 2011–2012 (Nov. 1959).

Geballe, T. H. Radiation effects in semiconductors: thermal conductivity and thermoelectric power. *J. Appl. Phys.* **30**(8), 1153–1157 (Aug. 1959), and *Bell Tele. Labs. Monograph* 3409.

Geballe, T. H., Herring, C., and Kunzler, J. E. Phonon-drag thermomagnetic effects in N-germanium. *Bell Tele. Labs. Monograph* 3504.

George, R. I., and McQuistan, R. B. Lead wire attachment technique for thin film studies. *Rev. Sci. Instr.* **32**, 855–856 (July 1961).

Geyling, F. T., and Forst, J. J. Semiconductor strain transducers. *Bell System Tech. J.* **39**, 705 (1960).

Glossary of terms frequently used in: I—Plasma Physics, II—Acoustics, III—Solid State Physics. *Amer. Inst. Phys.* (1960).

Greenland, K. M. Some aspects of research on thin solid films. *J. Sci. Instr.* **38**, 1–11 (Jan. 1961).

Greiner, E. S., Gutowski, J. A., and Ellis, W. C. Preparation of silicon ribbons. *J. Appl. Phys.* **32**, 2489–90 (Nov. 1961).

Grubbs, W. J. Hall effect devices. *Bell Sys. Tech. J.* **38**(3), 853–876 (May 1959).

Haisty, R. W. Photoetching and plating of gallium arsenide. *J. Electrochem. Soc.* (Aug. 1961).

Hall, R. O. The thermal expansion of silicon. *Acta. Cryst.* **14**, 1004 (Sept. 10, 1961).

Hannay, N. B. Semiconductors. Reinhold Publishing Corp., New York (1959).

Harman, T. C. Effect of zone-refining variables on segregation of impurities in indium-antimonide. *Electrochem. Soc. J.* **103**(2), 128–34 (Feb. 1956).

Harrick, N. J. Metal to semiconductor contacts: injection or extraction for either direction of current flow. *Phys. Rev.* **115**(4), 876–82 (Aug. 15, 1959).

Harrick, N. J. Rectification without injection at metal-to-semiconductor contacts. *Phys. Rev.* **118**(4), 986–7 (May 15, 1960).

Hemingway, T. K. Applications of the constant-current diode. *Electronics* **34**(42), 60–3 (Oct. 20, 1961).

Herkart, P. G., and Kurshan, J. Theoretical resistivity and hall coefficient of impure germanium near room temperature. *RCA Rev.* **14**, 427–440 (Sept. 1953).

Herring, C. Transport properties of a many valley semiconductor. *Bell System Tech. J.* **34**, 237 (1955).

Herring, C., and Vogt, E. Transport and deformation potential theory for many-valley semiconductors with anisotropic scattering. *Phys. Rev.* **101**, 944 (1956).

Herrington, R. B., Cecil, O. B., and Puckett, R. D. Semiconductor resistive element. *Texas Instr. Quarterly Report* No. 3 (ASTIA AD-274-965) (Jan.–Mar. 1962).

Heywang, W., and Zerbst, M. Resistance measurements in semiconductor techniques. *Arch. Tech. Messen.* **309**, 225–228 (Oct. 1961).

Hilsun, C., and Rose-Innes, A. C. Semiconducting III-V compounds. International Series of Monographs on Semiconductors, Vol. I, Pergamon Press (1961).

Hogarth, C. A. Some conduction properties of oxides of cadmium and nickel. *Phys. Soc. Proc.* **64**(380B), 691–700 (Aug. 1, 1951).

Hollander, L. E., Jr., and Castro, P. L. Piezoresistance in single-crystal p-type GaAs. Presented at Am. Phys. Soc. Meeting March 1962. Abstract and review in *Strain Gage Readings* **V**(2), 38 (June–July 1962).

Hollander, L. E., Jr., Diesel, T. J., and Vick, G. L. Piezoresistivity in the oxide semiconductor rutile (TiO_2). *Phys. Rev.* **117**, 1469–1472 (1960).

Hollander, L. E., Vick, G. L., and Diesel, T. J. The piezoresistive effect and its application. *Rev. Sci. Inst.* **31**(3) (March 1960).

Hollander, L. E., Jr., Vick, G. L., Diesel, T. J., Wilner, L. B., and Perls, T. A. Piezoresistivity in semiconductors for transducer applications. O.T.S. as PB 147-675 (LSMD Rpt. 49736) (June 1959).

Holmes, P. J. The electro-chemistry of semiconductors. Academic Press, New York, p. 400 (November 1961).

Holmes, P. J. Use of etchants in assessment of semiconductor crystal properties. *Instn. Elec. Engrs. Proc.* **106** (Pt. B, Supp. 17) 861–5 (May 1959).

Holmes, P. J., and Newman, R. C. State of etched semiconductor surfaces as revealed by electron diffraction. *Instn. Elec. Engrs. Proc.* **106** (Pt. B, Supp. 15) 287–92 (May 1959).

Honnold, V. R., and Perkins, C. W. Effects of nuclear radiation on electronic materials. *Electronic Industries* **21**(2), 99–101 (Feb. 1962).

Ioffe, A. F. Physics of semiconductors. Translation from Russian, Academic Press, p. 436 (1960).

IRE standards on electron devices: definitions of semiconductor terms. *Proc. IRE* **42**(10), 1506–8 (Oct. 1954).

Irvin, J. C. Resistivity of bulk silicon and of diffused layers in silicon. *Bell Sys. Tech. J.* **XLI**(2), 387–410 (Mar. 1962).

Irving, B. A. Shapes of etch hillocks and pits and their correlation with measured etch rates. *J. Appl. Phys.* **31**(1), 109–11 (Jan. 1960).

Iwersen, J. E., and Nelson, J. T. Method for applying a gold-silver contact onto silicon and germanium semiconductors and article. Pat. 3,028,663.

Johnson, V. A. Theory of electrical resistivity in tellurium. *Phys. Rev.* **74**, 1255(A) (1948).

Johnson, V. A., and Fan, H. Y. Temperature dependence of the energy gap in germanium from conductivity and hall data. *Phys. Rev.* **79**, 899 (1950).

Johnson, V. A., and Lark-Horovitz, K. Electronic mobility in germanium. *Phys. Rev.* **79**, 409 (1950).

Jones, A. R. Uses of semiconductor detectors in health physics monitoring. *Nucleonics* **18**, 86 (Oct. 1960).

Jones, E. Piezoelectric and piezoresistive strain gages. *Control Eng.* **8**, 134–137 (Sept. 1961).

Kaufman, A. B. Asymmetric bridge. *Instr. and Control Systems* **33**(4), 634–5 (Apr. 1960).

Kelen, A. Micromanipulator for electrical investigations of semiconducting materials. *Appl. Sci. Research* **3**(2), Sec. B 125–8 (1953).

Kennedy, A. J. Single crystal extensometer. *Rev. Sci. Instr.* **24**(7), 505–7 (July 1953).

Kennedy, D. P. Spreading resistance in cylindrical semiconductor devices. *J. Appl. Phys.* **31**, 1490–7 (Aug. 1960).

Kersta, L. G. Elastic conductor. Pat. 2,697,157.

Keyes, R. W. The electronic contribution to the elastic properties of germanium. *I.B.M. J. Res. and Devel.* **5**, 266–278 (Oct. 1961).

Keyes, R. W. Temperature dependence of the elastoresistance in N-type germanium. *Phys. Rev.* **100**, 1104 (1955).

Keyes, R. W., and Pollak, M. Effects of hydrostatic pressure on the piezoresistance of semiconductors, i-InSb, p-Ge, p-InSb, n-GaSb, *Phys. Rev.* **118**, No. 4 (May 15, 1960).

Klahr, C. N. Resistivity and hall constant of semiconductors. *Phys. Rev.* **82**, 109–110 (Apr. 1, 1951).

Knight, R. D. Equipment for the encapsulation of semiconductor devices; hydraulically operated ram. *J. Sci. Instr.* **37**, 197–9 (June 1960).

Knight, R. D. Production of islands and dice in semiconductor slices with ultrasonic drill. *J. Sci. Instr.* **37**(8), 263–5 (Aug. 1960).

Kolb, E. D., and Tanenbaum, M. Uniform resistivity p-type silicon by zone leveling. *Bell Tele. Labs. Monograph* 3365.

Konigsberg, E., and Allred, W. P. Research in solid state. *C.E.C. Recordings* p. 18 (Spring 1961).

Krinsky, A. Thin film strain gages. Presented at I.S.A. Conf., Los Angeles, Calif., Sept. 1961. Abstract and review in *Strain Gage Readings* **IV**(5) (1961).

Krinsky, A., and Parker, R. L. Electrical resistance strain characteristics of evaporated films at room temperature. Nat'l. Bur. Stds. In Preparation (Aug. 1962).

Kruidhof, E. W., and Moret, H. Measurement of the electrical resistance of metal layers evaporated on non-conducting foils. *J. Sci. Instr.* **39**, 132 (Mar. 1962).

Kuczynski, G. C., and Hochman, R. H. Light induced plasticity in germanium. *J. Appl. Phys.* **30**(2), 267 (Feb. 1959).

Kurtz, Anthony D., and Jones, Edgar J. An ultra-high output telemetering gage. *Instr. Soc. of Am. Conference Preprint* No. 145–LA–61 (Sept. 11–15, 1961.)

Landgren, C. R. Etching processes and solutions. Pat. 2,847,287.

Lauritzen, P. O. Experimental measurements of 1/f noise in germanium filaments. Stanford Univ. Solid-state Electronics Lab. TR-1704-1 (Nov. 30, 1960).

Lawrence, R. Temperature dependence of drift mobility in germanium. *Phys. Rev.* **89**, 1295 (1953).

Lax, B., and Mavroides, J. G. Solid-state devices other than semiconductors. *I.R.E. Proc.* **50**(5), 1011–1024 (May 1962).

Lax, M., and Sachs, R. Frequency dependence of the A.C. resistance of thin semiconducting films. *Phys. Rev.* **107**(3), 650–5 (Aug. 1, 1957).

Lee, S. Y., and Pastan, H. L. Design and application of semiconductor strain gage transducers. *Instr. Soc. of Am. Conference Preprint* No. 189–LA–61 (Sept. 11–15, 1961).

Lehovec, K., and Levitas, A. Fabrication of multiple junctions in semiconductors by surface melt and diffusion in solid state. *J. Appl. Phys.* **28**(1), 106–9 (Jan. 1957).

Logan, M. A. An A.C. bridge for semiconductor resistivity measurements using a four-point probe. *Bell. Sys. Tech. J.* **XL**(3), 885–919 (May 1961), and *Bell Tele. Labs. Monograph* 3894.

Logan, R. A., Augustyniak, W. M., and Gilbert, J. F. Electron bombardment damage in silicon esaki diodes. *J. Appl. Phys.* **32**, 1201–1205 (July 1961).

Logan, R. A., Pearson, G. L., and Kleinman, D. A. Anisotropic mobilities in plastically deformed germanium. *J. Appl. Phys.* **30**, 885–95 (June 1959), and *Bell Tele. Labs. Monograph* 3366.

Long, D. Effects of pressure on electrical properties of semiconductors. *Phys. Rev.* **101**(4), 1256–63 (Feb. 1956).

Long, D. Energy bands in semiconductors. *J. Appl. Phys.* **33**(5), 1682–1696 (May 1962).

Long, D. Stress dependence of the piezoresistance effect. *J. Appl. Phys.* **32**, 2050–2051 (Oct. 1961).

Lundquist, N., and Myers, H. P. Strain-gauge balance for ferromagnetic and paramagnetic measurements. *J. Sci. Instr.* **39**, 154–155 (Apr. 1962).

Lussana, Silvio. Effect of pressure on thermal and electric conductivity of metals and the Wiedemann-Franz law. *Nuovo Cimento* **25**(3–4), 115–130 (Mar.–Apr. 1923).

MacKintosh, I. M. Effects at high angle grain boundaries in indium antimonide. *J. Electronics* **1**(5), 554–8 (May 1956).

Magee, V. Production and evaluation of semiconductor-grade silicon. *Instn. Elec. Engrs. Proc.* **106** (Pt. B, Supp. 17) 879–82 (May 1959).

Marsh, D. M. Micro-tensile testing machine. *J. Sci. Instr.* (June 1961).

Masella, A. J., and Mould, R. T. Proportioners mix production gases; semiconductor crystal growing. *Electronics* **33**, 80 (Aug. 19, 1960).

Mason, W. P. Dislocation relaxations at low temperatures and determinations of the limiting shearing stress of a metal. *Phys. Rev.* **98**, 1136–1138 (May 1955) and *Bell Tele. Labs. Monograph* 2433.

Mason, W. P. A dynamic measurement of the elastic, electric and piezoelectric constants of rochelle salt. *Phys. Rev.* **55**, 775–789 (1939).

Mason, W. P. The elastic, piezoelectric, and dielectric constants of potassium dihydrogen phosphate and ammonium dihydrogen phosphate. *Phys. Rev.* **69**, 173–194 (1946).

Mason, W. P. Elastic, piezoelectric and dielectric properties of sodium chlorate and sodium bromate. *Phys. Rev.* **70**, 529 (1946).

Mason, W. P. Energy conversion in the solid state IV. *Bell Tele. Labs. Monograph* 3324.

Mason, W. P. Gauges using piezoresistive elements. Pat. 3,034,345.

Mason, W. P. High frequency electromechanical transducer. Pat. 2,939,106.

Mason W. P. Internal friction, plastic strain and fatigue in metals and semiconductors. *Bell Tele. Labs. Monograph* 3326.

Mason, W. P., and Jaffe, H. Methods for measuring piezoelectric, elastic and dielectric coefficients of crystals and ceramics. *IRE Proc.* **42**, 921–930 (June 1954), and *Bell Tele. Labs. Monograph* 2241.

Mason, W. P., and Shockley, W. Negative resistance amplifiers. Pat. 2,775,658.

Mason, W. P. Phonon viscosity and its effect on acoustic wave attenuation and dislocation motions. Third Int'l. Congress on Acoustics, Stuttgart, Germany (1959), and *Bell Tele. Labs. Monograph* 3601.

Mason, W. P. Physical acoustics and the properties of solids. D. Van Nostrand Co. (1958).

Mason, W. P., and Thurston, R. N. Piezoresistive materials in measuring displacement, force, and torque. *J. of the Acoustical Soc. of Am.* **29**, 1096 (1957).

Mason, W. P., and Pratt, J. S. Piezoresistive accelerometer. Pat. 2,963,911.

Mason, W. P. On semiconductor strain gages. Presented at Soc. for Exptl. Stress Anal., Hudson Mohawk Sect., Rensselaer Polytech. Inst., Troy, N.Y.

Mason, W. P. Semiconductors in strain gages. *Bell Labs. Record* **37**, No. 1, 7 (Jan. 1959).

Mason, W. P. Semiconductors in strain gauges. *Engineer's Digest* **20**(2), 76, 96 (Feb. 1959).

Mason, W. P. Semiconductor devices as pressure transducers. *Electronics* **35**(8), 35–9 (Feb. 23, 1962).

Mason, W. P., McSkimin, H. J., and Bateman, T. Third order elastic moduli of germanium. *J. Appl. Phys.* **32**, 928–936 (May 1961), and *Bell Tele. Labs. Monograph* 3938.

Mason, W. P. Ultrasonics. McGraw-Hill Encyclopedia of Sci. and Tech. **14**, 182–186 (Oct. 1960).

Mason, W. P. Use of semiconductor transducers and esaki diodes in measuring strains and pressures. *Instr. Soc. of Am. Conference Preprint* No. 44–LA–61 (Sept. 11–15, 1961). Reviewed and abstracted from oral presentation, *Strain Gage Readings* 4(5), 22 (Jan. 1962).

Mason, W. P. Variable resistance semiconductive devices. Pat. 2,939,317.

Matlow, S. L., and Gould, H. J. Chemical treatment for rendering silicon-doped aluminum solderable. *Electrochem. Soc.* **108**, 198–199 (Feb. 1961).

Matsuura, E., Matsui, K., and Hasiguti, R. R. Technique for ohmic connecting leads to silicon. *J. Appl. Phys.* 33(4), 1610–1611 (Apr. 1962).

McCall, D. W., Douglass, D. C., and Anderson, E. W. Diffusion in liquids. *Bell Tele. Labs. Monograph* 3561.

McGahan, T. E., and Spector, C. J. Precision lapping, damage and diffusion. Presented at Electrochem. Soc. Meeting, Chicago, Ill. (1960).

McKeown, P. J. A. Controlled chemical etching in the production of semiconductor dice. *Electrochem. Soc. J.* **109**, 269–270 (Mar. 1962).

McSkimin, H. J. Elastic moduli of single crystal germanium as function of hydrostatic pressure. *Bell Tele. Labs. Monograph* 3034.

McSkimin, H. J. Measurement of dynamic properties of materials. Pat. 2,966,058.

McSkimin, H. J. Measurement of ultrasonic wave velocities and elastic moduli for small solid specimens. *Bell Tele. Labs. Monograph* 3369.

McSkimin, H. J. Notes and references for the measurement of elastic moduli by means of ultrasonic waves. *J. Acoust. Soc. Am.* **33**, 606 (May 1961).

McSkimin, H. J. Use of high frequency ultrasound for determining the elastic moduli of small specimens. *Proc. Nat'l. Electronics Conf.* **12**, 351–362 (Apr. 15, 1957).

McSkimin, H. J., and Thomas, D. G. Elastic moduli of cadmium telluride. *J. Appl. Phys.* **33**, 55–59 (Jan. 1962).

Mechanical properties of intermetallic compounds. J. H. Westbrook, Editor. John Wiley and Sons (1960).

Miller, J. F. *et al.* Rare earth compound semiconductors. *Electrochem. Soc. J.* **106**, 1043–6 (Dec. 1959).

Moen, Arne S. New horizons in transducers utilizing solid state strain gages. *Instr. Soc. of Am. Conference Preprint* No. 114–LA–61 (Sept. 11–15, 1961).

Morin, F. J., Geballe, T. H., and Herring, C. Temperature dependence of piezoresistance of high purity silicon, germanium. *Phys. Rev.* **105, 525** (1957).

Morrison, S. J. Strain energy calculations in design of cat's whiskers for semiconductor devices. *Instn. Elec. Engrs. Proc.* **104** Pt. C (5) 148–53 (Mar. 1957).

Müller, C. Thin transparent films of metal. *Metallurgist* (Supp. to Engineer) **141** (3657) 6 (Jan. 29, 1926).

Murray, Thomas P. Automatic optical thickness gauge for thin film measurements. *Rev. Sci. Instr.* **33,** 172–176 (Feb. 1962).

Nathan, M. I. Current voltage characteristics of germanium tunnel diodes. *J. Appl. Phys.* 33(4), 1460–1469 (Apr. 1962).

Olshefski, P. J. Constant-current generator measures semiconductor resistance. *Electronics* **34,** 63 (Nov. 24, 1961).

Organic semiconductors: properties and applications. *Jet Prop. Lab. Lite.* Research 341 (Sept. 1961). Abstract and review in *Strain Gage Readings* V(2), 38 (June–July 1962).

Oroshnik, J. Precision 2 point probe for measuring of resistivity of semiconductors and metal-to-semiconductor contact resistance. *Sylvania Technologist* **10**(1), 17–20 (Jan. 1957).

Oroshnik, J., and Many, A. Evaluation of the homogeneity of germanium single crystals by photovoltaic scanning. *J. Electrochemical Soc.* (April 1959).

Parmee, J. L. Preparation of high purity single crystal silicon; the floating-zone technique. *The Engineer* **209,** 979–82 (June 10, 1960).

Patel, J. R., and Alexander, B. H. Plastic deformation of germanium in compression. *Acta Met.* **4,** 385–395 (July 1956).

Paul, W. The effect of pressure on the properties of germanium and silicon. Pergamon Press, Advances in Semi-Conductor Science (1959).

Pearson, G. L. Bibliography on diffusion of impurity elements in compound semiconductors. Stanford Univ. Solid-state Electronics Lab. TR-1801-1 (Apr. 7, 1961).

Pearson, G. L., and Bardeen, J. Electrical properties of pure silicon and silicon alloys containing boron and phosphorus. *Phys. Rev.* **75,** 865–883 (1949).

Pearson, G. L., Read, W. T., and Feldmann, W. L. Deformation and fracture of small silicon crystals. *Acta Metallurgica* **5,** 181 (1957).

Petritz, R. L. Contributions of materials technology to semiconductor devices. *I.R.E. Proc.* **50**(5), 1025–1038 (May 1962).

Pfann, W. G. Electromagnetic stirring method. Pat. 2,890,940.

Pfann, W. G. Isotropically piezoresistive semiconductors. *J. Appl. Phys.* 33(4), 1618–1619 (Apr. 1962).

Pfann, W. G., Hobstetter, J. N., and Indig, G. S. Preventing conductivity fluctuations during growth of a semiconducting crystal. *Bell Tele. Labs. Monograph* 3142.

Pfann, W. G., and Thurston, R. N. Semiconducting stress transducers utilizing the transverse and shear piezoresistance effects. *J. Appl. Phys.* 32(10), 2008–2019 (Oct. 1961).

Pfann, W. G. Suspension of liquid material. Pat. 2,904,411.

Pfann, W. G., and Olsen, K. M. Zone-melting. *Bell Labs. Rec.* **33,** 201–205 (June 1955).

Pfann, W. G. Zone-melting process. Pat. 2,875,108.

Pfann, W. G. Zone melting. *Sci. Magazine* **135,** 1101–1109 (Mar. 1962).

Phillips, R., and Lucas, J. H. Apparatus for the controlled orientation of crystallographic specimens for ultra-thin sectioning. *J. Sci. Instr.* **39**, 23–25 (Jan. 1962).

Photo and thermoelectric effects in semiconductors. International Series of Monographs on Semiconductors, Jan Tauc, Editor, Pergamon Press Vol. **12** (1961).

Pohl, P. Signal conditioning for semiconductors. *ISA J.* **9**(6), 33–34 (June 1962).

Pollack, M. Apparatus for piezoresistance measurement. *Rev. Sci. Instr.* **29**(7), 639–641 (July 1958).

Pollack, M. Piezoresistance in heavily doped N-type germanium. *Phys. Rev.* **111**, 798 (1958).

Potter, R. F. Piezoresistance of indium antimonide. *Phys. Rev.* **108**, 652–658 (1957).

Price, P. J. Intervalley noise. *J. Appl. Phys.* **31**, 949–53 (June 1960).

Prince, M. B. Method of producing cavities in semiconductor surfaces. Pat. 2,844,531.

Properties of elemental and compound semiconductors. Harry C. Gatos, Editor. Metallurgical Soc. Conf., Boston, Mass. Aug. 31–Sept. 2, 1959. Interscience Publishers, N.Y. Vol. **5** (1960).

Prussin, S., and Stevenson, A. Strain optic coefficient of silicon for infrared light. *J. Appl. Phys.* (March 1959).

Pudvin, J. F. Environmental and device cleanness and purity standards. *Instn. Elec. Engrs. Proc.* **106** (Pt. B, Supp. 17) 1125–9 (May 1959).

Questions of metallurgy and physics of semiconductors. D. A. Petrov, Editor. Acad. of Sci., USSR—A. A. Baikov Metallurgy Inst. Transactions of Second Conf. on Semiconducting Materials, Jan. 1956. Akademica Nauk Press, 1957, Moscow, USSR. (Translated by Morris D. Friedman, Inc., Needham Heights, Mass.).

Riggs, J. R. Vapor growth of semiconductors. *Elec. Manuf.* **66**, 11 (Aug. 1960).

Riney, T. D. Residual thermoelastic stress in bonded silicon wafers. *J. Appl. Phys.* **32**, 454–460 (Mar. 1961), and *Bell Tele. Labs. Monograph* 3876.

Rmaut, G., and Vennik, J. Observations on an electrical effect obtained during deformation of sodium chloride crystals. *Philosophical Magazine* **6**(61), 1–8 (Jan. 1961).

Robin, J. Influence of pressure on various properties of semiconductors. *J. de Physique et le Radium* **21**(2), 130–40 (Feb. 1960).

Rohrbach, Chr., and Czaika, N. On some properties of semiconductor strain gages. Paper 1–13 presented at Second International Stress Analysis Conf. sponsored by GAMAC, Paris, France. Abstract and review in *Strain Gage Readings* **V**(2), 31 (June–July 1962).

Rovinskii, B. M., and Sinaiskii, V. M. Crystal lattice load-strain curve obtained by the continuous recording method. *S.G.R.* Abstract & Rev. **V**(2), 75 (June–July 1962), *Industr. Labs.* (Nov. 1958) (I.S.A. Translation).

Rudenberg, H. G. Resistivity measuring techniques in semiconductors. *Nat'l. Electronics Conf. Proc.* **14**, 585–97 (1958).

Ruth, R. P., Marinace, J. C., and Dunlap, W. C., Jr. Vapor deposited single-crystal germanium. *J. Appl. Phys.* Vol. 31/6 (June 1960).

Saburi, O. Semiconducting bodies in the family of barium titanates. *Am. Ceramic Soc. J.* **44**, 54–63 (Feb. 1, 1961).

Sagar, A. Experimental investigation of conduction band of GaSb. *Phys. Rev.* **117**(1), 93 (Jan. 1, 1960).

Sagar, A. Piezoresistance in n-type InP. *Phys. Rev.* **117**, 101 (1960).

Sanchez, J. C. The Micro Sensor, a new tool for the experimental stress analyst. Presented at the Soc. for Experimental Stress Analysis (October 12, 1960).

Sanchez, J. C. The semiconductor strain gage and a state of the art summary. *Strain Gage Readings* **4**, No. 4 (1961).

Sanchez, J. C. Semiconductor strain gage. *Instruments and Control Systems* **36** No. 6, 1064–1065 (June 1961).

Sanchez, J. C., and Wright, W. V. Semiconductor strain gages—what can they do? *I.S.A. J.* **9**(5), 38–40 (May 1962).

Sanchez, J. C., and Wright, W. V. Recent advances in flexible semiconductor strain gages. *Instr. Soc. of Am. Conference Preprint* No. 46–LA–61 (Sept. 11–15, 1961).

Sauer, H. A., Flaschen, S. S., and Hoesterey, D. C. Piezoresistance and piezo-capacitance effects in barium strontium titanate ceramics. *J. Am. Cer. Soc.* **42**, 363 (1959), and *Bell Tele. Labs. Monograph* 3412.

Schawlow, A. L., Piksis, A. H., and Sugano, S. Strain effects on degenerate spectral line of chromium in MgO crystals. *Phys. Rev.* **122**, 1469–1476 (June 1, 1961), and *Bell Tele. Labs. Monograph* 3961.

Schlabach, T. D. The temperature dependence of electrical resistivity of laminated thermoset materials. *Bell Tele. Labs. Monograph* 3374.

Schmidt, P. F., and Keiper, D. A. On jet etching of n-type Si. *Electrochem. Soc. J.* **106**(7), 592–6 (July 1959).

Schwartz, D. S. Investigation of solid state instrumentation techniques. WADD TR-61-9 (Feb. 1961) (Also from O.T.A., Wash. 25, D.C.).

Schwertz, F. A., and Mazenko, J. J. Nonlinear semiconductor resistors. *J. Appl. Phys.* **24**, 1015–1024 (Aug. 1953).

Scrupski, S. E. Transducers—an Electronic Design feature report. Semiconductor and conventional transducers; typical characteristics and source list. *Electronic Design* **10**(13), 44–61 (June 21, 1962).

Sedlacek, R., and Halden, F. A. Method for tensile testing of brittle materials. *Rev. of Sci. Instr.* **33**, 298–300 (Mar. 1962).

Seitz, F. The plasticity of silicon and germanium. *Phys. Rev.* **88**(4), 722–724 (Nov. 15, 1952).

Semiconductor abstracts. Battelle Memorial Institute, Vol. **VII**, John Wiley and Sons, Inc., New York (1962).

Shadrin, V. S. Method for measuring the piezoresistance in semiconductors. Instruments and Experimental Techniques No. 5 (Sept.–Oct. 1961). I.S.A. Translation from Russian p. 1017–1018 (Apr. 1962).

Shilliday, Theodore S. Optical effects in semiconductors. *Battelle (Mem. Inst.) Tech. Rev.* **8**, No. 9, 7–13 (Sept. 1959).

Shlichta, P. J. A technique for simultaneous zone purification and single crystal growth. *J. Sci. Instr.* **39**(7), 392 (July 1962).

Shock and vibration handbook. Edited by Cyril M. Harris and Charles E. Crede. Section 16, part II. McGraw-Hill (in preparation in 1961).

Shockley, W. Electrons and holes in semiconductors. D. Van Nostrand Co. (1950).

Shockley, W. Transistor circuits with constant output current. Pat. 2,716,729.

Sikorski, M. E. Sensitive tunnel diode pressure transducers. Presented at I.R.E. Int. Solid-State Circuits Conf. held at Univ. of Pa. (Feb. 14–16, 1962).

Sikorski, M. E., and Andreatch, P. Tunnel diode hydrostatic pressure transducer. *Rev. Sci. Inst.* **33**(2), 155–160 (Feb. 1962).

Simon, R., *et al.* Uniformity of electrical current flow in cylindrical semiconductor specimens with cylindrical metallic end caps. *J. Appl. Phys.* **32**, 46–47 (Jan. 1961).

Smith, C. S. Solid state physics. Edited by F. Seitz and D. Turnbull, Academic Press, Inc., N.Y. **6**, 175 (1959).

Smith, Charles S. Piezoresistance effect in germanium and silicon. *Phys. Rev.* **94**, 42–49 (1954).

Smith, D. A., and Lewis, T. M. A. A buffer stage for piezo-electric strain gauges. *Electronic Eng.* (Feb. 1962).

Smith, R. S. Measurement of crystallite size and strain of electroplated films. *IBM J. of Res. and Devel.* **4**, No. 2, 205–207 (April 1960).

Sparks, M., and Pietenpol, W. J. Diffusion in solids—a breakthrough in semiconductor device fabrication. *Bell Labs. Rec.* **34**, 441–446 (Dec. 1956).

Spencer, E. G., and Le Craw, R. C. Magneto-acoustic resonance in yttrium-iron garnet. *Phys. Rev. Letters* **1**, 241–242 (Oct. 1958) and *J. Appl. Phys.* **30**, 1495–1505 (Apr. 1959).

Spitzer, W. G., Trumbore, F. A., and Logan, R. A. Properties of heavily doped n-type germanium. *J. Appl. Phys.* **132**, 1822–1830 (Oct. 1961).

Stambler, I. Semiconductor strain gages; small size high output. *Space/Aeronautics* **36**, 64–67 (Nov. 1961).

Stein, Peter K. Commercial solid state strain gages with gage factors of 140. *Strain Gage Readings* **2**, No. 6, 65 (Feb.–Mar. 1960).

Stein, Peter K. A photoelastic, resistance-strain sensitive material. *Strain Gage Readings* **2**, No. 2, 43 (June–July 1959).

Stein, Peter K. Semiconductor strain gages: gage factors in the hundreds. *Strain Gage Readings* **2**, No. 2, 39 (June–July 1959).

Stein, Peter K. Survey of commercially available semiconductor strain gages. *Strain Gage Readings* **3**, No. 5, 17 (Dec. 1960–Jan. 1961).

Steitz, F., and Turnbull, D. Solid state physics. Academic Press, **12** and **13** (1961).

Stillinger, F. H., Jr., and Kirkwood, J. G. Theory of the diffuse double layer. *J. Chem. Phys.* **33**, 1282–1290 (Nov. 1960).

Stubb, T. Measurement of conductivity in semiconductors with aid of microwaves. *Acta Polytechnica Scandinavica* No. 2 (Physics-Nucleonics Series No. 2) (1959).

Sullivan, M. V. New electrochemical technique for polishing semiconductor wafers. *Bell Labs. Rec.* **39**, 107 (Mar. 1961).

Swalin, R. A. The theory of diffusion in semiconductors. Third Tech. Rept. Dept. of Metallurgy, Univ. of Minn. (Minn. Univ. Nonr. 710 (27) T. R. 3) (Sept. 1, 1960).

Swieykowska, Z. Najkorzystniejszy dobor opornosci galezi mostka Wheatstone 'a przy uwzglednieniu dopasowania ukladu do opornosci krytycznej. *Archiwum Elektrotechniki* **6**(4), 733–742 (1957). (Summary in English).

Talmo, R. E. Semiconductor strain gages offer high sensitivity. *Electronics* **34**, 43–45 (Feb. 24, 1961).

Tanenbaum, M. and Mills, A. D. Preparation of uniform resistivity n-type silicon by nuclear transmutation. *Electrochem. Soc. J.* **108**, 171–176 (Feb. 1961).

Taylor, J. H. Pressure dependence of resistivity, hall coefficient, energy gap for InAs. *Phys. Rev.* **100**(6), 1593–5 (Dec. 15, 1955).

Taylor, J. H. Pressure dependence of resistance of germanium. *Phys. Rev.* **80**(5), 919–20 (Dec. 1, 1950).

Taylor, T. C. Thermally-induced cracking in fabrication of semiconductor devices. *Inst. Radio Engrs. Trans. on Electron Devices* ED–6(3), 299–301 (July 1959).

Terminology. IRE standards on solid-state devices: definitions of semiconductor terms, 1960. *IRE Proc.* **48**(10), 1772–5 (Oct. 1960). IRE Standard 60 IRE 28.S1.

Tomaino, M. F. Report on semiconductive plastics. *Electronics* **33**, 68 (Jan. 22, 1960).

Traite, M., Welkowitz, W., and Downs, R. Intracardiac catheter tip type piezo-resistive pressure gage. *Rev. Sc. Inst.* (Sept. 1960).

Trakhtenberg, A. D., and Fainshtein, S. M. Vyyavlenie dislokatsii v germanii i kremnii travleniem. Determining etching dislocations in silicon by etching, and search for suitable etching materials. *Fizika Tverdogo Tela* **1**(3), 373–7 (Mar. 1959).

Trumbore, F. A., and Isenberg, C. R. Two-phase germanium zinc "whiskers." *J. Appl. Phys.* Letters to Ed. **30**, 795–796 (May 1959).

Turner, D. R. Electropolishing silicon in hydrofluoric acid solutions. *Bell Tele. Labs. Monograph* 3107.

Turner, D. R. Electroplating metal contacts on germanium and silicon. *J. Electrochem. Soc.* **106**, 786–90 (Sept. 1959), and *Bell Tele. Labs. Monograph* 3413.

Turner, D. R. Electrolytic etching of semiconductors. *Electrochem. Soc. Monograph* pp. 285–310 (Aug. 1960).

Turner, D. R. Junction delineation on silicon in electrochemical displacement plating solutions. *Bell Tele. Labs. Monograph* 3439.

Turner, D. R., and Sauer, H. A. Ohmic contacts to semiconducting ceramics. *Electrochem. Soc. J.* **107**, 250–1 (March 1960).

Turner, T. Henry. Extra pure silicon (physical properties of). *The Engineer* **209**, 1012 (June 17, 1960).

Tuzzolino, A. Piezoresistance constants of P-type InSb. *Phys. Rev.* **109**, 1980 (1958).

Van de Pauw, L. J. A method of measuring specific resistivity and hall effects of discs of arbitrary shape. *Phil. Res. Rep.* **13**, 1 (1958).

Van Roosbroeck, W., and Pfann, W. G. Transport in a semiconductor with anisotropic mobilities and the photopiezoresistance effect. *J. Appl. Phys.* **33**(7), 2304–2309 (July 1962).

Varicak, M., and Saftic, B. Principle of a semiconductor manometer in the pressure range of 1 to 10^{-6} mmHg. *Rev. Sci. Instr.* **30**, 891–5 (Oct. 1959).

Vogt, C. O. Semiconductor strain sensors. Thesis for Master of Science Degree, Oklahoma State University (August 1960).

Vogt, C. O. The strainistor—a semiconductor strain sensor. Sixth National Flight Test Instrumentation Symposium, San Diego, California (May 2–5, 1960).

Vook, F. L. Low-temperature length change measurements of electron-irradiated germanium and silicon. *Phys. Rev.* **125**(3), 855–861 (Feb. 1, 1962).

Wagner, R. S., and Treuting, R. G. Morphology and growth mechanism of silicon ribbons. *J. Appl. Phys.* **32**, 2490–2491 (Nov. 1961).

Waltz, M. C. Method of plating silicon. Pat. 2,814,589.

Warner, R. M., Jr. Semiconductor resistance element. Pat. 2,989,713.

Warner, R. M., Jr., Jackson, W. H., Doucette, E. I., and Stone, H. A., Jr. A semiconductor current limiter. *Bell Tele. Labs. Monograph* 3087.

Watkins, H., and Kolk, A. Measurement of stress in very thin electro-deposits. *Electrochem. Soc. J.* **108**, 1018–1023 (Nov. 1961).

Watkins, J. A survey of thin-film technology. *Electronic Industries* **20**(9), 92 (Sept. 1961). (also Oct. p. 102).

Wernick, J. H. Effects of crystal orientation, temperature and zone thickness in temperature-gradient zone-melting. *J. Metals* **9**(10), Sec. 2 (Trans.) 1169–73 (Oct. 1957).

Wernick, J. H., and Wolfe, R. Search for new semiconductors. *Bell Labs. Rec.* **39**(11), 388–394 (Nov. 1961).

Wertheim, G. K. Radiation-induced defects in silicon. Semiconductor Nuclear

Particle Detectors, Nat'l. Acad. of Sci., Nat'l. Research Council 871, 128–135 (1961).

White, D. L. Beta quartz as a high temperature piezoelectric material. *J. Acoust. Soc. Am.* **31**, 311–314 (Mar. 1959), and *Bell Tele. Labs. Monograph* 3360.

Williams, E. L. Boron diffusion in silicon. *J. Electrochem. Soc.* **108**, 795–798 (Aug. 1961).

Winslow, F. H. Method of purifying volatile compounds of germanium and silicon. Pat. 2,812,235.

Wolff, M. F. How radiation affects semiconductor devices. *Electronics* **32**, 55–7 (Nov. 27, 1959).

Wolters, H. B., and Schapink, F. W. Tensile testing machine for whiskers. *J. Sci. Instr.* (June 1961).

Yamashita, T., and Ohta, T. Measurement of seebeck effect in plastically bent germanium. *J. Phys. Soc.* (Japan) **16**, 1565–1569 (Aug. 1961).

Zeigler, A. W. Methods for bonding silica bodies. Pat. 2,709,147.

Ziman, J. M. A theory of the electrical properties of liquid metals I: the monovalent metals. *Philosophical Magazine* **6**(68), 1013–1034 (Aug. 1961).

General Reference

Anderson, O. L. Adhesion of solids: principles and applications. *Bell Labs. Rec.* **35**, 439–445 (Nov. 1957).

Anonymous. The acoustoelectric effect in germanium. *Bell Labs. Rec.* **37**(4), 152 (Apr. 1959).

Anonymous. Basic study into the evaluation of transducer-type pressure gauges. *Instrument Practice* **13**, 303 (Mar. 1959).

Anonymous. Germanium resistance thermometer. *Bell Labs. Rec.* **36**, 261 (July 1958).

Anonymous. Strain gage handbook. Bulletin 4311A, Baldwin-Lima-Hamilton Corp., Waltham, 54, Mass. (May 1962).

Bassett, W. V., Cromwell, H., and Wooster, W. E. Improved techniques and devices for stress analysis with resistance wire gages. *S.E.S.A. Proc.* **3**(2), 76–88 (1946).

Bridgman, P. W. The failure of ohm's law in gold and silver at high current densities. *Proc. Am. Acad. of Arts and Sci.* **57**(6), 131–172 (Apr. 1922).

Bridgman, P. W. Measurements of the deviation from ohm's law in metals at high current densities. *Proc. Nat. Acad. Sci. U. S.* **10**, 299–303 (1921).

Bridgman, P. W. The measurement of hydrostatic pressures up to 20,000 Kg/cm². *Am. Acad. Arts and Sci. Proc.* **47**, 321 (1911).

*Characteristics and applications of resistance strain gages. National Bureau of Standards Circular No. 528, Superintendent of Documents, U. S. Government Printing Office, Washington, D.C. (1954).

Clough, W. R., Shank, M. E., and Zaid, M. The behavior of SR-4 wire resistance strain gages on certain materials in the presence of hydrostatic pressure. *S.E.S.A. Proc.* **10**(2), 167–176 (1953).

Day, E. E. Discussion of paper "characteristics of wire gages under various conditions." *S.E.S.A. Proc.* **9**(1), 139–40 (1951).

*Dobie, W. B., and Isaac, P. C. G. Electric resistance strain gauges. The English Universities Press Ltd., London (1948). In U.S.A. The MacMillan Co., New York.

Freudenthal, A. M. Stress analysis beyond the elastic range. *S.E.S.A. Proc.* **6**(2), 131–140 (1948).

Gador, L. Loading capacity of non-linear bridges. *Acta. Tech.* (Budapest) **28**(3–4), 281–308 (1960).

Gordy, E., and Hasenpusch, P. Constant current coupled transistor power supply. *Electronics* **32**, 60 (Oct. 9, 1959).

*Grundlagen und Anwendungen des Dehnungsmesstreifens. Kurt Fink, Editor, Verlag Stahleisen, M.B.H., Dusseldorf, Germany (1952).

Guerard, J. P., and Weissmann, G. F. Effect of hydrostatic pressure on SR-4 strain gages. *SESA Proc.* **16**(1), 151–156 (1958).

Gustafsson, G. V. A. Some basic characteristics of wire strain gauges and bridge circuits for these gauges. The Aeronautical Research Institute of Sweden, Stockholm. Report No. 22.

*Handbook of experimental stress analysis. M. Hetenyi, Editor. John Wiley & Sons, New York (1950).

*Handbuch der Spannungs und Dehnungsmessung. Edited by Kurt Fink and Christof Rohrbach, VDI, Verlag, Dusseldorf (1958).

Harris, F. K. Electrical measurements. John Wiley and Sons (1952).

Hylkema, C. G., and Bowersox, R. B. Experimental and mathematical techniques for determining dynamic response of pressure gages. *ISA J.* **1**(1), 27–32 (Feb. 1954).

*Jones, E., and Maslen, K. R. The physical characteristics of wire resistance strain gauges. Her Majesty's Stationery Office, London (1952).

*Koch, J. J., Boiten, R. G., Biermasz, A. L., and Roszbach, G. P. Strain gauges— theory and application. Philips Technical Library, Philips Industries, Eindhoven, Holland (1952).

*Lee, G. H. An introduction to experimental stress analysis. John Wiley & Sons, Inc., New York (1950).

Lessells, J. M. Discussion of paper "allowable working stresses." *S.E.S.A. Proc.* **3**(2), 102–3 (1946).

*Lion, K. S. Electrical instrumentation elements. Vol. **1**, Input Transducers, Mc-Graw-Hill Book Co., New York (1958).

Low, J. R., Jr., and Garofalo, F. Precision determination of stress-strain curves in the plastic range. *S.E.S.A. Proc.* **4**(2), 16–24 (1947).

Mack, D. R. Linearizing the output of resistance temperature gages. *S.E.S.A. Proceedings*, Vol. XVIII, No. 1 (1960).

Majors, H., Jr. Characteristics of wire gages under various conditions. *S.E.S.A. Proc.* **9**(1), 123–39 (1951).

Mason, W. P. Adhesion between metals and its effect on fixed and sliding contacts. *Bell Tele. Labs. Monograph* 3368.

Mason, W. P. Avoidance of fatigue effects under dynamic strain. Pat. 2,936,612.

Mason, W. P. Electrostrictive ceramics comprising barium titanate. Pat. 2,906,973.

Mason, W. P. Internal friction and fatigue in metals at large strain amplitudes. *J. Acoust. Soc. Am.* **28**, 1207–1218 (Nov. 1956), and *Bell Tele. Labs. Monograph* 2758.

McCall, D. W. Cell for the determination of pressure coefficients. *Bell Tele. Labs. Monograph* 2872.

*The measurement of stress and strain in solids. Institute of Physics, London, Cambridge University Press (1948).

Noll, G. C., and Lipson, C. Allowable working stresses. *S.E.S.A. Proc.* **3**(2), 89–101 (1946).

Noltingk, B. E. History of electrical devices for measuring strains and small movements. *J. Sci. Instr.* **32**(5), 157–8 (May 1955).

Pearlstein, E. New bridge circuit for comparing four-terminal resistors. *Rev. of Sci. Instr.* **33**(6), 610–612 (June 1962).

*Perry, C. C., Bean, W. T., Jr., Ellis, G., Gray, R. M., Lawton, C. W., and Stitz, E. O. Manual on experimental stress analysis techniques (preliminary edition). S.E.S.A., 21 Bridge Square, Westport, Conn. (1959).

*Perry, C. C., and Lissner, H. R. The strain gage primer. McGraw-Hill Book Co., New York (1955).

Planer, G. V., and Foster, A. Flame sprayed ceramic dielectric for transducers. *Brit. Inst. Radio Eng. J.* **19**, 699–702 (Nov. 1959).

Precision measurement and calibration. Nat'l. Bur. Stds. Handbook **77**, Electricity and Electronics Vol. 1 (1961). ($6.00 Supt. of Documents, Wash., D.C.).

*Proceedings of the society for experimental stress analysis, Vol. 1, No. 1 to date. S.E.S.A., 21 Bridge Square, Westport, Conn. (Vol. XV, No. 2 contains complete cumulative index of Vols. I-XV).

*Roberts, H. C. Mechanical measurements by electrical methods. The Instruments Publishing Co., Inc., Pittsburgh, Pa., 2nd Edition (1951).

Rondeau, H. F., and Tatnall, F. G. An introduction to the resistance wire strain gage. *ISA J.* **1**(2), 17–26 (Feb. 1954).

Sawicki, J. Compensated Wheatstone bridge for exact resistance measurement. *Archiwum Elektrotechniki* **7**(2), 479–506 (1958).

Stirling, P. H., and Ho, H. Trouble shooting with strain gages. *Industrial and Eng. Chem.* (May 1961).

*Strain gage readings. Vol. 1, No. 1, April–May 1958 to date. Stein Engineering Services, Inc., 5602 E. Monte Rosa, Phoenix, Ariz.

Stricker, S. Short note on conditions for maximum sensitivity of D.C. Wheatstone bridge. *Research Council of Israel Bull.* **7C**(1), 51–4 (Apr. 1959).

Swainger, K. The measurement and interpretation of post-yield strains. *S.E.S.A. Proc.* **5**(2), 1–8 (1948).

*Symposium on elevated temperature strain gages. Special Technical Publication No. 230, American Society for Testing Materials, 1916 Race St., Philadelphia 3, Pa. (1957).

*Testing topics reprints. F. G. Tatnall, Editor, Baldwin-Lima-Hamilton Corp., Waltham 54, Mass.

Thomson, W. (Lord Kelvin), Effects of mechanical strain and of magnetization on the thermo-electric qualities of metals, Part III of the Bakerian Lecture—on the electro-dynamic qualities of metals. *Philosophical Transactions of the Royal Society of London,* **146**, pp. 709–736 (1856).

Tomlinson, H. On the increase in resistance to the passage of an electric current produced on certain wires by stretching. *Proc. of the Royal Soc. of London* **26**, 401–410 (Mar. 1, 1877–Dec. 20, 1877).

Walker, D. E. A stabilized constant current power unit. *Electronic Eng.* **34**, 406–409 (June 1962).

Weinreich, G., Sanders, T. M., Jr., and White, H. G. Acoustoelectric effect in n-type germanium. *Bell Tele. Labs. Monograph* 3383.

*Yarnell, J. Resistance strain gauges. *Electronic Eng.*, 28 Essex St., Strand, London, W.C.2 (1951).

*Zelbstein, U. Technique et utilization des jauges de constrainte. Dunod, Paris, (1956).

Author Index

Numbers in parentheses are reference numbers and are included to assist in locating references when the authors' names are not mentioned in the text. Numbers in italic refer to the page on which the reference is listed.

A

Alter, H., 52(24), *69*
Anderson, J. R., 76, 79, *90*
Aukward, J. A., 60(75), *71*

B

Ball, L. M., 83, *91*
Barker, R. S., 83, 85, *91*
Bassiere, M., 78, *90*
Bergler, W. H., Jr., 52(32), 53(32), *69*
Black, J. M., 53, *70*
Blomquist, R. F., 53, *70*
Bloss, R. L., 126(16), *141*
Bodner, M., 157(2), *167*
Boiten, R. G., 139(28), *142*
Boller, K. H., 48(5), *68*
Boyer, A. G., 81, 83, *91*
Brennan, J. N., 139(24,25), *142*
Brewer, W. B., 157(2), *167*
Bridgnell, D., 49(15), *68*
Brodie, G. H., 80, *91*
Brosius, G. F., 123(12), *141*
Bruin, P., 48(11), *68*

C

Campbell, W. R., 73, 74, 80, 83, *90*, *91*, 123(10), 125(10), 130(17), 132(19), *141*, *142*
Carswell, T. S., 52(30), 53(30), *69*
Champetier, L., 80, *91*
Champion, F. C., 132(20), *142*
Chottiner, J., 59, *71*
Coover, H. W., 54, 58, *70*
Coulter, M., 80, *91*
Cressey, K., 60(73), 63(73), *71*
Crowe, W. D., 139(30), *142*
Czaika, N., 49(18,19,20), 66(18,19,20), *68*
69

D

Davidson, J. R., 48, 49(1b), *68*
Davis, J. E., 150(4), *167*

Davy, N., 132(20), *142*
Day, E. E., 73, 74, *90*, 123(11), 126(14), *141*
Dean, M., 139(29), *142*
deForest, A. V., 123(7), *141*
Delmonte, J., 60(73), 63(73), *71*
DeLollis, N. J., 53, *70*
Dimeff, J., 79, 81, *90*
Dobie, W. B., 123(2), *141*
Duggin, B. W., 65, *71*

E

Eikner, H. W., 48(6), 54(49,50,51,52) *68*, *70*
Eisner, R. L., 1(5), 2(5), 8(5), *18*
Engl, W., 95(1), *108*
Epstein, G., 52(27), 53(27), *69*

F

Feldmann, W. L., 110(8), *120*, 256(4), *257*, 259(3), *272*
Follis, G. R., 54, 58, *70*
Forst, J. J., 109(4), *120*, 169(5), 173(7), 183(7), *189*, 245(2), 252(3), *257*, 317 (4), 333(4), *345*
Fouretier, G., 49(16), *68*

G

Gayman, W. H., 80, *91*
Geballe, T., 1(4), 2(4), 5(4), *18*, 109(6), *120*, 180(9), *189*
Geiger, R. C., 83, *91*
Geyling, F. T., 109(4), *120*, 169(5), *189*, 245(2), *257*
Greenfield, J. F., 49(15), *68*
Guerke, R. M., 123(9), *141*
Gustafsson, G. V. A., 74, 80, *90*, *91*

H

Hansen, R. M., 79, *90*
Harris, C. R., 150(4), *167*
Hartley, D., 123(12), *141*

Subject Index*

A

Accelerometer, *see* transducers

Adhesives, general information, *see also* mounting techniques
accelerated cure, 73
application consequences, 51–52, 166
basic behavior, 52, 53
bond performance, 60, 61, 130, 139, 167
bond quality, 60, 83, 121, 167
bubble entrapment, 55, 121
clamping pressure, 56, 59, **317, 319**
complete cure, determination of, 63–65
creep, 52, 55, 59–63, 65, **111**, *322*
cure and post cure, 54, 59, 63
fatigue failure, impact, 139
gage performance, determined by, 45–67
glue-line thickness, 60, 63, 139
hygroscopic, 55, 58
hysteresis, 61, **111**
imperfect bond, 83, 88
incomplete cure, 64
insensitivity to moisture, 122
insulation resistance, 62–66
lap-joint tests, 48
mounting methods, 54–62
nuclear radiation, effects of, 141
organic, temperature weakening, 51, 64
properties, ideal, 47
qualitative relations, 53, 60
refrigeration for, 56, 139
resistance leakage to specimen, *see* waterproofing
resistance vs. cure, 63
shear strength, 48
short drying time, 58, 121
shrink during cure, 55–57, 59, 61, 62
state-of-the-art, 47
strain transmittal, 49, 167
stresses in layer, residual, 49, 58
summation of principles, 66

surface preparation for, 54, *170*, **171**, **317**
temperature effects on, 55–57, 59, 75, 80, 166, *312*
temperature limit of, 55, *312*
thermoplastic, for rapid survey, 58
zero shift, apparent, 64

Adhesives for semiconductor gages, *54*, **5, 172, 254, 317, 320**

Adhesives, types of
ceramic, 64, 65
chemical reaction
Araldite, 27
Armstrong A-2, 317
Baldwin EPY-150 and 400, 57, **172**, **317**
Budd SGAC No. 121 and 122, 317
epoxy, **5**, 57
Mithra No. 200, **172**
polymerizing, 122
contact (rapid mounting)
cyano-acrylate, 58, 139
Eastman 910, 58, 75, 83, **172**, **317**, **320**
discussion of, 54
solvent setting
cellulose nitrate, 54, 62
Duco cement, 54, 62
glycol phthlate, **254**
SR-4 cement, 54
thermoplastic
deKhotinsky cement, 58
thermosetting
Allen P-1, 154
epoxy, 57
Palmer Products BC-6035 (Bakelite), 56
phenolic, 23, 56, 59, 85, 139

Aeronautical Research Laboratories, 73

Alloys, *see also* germanium, silicon, substrate materials
Balco, 331

---

* Topics specifically related to semiconductor strain gages are indexed in boldface type. Italicized numbers refer to topics related to both semiconductor and conventional gages. Regular type denotes conventional gage topics.

**Boldface type: semiconductor gages—italicized: coincidental listings—regular type: con-
ventional gages—**

Boldface type: semiconductor gages—italicized: coincidental listings—regular type: conventional gages—

Boldface type: semiconductor gages—italicized: coincidental listings—regular type: conventional gages—

Boldface type: semiconductor gages—italicized: coincidental listings—regular type: conventional gages—

Boldface type: semiconductor gages—italicized: coincidental listings—regular type: conventional gages—

SAE type 1020, 165
stainless, 145
stainless type 316, 152, 153, 165
stainless type 302 (coefficient of expansion), 162–163
thermal expansion of, *see* temperature and temperature effects
thermal expansion of, 145, 162, **180, 271**
best-fit coefficient, 158, **271**
Dural, 85
heating rates, 150
titanium, 163
tool steel, 84
Surface preparation, *see* adhesives, general
Switch, *see also* relays
contact resistance, 100
semiconductor, **102**
unit, 23, 24, 26, 197

T

Telemetry, *see* crane scale; instrumentation, general
Temperature coefficient of expansion, gage elements, *see* temperature and temperature effects
Temperature compensation, *see also* calculations; evaluation, information on
apparent strain, errors due to, **271, 323**
auxiliary gage, copper wire, 85, 86
ballast resistance, 86, 150–157, **183, 269, 331, 339**
bridge output, **270**
compared to wire and foil types, **271, 307–308**
compensated gages, list of types, **272**
cryogenic region, 153–154
disadvantage, 162, 166
dual element, 132, 151, 160
dummy gage block, use of, 132
electrical, **276, 329**
of gage factor, **333**
gage factors, opposite (*p-n-*), use and theory of, **271, 317, 330, 339**
general, 4–5, 73–90, 94, 130, 143–167, **181–182**

linear, 83, 149
lot number, *see also*, lot number
lot number, 150, 157, 162
matching unmounted gages, 85, **182**
nonlinear, 83, 162
nonlinearity, residual, 132, 154, 158, 162
not required, **181, 345**
resistance circuit, **267–271**
selection of proper gage, discussion of, 166
self-temperature, 85, 130, 133, 145, 150, 158–167, **316, 329, 339**
element wire selection, 158
gage construction, 151, 157, 160
gage types, discussion of, 130
possible error source, 161
shunting active gage, **333, 334**
single gage
compensated type, 132, 156, 158, 160
dummy, 78, 130, 132, 147–150, 162, 166, **181, 184, 189, 271, 293, 327–328, 338**
uncompensated type, 77, 157
six-wire system, 156
stabilization, theory of, **263–272**
techniques used, **181, 328, 340**
thermistor (resistive) shunt, **316, 328, 331, 333, 339**
thermocouple, 130, 152, 157, 158
three-wire system, 135, 157, 167
unbonded gages, **330**
variable bridge excitation, 157
zero shift, **181, 329**
Temperature sensing
discussion of use, 132, 157, **181**
lead-wire junction, 79
platinum wire, 150
for gage compensation, 130, 152, 157
strain sensitivity of, 152, 155
thermistor, **181, 316, 328, 331**
thermocouple in bridge network, 157–158
thermocouple ice bath, use of, 193
Temperature and temperature effects, *see also* adhesives; calculations; evalua-

Boldface type: semiconductor gages—italicized: coincidental listings—regular type: conventional gages—